**Test Item File
to Accompany**

The Enduring Vision:

A History of the American People

Kenneth J. Blume

Albany College of Pharmacy, Union University

D. C. Heath and Company

Lexington, Massachusetts   Toronto

Preface

The *Test Item File to Accompany The Enduring Vision* offers the instructor a broad array of questions that test factual and conceptual comprehension of both narrow and wide-ranging material. Every chapter has about twenty-five names or terms for identification. There are also about forty-five multiple-choice questions per chapter to assess students' comprehension of important facts, generalizations, and sequences in the text. Each chapter further offers about ten essay questions that probe students' ability to evaluate, synthesize, explain, and apply what they have learned in their study of *The Enduring Vision*. Finally, most chapters have a map section that asks students to identify particular geographic locations.

In addition to the questions tailored to each text chapter, the *Test Item File* includes two sets of questions designed for use in final examinations. The first set, covering the Prologue and Chapters 1–15, follows Chapter 15 of the *Test Item File*; the second set, spanning Chapters 15–31, follows Chapter 31. The essay questions here are particularly broad-based. Instructors may wish to add their own final-exam questions or to incorporate questions from specific chapters.

Some questions in the *Test Item File* are coded with "SG" or "PT." "SG" indicates that the question also occurs in the *Student Guide to Accompany The Enduring Vision*. "PT" signifies that the question is derived from the "Place in Time" feature essay in the corresponding chapter of *The Enduring Vision*.

All of the test questions also appear in HeathTest Plus, a computerized testing program available in IBM PC, Macintosh, and Apple IIe formats. The *HeathTest Plus Computerized Testing Program* includes one program disk, test-item disks, and a User Manual. The program allows instructors to create customized quizzes and examinations by choosing from among the 80–90 questions in each chapter. Instructors can view and edit the questions and instructions on-screen before inserting them in the test and can add new questions to the database or to individual tests. In addition, the maps in the manual can be computer-generated through HeathTest Plus. The program also permits the random selection of items by chapter, automatically generates answer keys, and can save and print tests in multiple scrambled versions.

HeathTest Plus uses codes to make random searches through specified types of questions. Beyond the aforementioned "SG" and "PT" codes, these designations are:

I: identification questions
M: multiple-choice questions
S: essay questions
G: map (geographic) questions

I would like to thank Dr. Christine C. Kleinegger of the New York State Museum for her assistance in preparing these questions. It is certainly not too much to say that without her I would never have been able to finish this project.

Kenneth J. Blume

Contents

American Land, Native Peoples

IDENTIFICATIONS

Identify the following. Be as specific as possible, and include names, dates, and relevant facts as appropriate. Be sure to explain the *significance* of the person or term.

1. Pueblo culture

2. Precambrian, Paleozoic, Mesozoic

3. plate tectonics

4. Continental Divide

5. Chumash Indians

6. Mesa Verde   PT

7. Great Plains

8. Adena, Hopewell, and Mississippian cultures

9. Woodland culture

10. tidewater region

11. fall line

12. slash-and-burn

MULTIPLE-CHOICE QUESTIONS

Choose the answer that *best* completes the statement or answers the question.

13. Which of the following happened first?   a
    a. Precambrian era
    b. Paleozoic era
    c. Mesozoic era
    d. Ice Age

14. When did *Homo sapiens* evolve and begin migrating throughout the Old World?   **b**
    a. about 5 million years ago
    b. 100,000 to 300,000 years ago
    c. 25,000 years ago
    d. 1 billion years ago

15. Almost all native American peoples are descended from   **c**
    a. Polynesians who reached the Pacific coast about A.D. 400.
    b. hunters from central Europe who crossed the Polar ice cap and traveled south through what is now Canada.
    c. migrants who came from northwestern Asia over the Alaska-Siberia land bridge.
    d. *Homo sapiens* who evolved from North American apes.

16. Which part of the Western Hemisphere most closely resembles the land that North   **d**
    America's earliest migrants discovered?
    a. Kansas
    b. Central America
    c. Gulf of Mexico
    d. Alaska

17. Where in North America would you find the following climate: cool, humid, and   **d**
    foggy winters, a dense forest with immense trees, and wet westerly winds?
    a. the New England coast from Portland to Boston
    b. the Mississippi delta
    c. the Great Basin
    d. the Pacific coast from Anchorage to San Francisco

18. The region of the United States with the most uniformly temperate climate is   **a**
    a. the Pacific Coastal region.
    b. the Great Plains.
    c. New England.
    d. Atlantic seaboard region.

19. The Continental Divide is   **b**
    a. the imaginary line that separates the area of the nation receiving an abundance of rainfall each year from the area suffering an annual shortage.
    b. the watershed separating the rivers flowing eastward into the Atlantic from those draining westward into the Pacific.
    c. the process 200 million years ago by which the continents drifted apart to form the landmasses we know today.
    d. none of the above

20. Agriculture was first engaged in by the Indians of the   **c**
    a. Pacific Northwest.
    b. desert Southwest.
    c. midwestern heartland.
    d. Atlantic seaboard.

21. Which region of North America fits the following description: a wide, flat lowland,   d
heavily wooded with a mixture of broadleaf and coniferous forests, ribboned with
numerous small rivers, occasionally swampy, often miserably hot and humid in
summer.
    a. New England
    b. Pacific Northwest
    c. the Great Basin
    d. the tidewater region

22. The history of southwestern Indian cultures over many centuries demonstrates   a
    a. that human beings have a remarkable ability to thrive despite nature's
    inclemency.
    b. that myths and legends are more important than geography and climate in
    shaping a culture's history.
    c. that the destructive power of nature always triumphs.
    d. all of the above

23. The climate of the southwestern United States can be described as   b
    a. a stark, treeless tundra of grasses, lichens, and stunted shrubs, reborn in fleet-
    ing summers of colorful flowers and returning birds.
    b. arid, searingly hot on summer days and cold on winter nights, with dust
    storms, cloudbursts, flash floods, and plants and animals specially adapted to
    the environmental conditions.
    c. an area of broad, low hills, beautiful, isolated, and impoverished, with an
    intricate network of grassy swamps.
    d. a broad, rolling upland of rich, red soil and piney woods.

24. Why did the Mesa Verde dwellers probably abandon their pueblos and depart   b
from the region?   PT
    a. invasions by the Spanish *conquistadores*
    b. epidemics and climactic changes
    c. destructive floods
    d. earthquakes and tornadoes

25. Where can some of the world's richest deposits of iron and copper ore be found?   c
    a. New England
    b. the Caribbean basin
    c. the northern and western reaches of the Great Lakes region
    d. an arc beginning in the Pacific Northwest and crossing the Bering Strait into
    Siberia

26. The region with the greatest annual temperature range in the United States   d
is   SG
    a. New England.
    b. the Atlantic Southeast.
    c. the Pacific Northwest and Alaskan panhandle.
    d. the Great Plains.

27. The process that has transformed North America's heartland over many centuries   a
    has been
    - a. deforestation.
    - b. reforestation.
    - c. depopulation.
    - d. irrigation.

28. What did the Adena, Hopewell, and Mississippian cultures have in common?   b
    - a. They all built cities with populations of about 30,000.
    - b. They all buried their dead in earthen mounds.
    - c. They all lived in the Pacific Northwest.
    - d. They all lacked any knowledge of agriculture.

29. At the fall line   c
    - a. the rivers of North America divide either eastward to the Atlantic or westward
      to the Pacific.
    - b. North American trees change from those with leaves that turn colors in the
      autumn to those with leaves that fall without turning color.
    - c. rivers drop quickly to near sea level, thus making a series of rapids that block
      navigation upstream from the coast.
    - d. the underwater coastline of North America plunges deeply.

30. Which of America's rivers empties through an enormous delta with an intricate   c
    network of grassy swamps swarming with waterfowl, insects, alligators, and
    marine plants?
    - a. Hudson
    - b. Colorado
    - c. Mississippi
    - d. St. Lawrence

31. All of the following helped shape native Americans' social and cultural develop-   d
    ments prior to 1500 *except*:   SG
    - a. geographic isolation
    - b. great climate and geographic variations within the American environment
    - c. contact with Asian and African cultures from which they adopted many
      practices
    - d. long-term changes or cycles in weather such as warming trends or extended
      drought periods

ESSAY QUESTIONS

32. Compare and contrast the development and later decline of each of these major   SG
    Indian cultures: Hohokam, Pueblo, Hopewell, Mississippian, and Woodland.

33. How has the geological, geographic, and environmental history of North America affected the history of the people who have lived here over the centuries? Examine, for example, differences in climate, water, soil, and land formations in order to evaluate what your text describes as "the ultimate dependence of human beings on their environment."

34. Explain what the textbook means when it says that "geographical isolation and ecological variety have been the New World's most striking characteristics."

35. Compare the broad regions of North America—Northwest, Southwest, Heartland, and Atlantic Seaboard—in terms of natural features, environmental changes, and earliest human settlements.

MAP QUESTIONS

Choose the letter on the accompanying map of North America that correctly identifies each of the following:

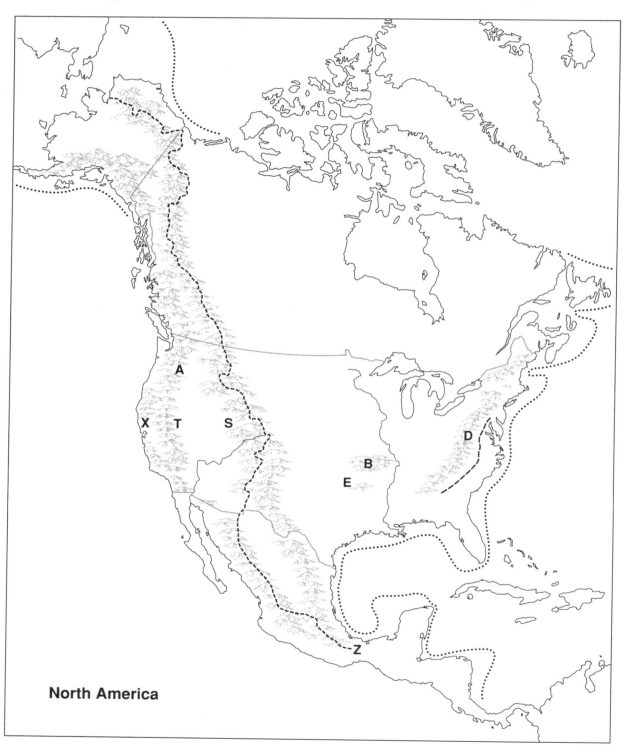

North America

36. Appalachian Mountains   **D**

37. Pacific Coastal Range   **X**

38. Sierra Nevada Range   **T**

39. Cascade Range   **A**

40. Rocky Mountains   **S**

41. Continental Divide   **Z**

42. Ozark Plateau   **B**

43. Ouachita Mountains   **E**

Choose the letter on the accompanying map of the United States that correctly identifies each of the following:

The United States of America

44. Arizona   **H**

45. California   **V**

46. Cape Cod   **L**

47. Colorado   **E**

48. Florida   B

49. Idaho   S

50. Indiana   Y

51. Louisiana   D

52. Michigan   Q

53. Minnesota   F

54. Missouri   Z

55. New Jersey   J

56. New Mexico   X

57. New York   A

58. Nevada   R

59. Oklahoma   M

60. Oregon   W

61. Utah   G

62. Washington   N

63. Wisconsin   T

Choose the letter on the accompanying map of the United States that correctly identifies each of the following:

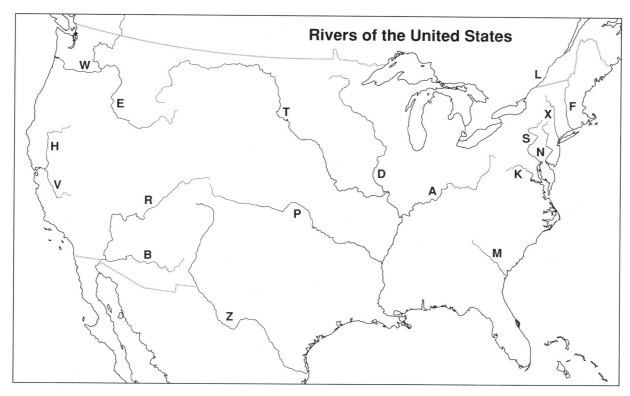

64. Sacramento River   H

65. Columbia River   W

66. Snake River   E

67. Colorado River   R

68. Gila River   B

69. Rio Grande   Z

70. Ohio River   A

71. St. Lawrence River   L

72. Mississippi River   D

73. Missouri River   T

74. San Joaquin River   V

75. Arkansas River   P

76. Hudson River   X

77. Connecticut River   F

78. Delaware River   N

79. Susquehanna River   S

80. Potomac River   K

81. Savannah River   M

Choose the letter on the accompanying map of North America that correctly identifies each of the following:

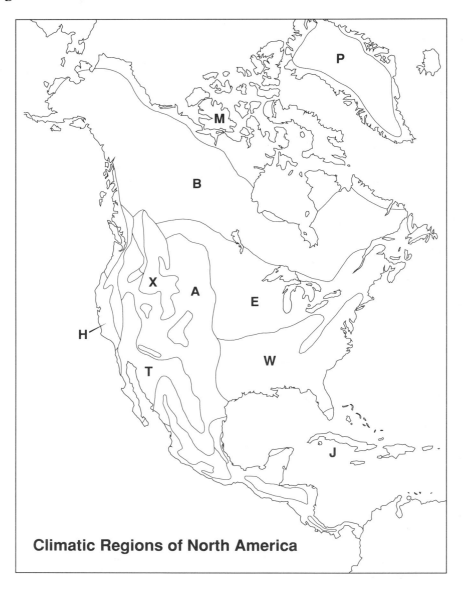

Climatic Regions of North America

82. ice cap P

83. tundra M

84. taiga (boreal forest) B

85. undifferentiated highlands X

86. semiarid regions A

87. desert T

88. humid continental regions E

89. humid subtropical regions W

90. Mediterranean area H

91. humid tropical areas J

CHAPTER 1

The New and Old Worlds

IDENTIFICATIONS

Identify the following. Be as specific as possible, and include names, dates, and relevant facts as appropriate. Be sure to explain the *significance* of the person or term.

1. nuclear and extended families

2. civil chiefs and war chiefs

3. caciques

4. manitou, shamans

5. social reciprocity

6. polygyny, bridewealth

7. European concept of "degree"

8. the family as a "little commonwealth"

9. Martin Luther, John Calvin

10. Anabaptists, Jesuits

11. Church of England

12. Puritanism

13. the "new slavery"

14. Vasco de Balboa, Ferdinand Magellan

15. Francisco Vásquez de Coronado, Hernán Cortés, Juan Ponce de Léon

16. Jacques Cartier, Samuel de Champlain

17. Elizabethan "sea dogs"

18. *conquistadores* and *encomiendas*

19. the "lost colony"

20. Richard Hakluyt

21. Virginia Company of Plymouth, Virginia Company of London

22. Captain John Smith

23. Jamestown's "starving time"

24. Pocahontas and Opechancanough

25. Fort Nassau, New Amsterdam, New Netherland

26. Peter Minuit

27. "beaver wars"

28. Mayflower Compact

29. Squanto and Samoset

MULTIPLE-CHOICE QUESTIONS

Choose the answer that *best* completes the statement or answers the question.

30. How did Columbus react to the natives when he reached the New World?   a
    a. He thought they could be Christianized and become good servants.
    b. He thought they were gullible fools.
    c. He thought they were descendants of earlier Viking explorers.
    d. all of the above

31. At the time of Columbus's arrival in the New World, where were the thickest clus-   b
    terings of native Americans?
    a. the Great Basin of North America
    b. Mexico, Central America, the Caribbean, and Peru
    c. Canada and New England
    d. none of the above

32. In 1492, the most important Indian social groups included all of the following   c
    except:
    a. the village
    b. the clan
    c. the tribal confederation
    d. the family

33. Which of the following best describes patterns of divorce in Indian societies at the   d
time of the first European contacts?

    a. Divorce was virtually unknown because Indian marriage was an ironclad
       arrangement.
    b. Divorce was unknown because Indians had no system of marriage.
    c. Divorce was very common because Indians placed little value on sexual
       fidelity or spiritual values.
    d. Divorce was generally a simple process because kinship was more important
       than marriage.

34. Which of the following would *not* have been a responsibility of women in north-   a
eastern Indian tribes?

    a. fishing
    b. field work
    c. preparation of animal hides
    d. gathering wild vegetation

35. The most common foundation of North American Indian life at the time of the first   b
European contacts was

    a. the nuclear family.
    b. the extended family.
    c. the nomadic tribe.
    d. river-trader societies.

36. Which of the following is *not* true about Indians and their religious beliefs at the   c
time of the initial European contacts?

    a. They prayed to the spirits of the animals that they were about to kill for food.
    b. They depended on shamans to understand the unseen.
    c. They believed that God has given humanity domination over nature.
    d. They explained the origins of the human race in deeply moving myths.

37. The culture of most Indian societies included   d

    a. a belief that their group should be economically self-sufficient to eliminate
       the need to trade with other tribes.
    b. the notion that property ownership conferred perpetual and exclusive con-
       trol of land.
    c. a simple, noncompetitive attitude that encouraged equality and consensus.
    d. a life that was strictly regulated and allowed little room for nonconformity.

38. The West African empires prior to 1600   a

    a. engaged in vigorous trade, were Islamic, and were known for their wealth.
    b. were infested with tsetse flies and therefore unable to develop a state
       bureaucracy.
    c. were generally warrior states with little inclination to develop agriculture.
    d. were ruled over by kings whose absolute political power was based on ruth-
       less use of force.

39. Which of the following is *not* true of both African and Indian religion?   **b**
    a. Both placed great importance on practicing magic and placating spiritual powers.
    b. Both regarded the dead ancestors of the living with uneasiness, lest they become harmful ghosts.
    c. Both recognized spiritual presences pervading nature.
    d. Both believed in witches.

40. Europeans' attempts to preserve "reciprocity" included all the following *except*:   **a**
    a. converting jointly owned "commons" to private property.
    b. prohibitions against usury.
    c. bans on dressing inappropriately to one's social rank.
    d. maintaining a "just price" that allowed the seller a reasonable standard of living but no more.

41. When people of sixteenth- and seventeenth-century Europe spoke of a "little commonwealth," they were referring to   **b**
    a. the generally local focus of most political activity.
    b. the family unit and the role of fathers, mothers, and children within that unit.
    c. England.
    d. the structure of African and Indian societies.

42. Which of the following sixteenth-century European religious groups was the most socially and politically radical?   **c**
    a. Calvinists
    b. Jesuits
    c. Anabaptists
    d. Lutherans

43. Which of the following is *not* a legacy of the Reformation?   **d**
    a. the major Christian traditions of America
    b. a belief in the importance of reading
    c. the ideas that all work is dignified and clergy have no special powers
    d. pursuit of wealth and replacement of traditional reciprocity with marketplace values

44. The group that wished to cleanse the Church of England of popish abuses was called the   **c**
    a. Anglicans.
    b. Lutherans.
    c. Puritans.
    d. Jesuits.

45. Which of the following characterized English society in the fifteenth and sixteenth   d
   centuries?
   a. a stagnant economy
   b. a rapidly growing population
   c. declining per capita output and real household income
   d. all of the above

46. Which of the following was *not* a development of the "maritime revolution" of the   a
   fifteenth century?
   a. new materials for constructing ships
   b. a more maneuverable ship
   c. a new type of sail
   d. better use of the compass and astrolabe

47. Which of the following nations was first in the new explorations that began in the   b
   fifteenth century?
   a. England
   b. Portugal
   c. Spain
   d. France

48. Which of the following statements about the slave trade that developed from the   c
   fifteenth century onward is correct?
   a. Slavery already existed in West African societies and was a much harsher, less
      humane form of slavery than that practiced by the Europeans.
   b. The only motivation was economic, and race had no role.
   c. Africans taken into slavery were often frightened by the horrible looks, red
      faces, and long hair of whites.
   d. Those sold into slavery by African kings were primarily undesirables such as
      lawbreakers or persons accused of witchcraft.

49. The European slavery that arose in the fifteenth century differed from other forms   d
   of European slavery because
   a. the "new slavery" was a high-volume business.
   b. slaves taken under the "new slavery" were treated harshly and were destined
      for exhausting, mindless labor rather than domestic service.
   c. the "new slavery" was based explicitly on the blackness and cultural differ-
      ences of Africans.
   d. all of the above

50. Which of the following statements about Christopher Columbus is correct?   a
   a. He was using outdated calculations and estimates about the earth's circum-
      ference and Asia's eastward thrust.
   b. He embarked on his expedition with limited navigating experience.
   c. His sole goal was to glorify his god, and he thought nothing of personal gain
      or even the finances of his expedition.
   d. He was simply one of about a dozen would-be explorers who roamed Europe
      endlessly hawking their enterprises.

51. Which of the following statements is correct?   **b**

    a. Ferdinand Magellan explored the North American coast from the Carolinas to Newfoundland.
    b. Jacques Cartier explored the coasts of Newfoundland, Quebec, and Nova Scotia and ascended the St. Lawrence.
    c. John Cabot rounded South America and crossed the Pacific to the Philippines, where he died; one of his ships became the first to sail around the world.
    d. Christopher Columbus crossed the Isthmus of Panama and reached the Pacific.

52. Which of the following does *not* correctly portray one aspect of the exchange between the Old World and the New World?   **c**

    a. The Old World sent horses and sheep to the New World.
    b. The New World sent corn and potatoes to the Old World.
    c. The Old World brought venereal syphilis to the New World.
    d. The New World sent canoes and hammocks to the Old World.

53. Which of the following is a correct statement about Spanish conquests in the New World?   **d**

    a. The Spanish triumphed because the Americas lacked any organized, advanced civilizations.
    b. Spanish conquests halted a century-long decline in population throughout Central and South America.
    c. The racist underpinnings of Spanish society prevented any mixing of Europeans and native peoples in the Americas.
    d. The Spanish church and government attempted to curb the excesses and abuses of the *conquistadores*.

54. One of the events considered to have been pivotal for the Plains Indians was   **a**

    a. the introduction of the horse between the sixteenth and eighteenth centuries.
    b. the founding of Santa Fe in 1610.
    c. the death of Juan Ponce de León.
    d. the arrival of French soldiers and sailors in 1541.

55. What was the primary object of Spanish explorers in the Northwest?   **b**

    a. agricultural land
    b. gold
    c. a fountain of youth
    d. furs

56. The first permanent European settlement on future United States soil was   **c**

    a. Jamestown, Virginia.
    b. Quebec, Canada.
    c. St. Augustine, Florida.
    d. Santa Fe, New Mexico.

57. Which of the following was the location of a successful early French settlement in   **d**
North America?
    a. the St. Lawrence Valley
    b. South Carolina
    c. Jacksonville, Florida
    d. none of the above

58. In the 1570s, what were England's objectives in the Western Hemisphere?   **a**
    a. to find the Northwest Passage and to harass the Spanish
    b. to convert the Indians to Protestantism and to establish colonies
    c. to discover new sources of gold and to develop new markets for English
       goods
    d. to lay claim to new fishing beds and to find an outpost to which they could
       exile Irish rebels

59. In their dealings with which of the following people did the English learn impor-   **b**
tant lessons and establish valuable precedents that they would later use in handling the North American Indians?
    a. the Spanish
    b. the Irish
    c. the Africans
    d. the French

60. Which of the following was considered a "sea dog"?   **c**
    a. Jacques Cartier
    b. Richard Hakluyt
    c. Sir Francis Drake
    d. John Smith

61. The first successful permanent British colony in North America was located at   **d**
    a. Plymouth, Massachusetts.
    b. Roanoke Island, North Carolina.
    c. New London, Connecticut.
    d. Jamestown, Virginia.

62. What was the main problem that crippled the Roanoke colony?   **a**
    a. The English settlers refused to work.   **PT**
    b. The native Americans refused to trade with the English settlers.
    c. The British refused to send more supplies.
    d. The blacks brought by the English refused to live in harmony with the native
       Americans.

63. A major casualty of the failed "Lost Colony" was the idea that   **b**
    a. tobacco could be grown successfully in North America.   **PT**
    b. English, Indians, and blacks could live together freely and productively.
    c. colonies could be established by private initiative rather than government
       direction.
    d. all of the above

64. Which of the following is *not* a reason why Captain John Smith succeeded in Jamestown where others had failed?   **c**
    a. He organized all settlers in well-supervised work gangs.
    b. He established rules for maintaining sanitation and hygiene.
    c. He successfully defeated all neighboring Indian tribes.
    d. He imposed military discipline on the colony.

65. After fifteen years, the Virginia colony still faced serious problems, including   **d**
    a. corrupt local officials who defrauded the shareholders.
    b. an exceptionally high death rate.
    c. deteriorating relations with the Indians.
    d. all of the above

66. How were the early English efforts at settlement paid for?   **a**
    a. through the issuance of company stock
    b. through the floating of government bonds
    c. through the raising of income taxes
    d. through deficit spending by the government

67. The French, Dutch, and Swedish settlements in North America were similar in that   **b**
    a. they all were ethnically diverse.
    b. they all existed mainly to engage in fur trading.
    c. they all enjoyed cordial relations with the neighboring Indian tribes.
    d. they all were populated by fervently religious settlers.

68. New Netherland was characterized by all the following *except*:   **c**
    a. greedy settlers.
    b. bad relations with Indian tribes.
    c. religious and ethnic uniformity.
    d. military weakness.

69. What was one of the purposes of the settlement that came to be known as Plymouth Plantation?   **d**
    a. to form a religious outpost to convert the native Americans to Christianity
    b. to establish a community in which all members could freely practice the religion of their choice
    c. to compete with the Virginia colony for furs
    d. to provide lumber, furs, and fish for London merchant Thomas Weston

70. What was the purpose of the Mayflower Compact?   **a**
    a. to establish a civil government, because the settlers had no legal right to be where they were
    b. to reach an agreement on who would pay for the *Mayflower* should the vessel be lost in a storm
    c. to force the native Americans to agree to abide by English laws and customs
    d. none of the above

71. Which of the following events is out of chronological order?　　　**b**
    a. the founding of Jamestown
    b. the founding of St. Augustine
    c. the founding of Quebec
    d. the founding of New Netherland

72. By the 1500s the nuclear family unit was becoming increasingly important among　　**a**
    SG
    a. western Europeans.
    b. South American Indians.
    c. North American Indians.
    d. West Africans.

73. Which of the following statements about West African society at the time of first　**d**
    contact with Europeans is correct?　　**SG**
    a. Slavery was unknown in West Africa.
    b. The majority of West Africans were either Moslems or Christians.
    c. Agriculture had not yet developed. The majority of West Africans were
       hunters and gatherers.
    d. Polygyny was permitted, and kinship groups were very important.

74. The primary aim of the explorations of Balboa, Magellan, Verrazano, and Cartier　**a**
    was to find　　**SG**
    a. a water passage through the Americas and reach Asia.
    b. the fabled fountain of youth.
    c. the Seven Cities of Gold.
    d. favorable places for their respective nations to establish new colonies.

75. Which of the following statements about Britain's Queen Elizabeth I is incorrect?　**a**
    a. She eagerly embraced Puritanism and denounced the vestiges of Catholicism　**SG**
       in the Church of England.
    b. She helped finance the raids of the English "sea dogs" on Spanish ports and
       ships and shared in the plunder.
    c. She secretly aided Protestant revolts in Europe against Spanish domination.
    d. After the pope declared her a heretic, she viewed English Catholics as poten-
       tial traitors.

76. Which of the following statements about English Puritans is incorrect?　　**b**
    SG
    a. They were Calvinists.
    b. They rejected the doctrine of predestination.
    c. The majority of them did not want to separate from the Church of England,
       but to reform it from within.
    d. They rejected magnificent cathedrals and ornate rituals in favor of plain ser-
       mons in ordinary churches.

ESSAY QUESTIONS

77. Describe the native American tribal social structure that might have been observed at the time of the first European contacts. What were the patterns of family structure, sex roles, property ownership, work, and religion? How did Europeans interpret—or misinterpret—these patterns?

78. According to the textbook, "The transplantation of Europeans into North America was hardly a story of inevitable triumph." Explain why.

79. Compare and contrast black African and native American societies before European contacts.

80. European society in the sixteenth and seventeenth centuries was characterized by hierarchy, economic change, and religious upheaval. Explain how these three factors affected European exploration and settlement of the New World.

81. What did the French, Dutch, and Swedish colonies have in common? How were they different? Why were those colonies significant? What impact did they have on the Indian populations of North America?

82. Explain the economic, political, and technological changes that enabled European expansion after 1460. Describe the major explorations of the New World during the fifteenth and sixteenth centuries. What did the leading nations desire? Who were the explorers? What did they find?

83. Discuss the "new slavery" that emerged in the fifteenth and sixteenth centuries. What nations were involved? What were the reasons for the slave trade? How did it affect African societies and politics? How did the "new slavery" differ from previous slavery?

84. What were the goals of the Spanish in the New World? What were their methods? To what extent were they successful? What impact did Spanish efforts have on existing American cultures, and what impact did those cultures have on the Spanish?

85. Compare the experiences of the first English settlements: Roanoke, Jamestown, **PT** and Plymouth. Compare motivations for settlement, economic conditions, and race relations. What problems did the settlers face, and how, if at all, did they overcome those problems? What lessons did the English learn from their experiences in each colony?

86. Why were the English late in joining the European expansion that began in the sixteenth century? What factors eventually stimulated English expansion? How did the goals and techniques of the English differ from those of other European nations? To what extent were they similar?

MAP QUESTIONS

Choose the letter on the accompanying map of Africa that correctly identifies each of the following:

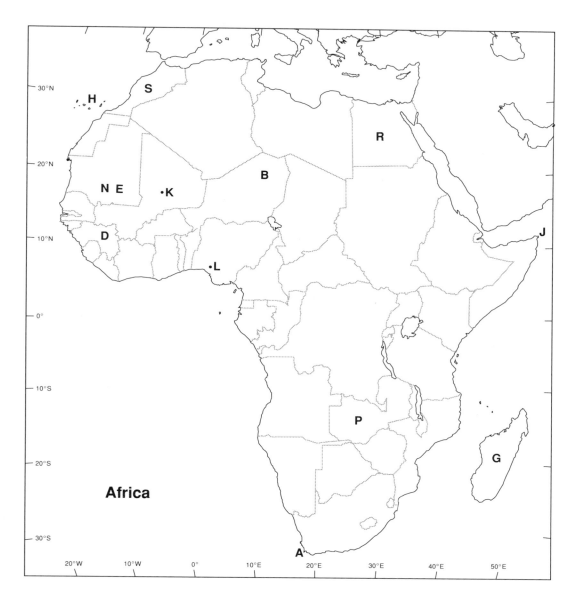

Africa

87. Sahara Desert   B

88. Ghana   E

89. Timbuktu, Mali   K

90. Senegambia   **N**

91. Benin   **L**

92. Guinea   **D**

93. Cape of Good Hope   **A**

94. Canary Islands   **H**

Choose the letter on the accompanying map of the Caribbean and Latin America that correctly identifies each of the following:

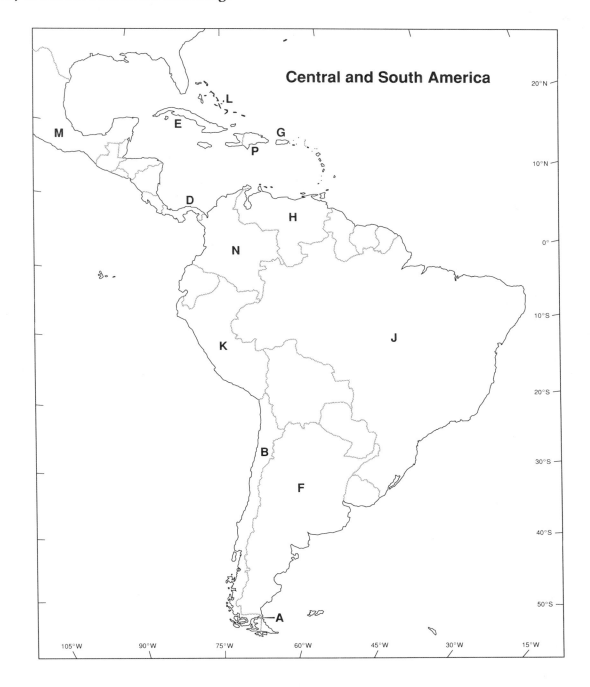

95. San Salvador   L

96. Hispaniola   P

97. Puerto Rico   G

98. Mexico   M

99. Argentina   F

100. Peru   K

101. Venezuela   H

102. Isthmus of Panama   D

103. Strait of Magellan   A

104. Brazil   J

Choose the letter on the accompanying map of the United States that correctly identifies each of the following:

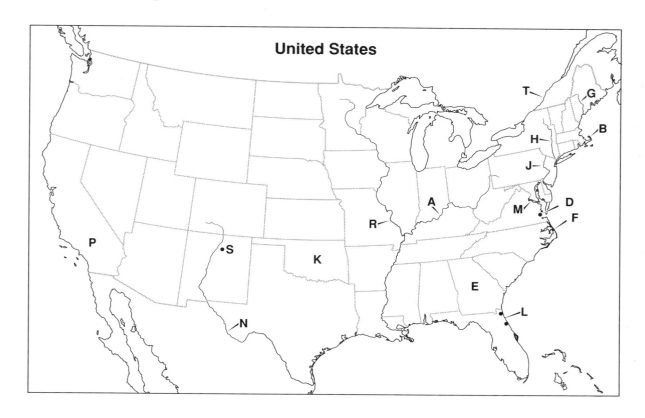

106. Mississippi River   R

107. Roanoke Island, North Carolina   F

108. Potomac River   M

109. Kennebec River, Maine   G

110. Jamestown, Virginia   D

111. Rio Grande   N

112. Sante Fe, New Mexico   S

113. Jacksonville–St. Augustine, Florida   L

114. St. Lawrence River   T

115. Hudson River   H

116. Delaware Valley   J

117. Cape Cod, Massachusetts   B

Choose the letter on the accompanying map of Europe that correctly identifies each of the following:

118. Portugal   **B**

119. Venice   **D**

120. England   **E**

121. France   **H**

122. Spain   **J**

123. Holland   **S**

Choose the letter on the accompanying map of the North Atlantic region that correctly identifies each of the following:

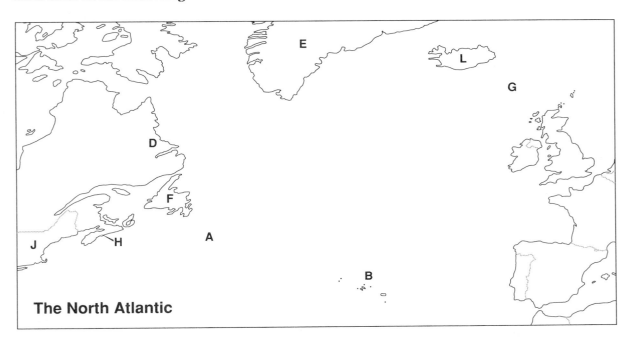

124. Iceland   **L**

125. Greenland   **E**

126. Grand Banks   **A**

127. Newfoundland   **F**

128. Nova Scotia   **H**

129. New England   **J**

CHAPTER 2

Godly Order and Slavery: Seventeenth-Century New England, Caribbean, and Chesapeake Society

IDENTIFICATIONS

Identify the following. Be as specific as possible, and include names, dates, and relevant facts as appropriate. Be sure to explain the *significance* of the person or term.

1. Captain John Smith

2. Separatist Puritans, Non-Separatist Puritans

3. James I, Charles I

4. John Winthrop, Massachusetts Bay Colony

5. Reverend John Cotton, congregationalism

6. the New England Way

7. Roger Williams

8. Anne Hutchinson, Antinomianism

9. Oliver Cromwell

10. the Stuart restoration

11. the Half-Way Covenant

12. the Pequot War

13. praying Indians, praying towns

14. King Philip's War

15. jeremiads

16. hiving out, outlivers

17. Tituba

18. slave codes, the Barbados code

19. Lord Baltimore

20. Bacon's Rebellion

MULTIPLE-CHOICE QUESTIONS

Choose the answer that *best* completes the statement or answers the question.

21. The country with the greatest number of people emigrating in the seventeenth century was   c
    a. France.
    b. Spain.
    c. England.
    d. Ireland.

22. The typical English immigrant to the New World was   c
    a. wealthy enough to afford the passage.
    b. sponsored by the English government as part of an official plan for colonial expansion.
    c. young.
    d. all of the above

23. The Pilgrims migrated to New England *mainly* in search of   d
    a. fertile land for farming.
    b. employment.
    c. political rights.
    d. religious freedom.

24. The Puritans wished to reform the Church of England by   b
    a. reverting to purer Roman Catholic rituals.
    b. purifying it of Roman Catholic rituals.
    c. clearly distinguishing between the clergy and the congregation.
    d. discouraging laypeople from interfering in church affairs.

25. A major difference between Separatist and Non-Separatist Puritans was over   a
    a. advocacy or rejection of a state church.
    b. acceptance or rejection of slavery.
    c. full participation by women in church affairs.
    d. the necessity of a conversion experience.

26. The Puritan conversion experience required   d
    a. self-denial.
    b. self-examination.
    c. repentance.
    d. all of the above

27. What did James I mean when he said, "No bishop, no king"?   b
    a. A king should not also serve as a bishop, in order to preserve the separation of church and state.
    b. The monarchy would be in jeopardy if there were no bishops to control dissenting clergy and to support monarchical policies in the House of Lords.
    c. He favored the abolition of all authority figures.
    d. The monarchy would not support any policy which did not have the backing of the bishops.

28. Economic conditions in England in the late sixteenth and early seventeenth centuries were marked by   c
    a. high prices for agricultural products.
    b. boom-bust cycles and inflation.
    c. bad harvests, depressions, and unemployment.
    d. increased demand for cloth because the Thirty Years' War required Germany to import English cloth.

29. What was described as "a city upon a hill"?   d
    a. London, England
    b. Plymouth, England
    c. Plymouth, Massachusetts
    d. Massachusetts Bay colony

30. Governor John Winthrop of Massachusetts Bay colony advocated a social philosophy that emphasized   a
    a. social reciprocity.
    b. class struggle.
    c. survival of the fittest.
    d. equality between the sexes.

31. Congregationalism as advocated by the Reverend John Cotton   a
    a. placed control of the church in the hands of the male "saints" of the congregation.
    b. distributed decision making equally between men and women in the congregation.
    c. placed control of the church in the hands of the gentry.
    d. granted greater authority to the Anglican bishops.

32. Harvard was founded to train   c
    a. physicians.
    b. lawyers.
    c. ministers.
    d. teachers.

33. Which of the following was *not* considered a religious dissenter in Massachusetts?   b
    a. Roger Williams
    b. John Cotton
    c. Anne Hutchinson
    d. Thomas Hooker

34. The first colony in British America that separated church and state and practiced   c
    religious tolerance was   SG
    a. Maryland.
    b. Massachusetts.
    c. Rhode Island.
    d. Virginia.

35. What was the most fundamental threat to the Puritan social order?   d
    a. theocracy
    b. feminism
    c. socialism
    d. the market economy

36. Which of the following epitomized the democratic nature of New England   b
    government?
    a. universal suffrage
    b. the town meeting
    c. communal ownership of property
    d. all of the above

37. The first generation of New England land settlement was characterized by   d
    a. communal ownership of property.
    b. a few elite families acquiring rights to most of the property.
    c. farms scattered around the countryside, away from village centers.
    d. households situated in the village, with farmland placed outside the village.

38. Puritan society was organized around   b
    a. the individual.
    b. the family.
    c. a social hierarchy based on wealth.
    d. a social hierarchy based on education.

39. New England wives   a
    a. were legally protected against domestic violence and nonsupport.
    b. had extensive property rights under English Common Law.
    c. were denied the option of divorce because it was prohibited by their Puritan faith.
    d. were considered equal in authority to their husbands within the family.

40. Which statement best describes the demography of New England in the early sev-   b
    enteenth century?
    a. Because of the harsh New World environment, New Englanders had a shorter life span and raised fewer children to adulthood than people living in England.
    b. Because of better diets and the slow spread of infection, New Englanders had a longer life span and raised more children to adulthood than people living in England.
    c. Rapid population growth in New England resulted more from immigration than from childbearing.
    d. Population growth in New England was relatively slow compared with the population explosion England was experiencing.

41. Early-seventeenth-century New Englanders depended primarily on which of the   d
    following for labor?
    a. slaves
    b. indentured servants
    c. hired laborers
    d. their children

42. The demise of Puritanism in New England was signaled by   a
    a. the unwillingness of second-generation Puritans to submit to the public conversion relation in order to become saints.
    b. the ascension of Oliver Cromwell as "Lord High Protector."
    c. an influx of Irish-Catholic immigrants.
    d. all of the above

43. The Half-Way Covenant was adopted because   a
                                                                                SG
    a. too few second- and third-generation Puritans were willing to testify publicly about their conversion experiences.
    b. Puritans believed that Indians were not capable of becoming fully Christian.
    c. Puritans wanted to justify enslavement of converted Indians and Africans.
    d. Puritans wanted to show Anglicans that they were willing to meet them half-way on resolving differences over religious doctrine.

44. The native American population in New England was reduced by all of the follow-   d
    ing *except*:
    a. diseases introduced by Europeans
    b. the Pequot War
    c. King Philip's War
    d. the Thirty Years' War

45. The Puritan attitude toward converting Indians was   c
    a. to allow Indians to maintain their own cultural and religious beliefs.
    b. to attract Indians to Puritanism by appealing to the Indians' appreciation of ceremony while relating Puritan doctrine to Indian beliefs.
    c. to organize "praying Indians" into "praying towns" where Indians were taught alien Puritan ways.
    d. colored by the deep hatred whites felt for the Indians, which caused the Puritans to avoid any contact with them.

46. Late-seventeenth-century New England was characterized by   b
    a. a population that was tightly clustered in town centers.
    b. a complex occupational structure.
    c. a subsistence economy in which farmers and artisans produced their own necessities or bartered for them.
    d. all of the above

47. Conflict in Salem, Massachusetts, in the late seventeenth century, arose between   c
    a. farmers and ministers.
    b. fishermen and merchants.
    c. farmers and merchants.
    d. fishermen and sailors.

48. Those accused of witchcraft in the Salem trials   d
    a. were almost exclusively the poor and powerless in the community.
    b. were young, troubled girls.
    c. were slaves.
    d. included both low-status individuals and prominent citizens.

49. All of the following were factors in the Salem witch trials *except*:   b
    a. rivalry between two families, one prominent and one that had lost prestige
    b. rising sinfulness as later generations abandoned the disciplined habits of the founding generation
    c. conflict between communally oriented rural residents and individualistic urban residents
    d. displaced resentment young girls felt for their mothers and other older women

50. In which of the following ways did the West Indies not influence British North America?   d
    a. The Caribbean islands became the major market for New England's surplus foodstuffs, dried fish, and lumber.
    b. The West Indies pioneered techniques of racial control that would later appear in the mainland colonies' plantation societies.
    c. After 1660 a large outmigration of English islanders added significantly to British North America's population.
    d. New Englanders became acquainted with beliefs about witchcraft from Caribbean islanders.

51. During the seventeenth century the greatest extremes of inequality in landowner-   **c**
ship were found in   **SG**
    a. New England.
    b. Maryland.
    c. the West Indies.
    d. Virginia.

52. Which of the following *best* describes the diplomatic situation of the West Indies   **a**
in 1600?
    a. The West Indies was a no-man's-land where undeclared war was the normal state of affairs.
    b. Through an elaborate system of treaties, England, Spain, France, and the Netherlands divided up the Caribbean islands.
    c. Spain maintained its dominance of the West Indies and successfully kept out the English, French, and Dutch.
    d. England ousted the Spanish and oversaw peaceful colonial expansion.

53. Which crop changed the British West Indies from a society of independent small   **d**
landowners utilizing white servant labor to a society of large plantation owners
utilizing black slave labor?
    a. tobacco
    b. cotton
    c. peanuts
    d. sugar

54. Most people in the British West Indies in the early eighteenth century were   **b**
    a. white.
    b. black.
    c. Indian.
    d. of mixed race.

55. The Barbados code was   **c**
    a. an unwritten standard among seamen as to what constituted piracy.
    b. a set of laws that outlined the treatment of Indians, essentially stripping them of all rights.
    c. a set of laws that outlined the treatment of slaves, essentially stripping them of all rights.
    d. a standard of chivalry in planter society regarding the treatment of women.

56. The typical family structure among whites in the seventeenth-century British West   **d**
Indies was
    a. the nuclear family—parents and children.
    b. the extended family—parents, children, and other relatives.
    c. polygyny—planters having more than one wife.
    d. bachelorhood.

57. According to the old Caribbean joke about national differences in the West Indies, **b**
   "Upon founding a new settlement,
   a. the Dutch first constructed a church, the Spanish first built a fort, and the English immediately set up a bar."
   b. the Spanish first constructed a church, the Dutch first built a fort, and the English immediately set up a bar."
   c. the English first constructed a church, the Spanish first built a fort, and the Dutch immediately set up a bar."
   d. the Spanish first constructed a church, the English first built a fort, and the French immediately set up a brothel."

58. Black slave life in the Caribbean was characterized by all the following *except*:   **a**
   a. large-scale conversion to Christianity
   b. a near-equal ratio of males to females
   c. a high mortality rate
   d. the re-creation of African family structures

59. The county-court system in Virginia   **d**
   a. was undemocratic because the justices were appointed.
   b. was modeled after the court system in England.
   c. constructed and maintained roads, bridges, and public buildings.
   d. all of the above

60. By 1710 the basic unit of local government *south* of New England was   **b**
   a. the town meeting.
   b. an unelected county court.
   c. an elected county court.
   d. rule by a royal governor.

61. Which of the following statements about Virginia is correct?   **b**
   a. Unlike Massachusetts, it had no established church.   SG
   b. It was governed by an appointed royal governor and governor's council and a House of Burgesses elected by landowners.
   c. By 1640 the great majority of its plantation laborers were African slaves.
   d. The indentured servants' chances of upward social mobility improved in the second half of the 1600s.

62. Religion in the Chesapeake region in the seventeenth century   **c**
   a. was a driving force in cultural life.
   b. thrived because clergymen flocked to the area.
   c. was not as important a force as in New England.
   d. was virtually nonexistent.

63. Which colony was intended as a haven for Catholics in the seventeenth century?   **a**
   a. Maryland
   b. Massachusetts
   c. New York
   d. Virginia

64. The Act for Religious Toleration in 1649   **d**
    a. was passed to protect Puritans in Massachusetts from religious persecution and was America's first law affirming freedom of worship.
    b. allowed Indians to perform their own religious rites in "praying towns."
    c. embodied the fundamental anti-authoritarian tenets of the Antinomians.
    d. was passed to protect Catholics in Maryland from religious persecution and was America's first law affirming freedom of worship.

65. Which of the following characterized life in the Chesapeake region in the early seventeenth century?   **b**
    a. a relatively long life expectancy compared with that in the harsh environment of New England
    b. the presence of many more men than women, giving women somewhat greater status because of their scarcity
    c. rapidly developing urbanization
    d. a population density which required residents to live in close proximity to neighbors

66. The economy in the Chesapeake in the second half of the seventeenth century   **d**
    a. remained stable because self-sufficient Chesapeake farmers concentrated on subsistence farming.
    b. was marked by boom-bust cycles linked to fluctuations in the price of cotton.
    c. boomed as tobacco prices skyrocketed.
    d. was marked by depression as tobacco prices fell.

67. Bacon's Rebellion stemmed from violent attacks of   **b**
    a. Protestants against wealthy Catholics.
    b. poor white settlers against Indians.
    c. black slaves against plantation owners.
    d. white indentured servants against plantation owners.

68. Class tension in the Chesapeake lessened after 1690 because   **c**
    a. more land became available to small farmers.
    b. the rise in tobacco prices allowed small farmers a better standard of living.
    c. poor whites shared a common interest with upper-class whites in maintaining social control over blacks.
    d. poor whites shared a common interest with upper-class whites in maintaining social control over Indians.

69. Seventeenth-century New England and the West Indies   a
    a. were interdependent because the sugar islands could not feed themselves or supply their own lumber, and New England relied on the Caribbean to purchase its surpluses.
    b. were interdependent because New England's short growing season required the importation of food from the Caribbean islands.
    c. were interdependent because New Englanders used the Caribbean as a "safety valve" for excess population in search of farmland.
    d. had virtually nothing to do with each other because the vast distance between them prohibited economic or cultural exchange.

70. A man's right to vote for governor and members of the General Court in   d
    seventeenth-century Massachusetts was based on   SG
    a. landownership.
    b. wealth.
    c. length of residence in America.
    d. church membership.

71. The following accounts for the transformation that occurred in the populations of   c
    settlements such as Middlesex County, Virginia, between the late seventeenth cen-   PT
    tury and mid eighteenth century:
    a. Because of improvements in medical care, the death rate among poor whites dropped dramatically.
    b. The black population surged as local slave codes became more humane.
    c. The percentage of slaves swelled to more than half of the population as the supply of indentured English servants dried up.
    d. The white population increased rapidly as new waves of indentured servants from England and white farmers from the interior arrived to take advantage of the new economic opportunities offered by tobacco growing.

ESSAY QUESTIONS

72. What were the reasons for the "Great Migration" that took place in the seventeenth century? Explain how English men and women almost absentmindedly built an empire for their mother country.

73. Compare the three different societies that composed English North America: New England, the West Indies, and the Chesapeake. To what extent can New England and the English West Indian colonies be considered "polar opposites," and the Chesapeake colonies a middle ground? Consider the following: land use; labor; economy; attitudes toward commercial activity; religion; freedom of thought; family and community life; relations between whites and blacks, and between Europeans and native Americans; environmental factors; and local government.

74. What did John Winthrop mean when he spoke of his "city upon a hill"? To what extent were the Puritans successful in building that city? How and why did the market economy threaten and ultimately transform their city?

75. Discuss the role of religion in shaping New England society. What was the importance—and the fundamental weakness—of the "conversion experience"? Why did New England's religious institutions—and consequently political institutions—become far more democratic than those in the mother country?

76. Discuss the Salem witch trials, detailing first the known facts about what hap- SG pened and then reviewing and evaluating the interpretations offered in your text of the causes of the witchcraft accusations and hysteria.

77. Describe the role of women and the family in Puritan society. What position did women have in the Puritan family and in New England society generally? To what extent was the lot of New England women better than it had been in England, and to what extent was it much the same?

78. "Born of war, England's West Indian colonies matured in turmoil." Explain this statement from your text. How does this statement help explain the differences between the British colonies in the Caribbean and the British colonies on the North American mainland?

79. What were the economic foundations of the British West Indies? Compare the costs and benefits of the two main crops. How did the planters on the islands maintain a labor supply? How did the "sugar revolution" transform the British Caribbean colonies into "a starkly unequal world of haves and have-nots"?

80. Explain how Chesapeake politics and society were shaped by the following factors: royal indifference, the need for additional taxes, demographic patterns, economic successes and failures, and labor problems.

81. What were the causes of Bacon's Rebellion? What does the rebellion reveal about race and class relations in seventeenth-century Virginia?

MAP QUESTIONS

Choose the letter on the accompanying map of the Caribbean that correctly identifies each of the following:

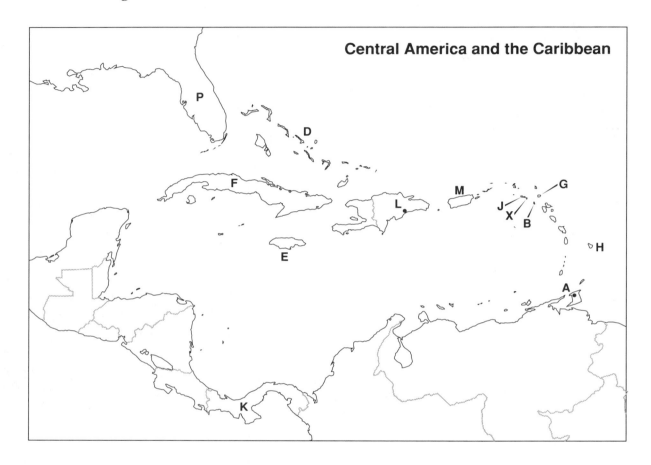

Central America and the Caribbean

82. Barbados   H

83. St. Kitts   J

84. Montserrat   B

85. Nevis   X

86. Antigua   G

87. Jamaica   E

88. Cuba   F

89. Santo Domingo (Hispaniola)   L

90. Puerto Rico   M

Choose the letter on the accompanying map of the southeastern seaboard that correctly identifies each of the following:

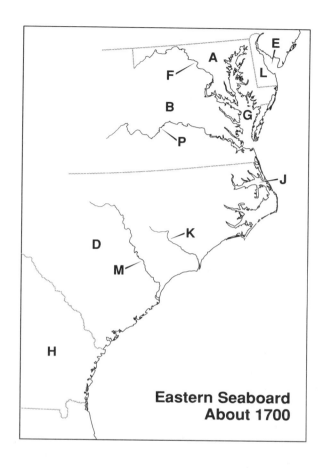

**Eastern Seaboard
About 1700**

91. the Carolinas   D

92. Chesapeake Bay   G

93. Maryland   A

94. Potomac River   F

95. Virginia   B

Choose the letter on the accompanying map of New England that correctly identifies each of the following:

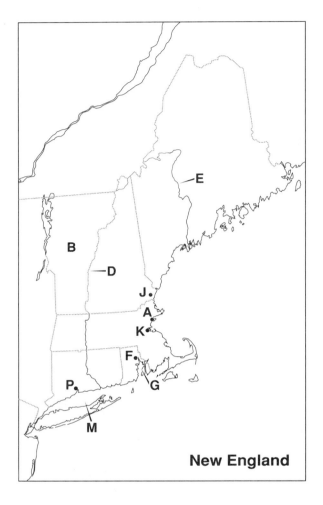

New England

96. Salem, Massachusetts   A

97. Boston, Massachusetts   K

98. Providence, Rhode Island   F

99. Narragansett Bay   G

100. Exeter, New Hampshire   J

101. Connecticut River   D

102. New Haven, Connecticut   P

CHAPTER 3

Colonial Society Comes of Age, 1660–1750

IDENTIFICATIONS

Identify the following. Be as specific as possible, and include names, dates, and relevant facts as appropriate. Be sure to explain the *significance* of the person or term.

1. Navigation Acts

2. proprietors, landgraves, and caciques

3. Tuscarora and Yamasee wars

4. Stono Rebellion

5. patroons

6. George Fox, Society of Friends

7. the Sieur de La Salle

8. *coureurs de bois*

9. Louis Jolliet and Jacques Marquette

10. Pope

11. Eusebio Kino, Father Junípero Serra

12. Charles II, James II

13. Dominion of New England, Sir Edmund Andros

14. William and Mary

15. the Glorious Revolution

16. Leisler's Rebellion

17. John Coode, the Protestant Association

18. King William's War (War of the League of Augsburg)

19. Queen Anne's War (War of the Spanish Succession)

20. demographic takeoff

21. James Oglethorpe

22. mercantilism

23. tasking

24. "swilling the planters with bumbo"

25. the Enlightenment

26. Benjamin Franklin, *Poor Richard's Almanack*

27. Deists

28. the Great Awakening

29. George Whitefield, Jonathan Edwards

30. New Lights vs. Old Lights

MULTIPLE-CHOICE QUESTIONS

Choose the answer that *best* completes the statement or answers the question.

31. According to George Whitefield,   **d**
    a. the Anglican clergy had abandoned Calvinist doctrine in favor of reason.
    b. wives should question their husbands' piety.
    c. slaves had souls.
    d. all of the above

32. After 1660, the English   **a**
    a. began a new wave of colony building.
    b. turned inward to reform their own society rather than establish new societies across the seas.
    c. embarked on an era of free trade by repealing most parliamentary acts dealing with overseas commerce.
    d. outlawed royal ownership of overseas colonies.

33. The economy of southern Carolina was based on   **b**
    a. sugar.
    b. rice.
    c. cotton.
    d. tobacco.

34. The only British colony on the North American mainland to have a black majority   c
in the eighteenth century was
    a. Georgia.
    b. Virginia.
    c. South Carolina.
    d. Delaware.

35. Which of the following is one of the reasons that the cultivation of rice changed   a
South Carolina society dramatically?
    a. Rice cultivation required the use of slaves.
    b. The discovery of a profitable crop meant that there would be more work for
       thousands of indentured servants.
    c. Because rice could be grown on small farms, with minimal capital investment,
       South Carolina became a society of small farmers.
    d. Vast areas of the interior were opened up to rice cultivation.

36. The treatment of the Tuscarora and Yamasee Indians in North Carolina during the   b
early eighteenth century demonstrated that
    a. English settlers should have been able to use Indians instead of black slaves
       for rice and tobacco cultivation.
    b. Indian resistance would not significantly hinder white expansion in the
       Carolinas.
    c. native American tribes could resist white expansion by remaining unified.
    d. the British Parliament was too quick to send troops when it thought that
       English settlers were in danger.

37. As a result of the Stono Rebellion,   c
    a. South Carolina planters engineered a series of reforms that helped create a
       more open and equal society.
    b. the king of England took direct control by ending proprietary rule and trans-
       forming North and South Carolina into royal colonies.
    c. a harsh new code was instituted to keep slaves under constant surveillance
       and ensure that masters disciplined their slaves.
    d. the last vestiges of Indian resistance to white expansion were eliminated.

38. Generally, proprietors of Restoration colonies such as Carolina, New York, and   d
New Jersey
    a. attempted to encourage widespread participation in the affairs of the colony.
    b. never had the confidence of the British crown in their handling of their
       colonies.
    c. re-created a European-style system of lords of the manor and oppressed
       tenants.
    d. wished to create a hierarchical society in which they could profit from set-
       tlers' rents.

39. Why did the patroons fail to become European-style lords who oppressed peasant   a
    tenants?

    a. There was always plenty of good land, and there were always too few farmers.
    b. No single family, or small group of families, could gain control of large
       amounts of land in the Hudson River valley.
    c. The residents of the Hudson River valley would not permit the establishment
       of a landed elite.
    d. The Dutch heritage of small landholding remained firmly entrenched in the
       area.

40. Which of the following was *not* a Quaker belief?   b

    a. The Holy Spirit could inspire every soul.
    b. An individual's Inner Light could best be revealed through the ceremony and
       music of a religious service.
    c. Individuals deserved recognition for their spiritual state rather than their
       wealth or family status.
    d. Women and men were equal in their ability to understand the Inner Light.

41. Prior to 1720, which two Restoration colonies received most of their settlers from   c
    Europe rather than from other colonies?

    a. Pennsylvania and South Carolina
    b. West Jersey and North Carolina
    c. Pennsylvania and West Jersey
    d. New York and East Jersey

42. Under William Penn, government in Pennsylvania was characterized during the   d
    early years by

    a. a strong executive and an assembly with limited power.
    b. Quaker domination of politics.
    c. a desire to keep the rabble in check and prevent haphazard growth and social
       turmoil.
    d. all of the above

43. Why did the year 1663 mark a turning point for New France?   a

    a. The French crown took direct control of the colony.
    b. The trading company that had founded the colony finally began to earn a
       profit.
    c. The English turned their attention southward and allowed the French
       colonists several generations of peace and security.
    d. The Sieur de La Salle arrived and began converting the Indians to
       Christianity.

44. What was the main purpose of France's North American empire?   b

    a. to convert native Americans to Christianity
    b. to support trade with the Indians for furs
    c. to pressure the British into ending their expansion
    d. to provide a location for French Protestants to worship without fear of
       persecution

45. What was the *most* important factor in France's ability to hold its vast North American domain against Spanish and English expansion?   c
    a. the presence of a large and expensive French army
    b. the construction of fortified missions by the *coureurs de bois*
    c. good relations with the Indians
    d. the establishment of thriving and stable communities throughout New France

46. In the late seventeenth century, the Spanish neglected Texas because   d
    a. the French were already firmly in control of the area.
    b. Spanish missionaries were preoccupied with California.
    c. Spain and England were engaged in a series of bloody European wars.
    d. an Indian revolt posed a serious threat to Spanish rule in New Mexico.

47. Spanish colonization of the borderlands depended mainly on the efforts of   a
    a. Catholic missionaries.
    b. cattle herders.
    c. farmers.
    d. fur traders.

48. During the late seventeenth and early eighteenth centuries, how did native Americans fare in Spain's American territories?   b
    a. Mission life helped them to keep together and preserve their traditional work habits and language.
    b. Because they were exposed to Old World diseases, they fell victim to terrible epidemics.
    c. Spanish soldiers slaughtered native Americans whenever they resisted the efforts of missionaries.
    d. all of the above

49. Which of the following statements accurately compares the French and Spanish colonists' relations with native Americans with those of the British colonists by the eighteenth century?   c
    a. Spanish and French colonies were concentrated in strategic missions or trading posts to fight the Indians, while the English colonists ranged throughout eastern North America and enjoyed cordial relations with Indians.
    b. The Spanish, French, and English colonies all had antagonistic relations with native Americans.
    c. Spanish and French colonies were spread thin and depended on Indian goodwill, while the English colonies were compact, expansionist, and antagonistic toward native Americans.
    d. English settlers had strong religious convictions and therefore cultivated Indian goodwill, while French and Spanish settlers attempted to exterminate native Americans.

50. The last two Stuart kings   d
    a. tried to reign as absolute monarchs.
    b. disliked representative government.
    c. tried to centralize colonial government.
    d. all of the above

51. Who was responsible for the following: jailing citizens; forcing a Boston Puritan   c
    congregation to share its meetinghouse with an Anglican minister; looking into
    the finances of Harvard College; enforcing the Navigation Acts; and suppressing
    the colonial legislature.
    a. William of Orange
    b. Jacob Leisler
    c. Sir Edmund Andros
    d. Thomas Hutchinson

52. The Glorious Revolution in England touched off rebellion in all of the following   d
    colonies *except*:   SG
    a. Massachusetts
    b. New York
    c. Maryland
    d. South Carolina

53. Which of the following correctly describes the impact of the Glorious Revolution   a
    in one of the colonies?
    a. Maryland: Protestants seize the capital, Maryland becomes a royal colony, and
       Catholics lose the right to vote.
    b. Massachusetts: Dominion of New England is dismantled, the colony regains
       the right to elect its own governor, and New Hampshire is reunited with Mas-
       sachusetts.
    c. New York: Revolt by a captain in the militia is swiftly suppressed, and New
       York remains a Stuart stronghold until 1720.
    d. Pennsylvania: Quakers are ousted from most government positions and the
       colony becomes a royal province with a governor chosen by the king.

54. Which of the following resulted from King William's and Queen Anne's wars?   c
    a. The French were driven from the North American continent.   SG
    b. The Stuart kings were driven from power.
    c. The wars heightened Anglo-Americans' sense of British identity and made
       them feel dependent on the mother country for protection.
    d. The British captured New Orleans and started to settle Louisiana.

55. Who bore the bloodiest fighting in the course of King William's War?   b
    a. the English
    b. the Iroquois
    c. the French
    d. the Spanish

56. The role of Iroquois women was to
    a. provide most of the family's food.
    b. influence the choice of leaders and other political decisions.
    c. preserve the memory of the past and pass traditions on to children.
    d. all of the above

    d
    PT

57. What was the main reason the population of the British North American colonies shot up in the eighteenth century?
    a. good nutrition and a healthier environment
    b. immigration
    c. discovery of wonder drugs to cure diseases
    d. conclusion of the wars with the Spanish and French

    a

58. On average how many children did colonial women have?
    a. 5
    b. 8
    c. 15
    d. 1.3

    b

59. Eighteenth-century immigrants to the British North American colonies
    a. tended to settle in large urban areas in New England, New York, and New Jersey.
    b. were usually middle- and upper-middle-class professionals or skilled artisans.
    c. included large numbers of Irish and Germans and declining proportions of English.
    d. included large numbers of murderers dumped on American shores by the British government.

    c

60. Which of the thirteen colonies was the last to be settled and the only one to receive some financial assistance from the British government?
    a. Georgia
    b. the Carolinas
    c. Pennsylvania
    d. Delaware

    a
    SG

61. Which of the following statements about Georgia is *not* correct?
    a. It was supposed to flourish by exporting expensive commodities such as wine and silk.
    b. For a time it was the only English colony where slavery was forbidden.
    c. It enjoyed good relations with southeastern Indian tribes.
    d. It was populated by large numbers of debtors who otherwise would have had to rot in jail.

    d

62. Mercantilism was   **b**
    a. an economic theory carefully elaborated by Adam Smith in *The Wealth of Nations*.
    b. a government policy aimed at achieving national economic self-sufficiency.
    c. a colonial American policy of trading primarily with England in order to strengthen political and economic ties.
    d. all of the above

63. The British Navigation Acts affected the economics of colonial America in all the   **c**
    following ways *except*:
    a. American producers of items such as silk, iron, dyes, hemp, and lumber were paid bounties by the British government
    b. imperial trade had to be carried in British ships
    c. colonial clothing and steel manufacturers were heavily subsidized so that they could meet the demand in England
    d. colonial products such as tobacco, rice, furs, indigo, and naval stores had to be shipped through England before going to foreign nations

64. Why did few colonial Americans object to the British navigation system after 1700?   **d**
    a. The restrictions stimulated the development of an American merchant marine and American maritime industries.
    b. Parliament never restricted products such as grain, livestock, fish, lumber, or rum, which accounted for 60 percent of colonial exports.
    c. Tobacco growers were given a monopoly of the British market, and their income was reduced only slightly.
    d. all of the above

65. In general, eighteenth-century colonial living standards   **a**
    a. rose dramatically, to the point where they exceeded those of Scotland and Ireland and approximated those of England and Wales.
    b. stagnated under the weight of British mercantilistic policies.
    c. declined under the burden of wartime taxation and the demands placed on primitive American industry by the great European wars.
    d. peaked about 1733 and then fluctuated wildly.

66. Which section of British North America enjoyed the highest standard of living in   **b**
    the eighteenth century?
    a. the Chesapeake
    b. the mid-Atlantic
    c. New England
    d. the tidewater

67. Which of the following statements about women in eighteenth-century America is   c
    correct?   SG
    a. Women could not inherit their parents' land. Only sons could legally inherit family estates.
    b. Women could not choose their own husbands. The choice was made by their parents.
    c. Women in rural and urban families played an important part in helping to support their households.
    d. Women had legal control over their dowries and other property that they brought with them into marriage.

68. Which of the following correctly suggests the conditions of landownership among   d
    farm families in well-settled areas?
    a. Land was usually cheaper than manure.
    b. Those who wished to own land usually had to concentrate on full-time agricultural work.
    c. Because of low interest rates and small down payments, families were able to pay off their mortgages within five years.
    d. The great majority of landowners could not provide their children with land when they married.

69. Which of the following was *not* a typical condition in eighteenth-century American   a
    cities?
    a. declining population because of out-migration to regions beyond the mountains where land was available
    b. poor rolls that were bulging with the survivors of mariners lost at sea
    c. contagious disease running rampant because of poor sanitation
    d. longer spells of unemployment and declining wages

70. Compared with indentured servants, slaves   b
    a. ate more.
    b. worked for a far longer portion of their lives.
    c. were healthier.
    d. all of the above

71. If you lived in 1750 and were talking about a member of the gentry, what might   c
    you say about him?
    a. "He says that it is more sensible to buy land, servants, or slaves than luxuries."
    b. "I often see him driving his wagon to cockfights."
    c. "He recently received a shipment of costly English fashions and expensive chinaware that he is going to use at the elegant formal he is holding three weeks hence."
    d. "The town gossip is that he is deeply in debt and has yet to accumulate enough savings to purchase a farm of his own."

72. After the middle of the eighteenth century, what was the generally accepted objective of Chesapeake landowners such as George Washington and Thomas Jefferson?   d

    a. to concentrate all the estate's resources on the profitable cultivation of one crop
    b. to refinance their operations by using slaves as collateral for new loans
    c. to free themselves from the economic cycles of the English market by developing new markets in France or Spain
    d. to achieve self-sufficiency on their estates and to diversify away from dependence on a single crop

73. What was the typical qualification for holding office in eighteenth-century English colonies, outside of New England?   a

    a. property ownership of at least 1,000 acres
    b. there were none; any voter could hold office
    c. membership in the Anglican church
    d. being born in the colonies, or having lived there at least thirty-five years

74. Which of the following could vote in the English colonies?   d

    a. women
    b. blacks
    c. Indians
    d. none of the above

75. To which branch of government did the colonial gentry turn to defend their own interests?   b

    a. the crown in London
    b. the lower house of the legislature (the assembly)
    c. the upper house of the legislature (the council)
    d. the executive branch (the governor)

76. The considerable powers that colonial governors possessed included all of the following *except*:   c

    a. the right to veto acts
    b. the power to call or dismiss assembly sessions at will
    c. control over taxes and the budget
    d. the authority to schedule elections at any time

77. Which of the following was *not* one of Benjamin Franklin's accomplishments?   a

    a. initiating a movement to encourage organized churches to resolve their theological differences
    b. establishing Philadelphia's first volunteer fire company
    c. organizing the American Philosophical Society
    d. inspiring the creation of a circulating library

78. What did most eighteenth-century American intellectuals think about science?

    a. They suspected that the mysteries of the universe were too complex for any human to truly understand.
    b. They believed that science could be useful because it could make everyone's life more comfortable.
    c. They feared that science could pose the greatest threat to organized religion since the Reformation.
    d. all of the above

    b

79. Deists

    a. argued that the only true knowledge was religious truth, and that God was unknowable.
    b. insisted that where the Bible conflicted with reason, one should follow the words of the Bible rather than the false dictates of reason.
    c. believed in a God who had created a perfect universe and then allowed it to operate according to natural laws.
    d. claimed that the best argument against the existence of God could be derived through the study of nature's harmony and order.

    c

80. The Great Awakening was

    a. an attempt at opening the eyes of Americans to the need for a more rational American religion.
    b. the realization by the colonial elites that regulations imposed upon them by the Board of Trade were restricting their liberties.
    c. a movement by American religious leaders to reunite many warring sects into one Protestant church.
    d. a revival movement that emphasized the corruption of human nature, the fury of divine wrath, and the need for immediate repentance.

    d

81. New Light preachers like Gilbert Tennent shook the foundations of the social order by sowing seeds of doubt about

    a. ministers.
    b. merchants.
    c. royal governors.
    d. imperial tax collectors.

    a

82. Which of the following was *not* a long-term effect of the Great Awakening?

    a. the founding of new colleges such as Columbia, Princeton, Brown, Rutgers, and Dartmouth
    b. the decline in the influence of Presbyterians, Baptists, and Methodists, and the increasing importance of Quakers, Anglicans, and Congregationalists
    c. the emergence of black Protestantism
    d. the fostering of religious toleration by blurring theological differences among New Lights

    b

ESSAY QUESTIONS

83. How did the Great Awakening and the Enlightenment influence colonial American intellectual and religious life, and colonial life generally? What were the possible political ramifications? Discuss, especially, Benjamin Franklin and George Whitefield.

84. Compare the "Restoration" colonies: Carolina, New York, New Jersey, and Pennsylvania. Why were they founded, who settled there, and what were the economic and political successes and failures in each colony? How did the social, economic, and political systems of those colonies compare?

85. Why did slavery develop in the Carolinas? How did northern and southern Carolina differ? Did slave conditions improve or worsen over the years? Discuss how slaves lived and worked, and compare their lives with those of indentured servants.

86. Compare the Spanish and French attempts at developing their American colonies in the seventeenth century. Why were the colonies established? What were the main successes and failures? Discuss their economies, their relations with native Americans, and the extent to which the imperial governments exercised control over Spanish and French colonists.

87. What were the causes of the Glorious Revolution? What was its immediate (short-term) impact on the English colonies? Discuss, especially, Massachusetts, New York, and Maryland. What was the long-term impact?

88. Explain how North America became an extension of Europe's battlefields from the late seventeenth century to the mid eighteenth century. What impact did these wars have on the relationship between the colonies and the government in England?

89. How did European expansion affect native American culture? How did native Americans affect European expansion in North America? What was the role of women in native American culture?

90. In what sense was the colonial economy and society "maturing" during the eighteenth century? Discuss economy, population, standard of living, literacy, colonial elites, and politics.

91. Historians have long debated the impact of Britain's mercantilist economic policy on the colonies. Explain the mercantilist economic theory and show how Parliament incorporated it in the "navigation system." According to Chapter 3, in what ways did that system hurt and benefit America? Does the author believe the harm outweighed the benefits?

92. Describe the gentry and the urban elite in eighteenth-century colonial America. What role did they play in politics? How did they set the tone for society generally?

MAP QUESTIONS

Choose the letter on the accompanying map of the United States that correctly identifies each of the following:

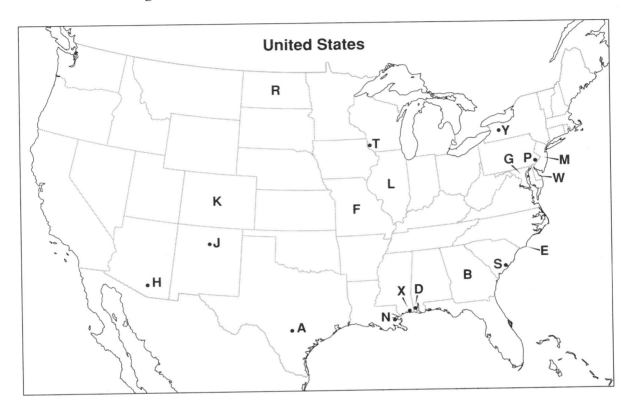

93. Charles Town, South Carolina

94. Cape Fear, North Carolina

95. New Jersey

96. Philadelphia, Pennsylvania

97. Delaware

98. Maryland

99. Prairie du Chien, Wisconsin

100. Biloxi, Mississippi

101. Mobile, Alabama

102. New Orleans

103. San Antonio

S

E

M

P

W

G

T

X

D

N

A

104. Sante Fe   J

105. Tucson   H

106. Geneseo, New York   Y

107. North Dakota   R

108. Colorado   K

109. Missouri   F

110. Illinois   L

111. Georgia   B

Choose the letter on the accompanying map of North America that correctly identifies each of the following:

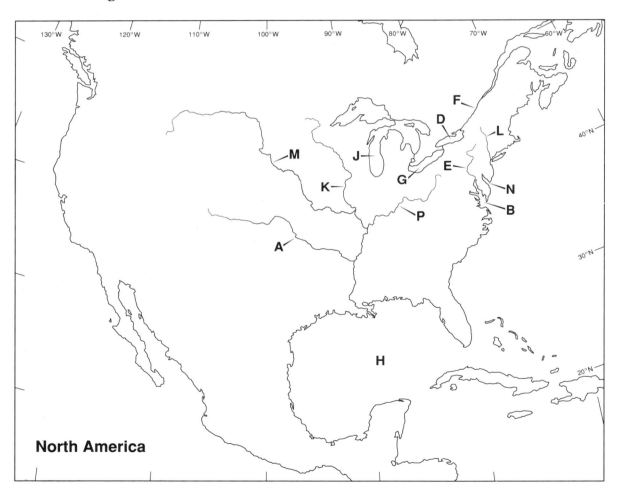

112. Chesapeake Bay   **B**

113. St. Lawrence River   **F**

114. Mississippi River   **K**

115. Arkansas River   **A**

116. Ohio River   **P**

117. Gulf of Mexico   **H**

118. Lake Ontario   **D**

CHAPTER 4

The Road to Revolution, 1748–1776

IDENTIFICATIONS

Identify the following. Be as specific as possible, and include names, dates, and relevant facts as appropriate. Be sure to explain the *significance* of the person or term.

1. King George's War, French and Indian Wars

2. Albany Plan of Union

3. Thomas Hutchinson

4. Louisbourg, Fort Duquesne, Fort Necessity

5. Treaty of Paris of 1763

6. Pontiac's Rebellion

7. Proclamation of 1763

8. salutary neglect

9. Frederick, Lord North

10. writs of assistance

11. Sugar Act

12. Stamp Act, Stamp Act Congress

13. virtual representation

14. the Loyal Nine, the Sons of Liberty

15. Declaratory Act

16. Charles Townshend, Revenue Act of 1767

17. John Dickinson, *Letters from a Farmer*

18. Samuel Adams's circular letter and *Journal of the Times*

19. non-importation and nonconsumption agreements

20. American Board of Customs Commissioners

21. Boston Massacre

22. Regulator movement

23. committees of correspondence

24. *Gaspee* incident

25. Tea Act of 1773, Boston Tea Party

26. Coercive Acts, Quebec Act, Intolerable Acts

27. Suffolk Resolves

28. Continental Association

29. Olive Branch Petition

30. Thomas Paine, *Common Sense*

MULTIPLE-CHOICE QUESTIONS

Choose the answer that *best* completes the statement or answers the question.

31. King George's War and the French and Indian Wars resulted in all of the following   **a**
    except:
    a. expulsion of Spain from North America
    b. expulsion of France from North America
    c. fusing the bonds between the British and Anglo-Americans
    d. planting seeds of misunderstanding, suspicion, and hostility between the British and Anglo-Americans

32. Which of the following European wars is correctly matched with its American   **b**
    name?
    a. Seven Years' War: Queen Anne's War
    b. War of the Austrian Succession: King George's War
    c. War of the Spanish Succession: French and Indian Wars
    d. none of the above

33. As a result of King George's War,   **c**
    a. the French were expelled from North America.
    b. four thousand New Englanders were killed in a futile assault on the French bastion of Louisbourg.
    c. the English captured and then returned the French fort on the northern tip of Nova Scotia, guarding the entrance to the St. Lawrence River.
    d. France was established as the dominant power in North America.

34. The Albany Plan of Union   d
    a. was largely based on the ideas of Benjamin Franklin and Thomas Hutchinson.
    b. came to nothing because no colonial legislature would surrender control over its powers of taxation.
    c. called for a Grand Council that would devise military and Indian policies and demand funds from the colonies.
    d. all of the above

35. Both the Proclamation of 1763 and the Quebec Act of 1774   a
    a. interfered with colonial claims to western lands.
    b. extended religious freedom to Catholics.
    c. were repealed after colonial protests.
    d. imposed new taxes on goods imported from Europe.

36. Troops under this commander provoked an incident that led to the Seven Years'   b
    War:
    a. William Pepperell
    b. George Washington
    c. Louis Montcalm
    d. Jeffrey Amherst

37. In the early years of the French and Indian Wars, the French were able to maintain   c
    the offensive against the Anglo-Americans for all of the following reasons *except*:
    a. The French had overwhelming Indian support.
    b. Nearly every able-bodied Canadian had been mobilized into a formidable militia.
    c. Canadians outnumbered the Anglo-Americans by about twenty to one.
    d. The American colonies balked at providing many troops and frequently sent poorly trained men.

38. How did William Pitt plan to encourage the Americans to assume the military bur-   c
    den in the French and Indian Wars?
    a. by promising to open the lands west of the Appalachian Mountains to settlement
    b. by hinting broadly at increased colonial self-government in the post-war world
    c. by promising that if the colonies raised the necessary men, Parliament would bear the financial burden
    d. all of the above

39. As a result of the Treaty of Paris of 1763,   d
    a. France lost all its possessions in the New World.
    b. most of Spain's New World empire was transferred to France.
    c. Louisbourg was returned to the French in exchange for a British outpost in India that the French had taken during the war.
    d. the British gained Florida and Canada and became supreme in eastern North America.

40. Pontiac's Rebellion occurred because   **a**

    a. the Indians feared that Anglo-American settlers would flock to areas west of the Appalachian Mountains.
    b. the British had abandoned their western forts to the French.
    c. the colonial government of Virginia had been pressuring Iroquois tribes to move west so that white settlement could expand.
    d. some Indian tribes objected to the alliance that had been formed with the French.

41. A writ of assistance   **b**

    a. helped colonial merchants cut through the red tape of imperial trade regulations.
    b. allowed the British to ransack a colonial merchant's house in search of illegal goods.
    c. required prosecutors to present evidence of probable cause for suspicion of smuggling.
    d. required that specified colonial products be landed in Britain before being shipped to other countries.

42. The Sugar Act   **d**

    a. placed a 3 pence per gallon duty on foreign molasses.
    b. required that colonists exporting lumber, iron, whalebone, and other commodities to foreign countries first land their shipments in Britain.
    c. slapped a heavy tax on American merchants carrying duty-free Portuguese wines to the colonies.
    d. all of the above

43. Colonial objections to the Sugar Act were based on   **a**

    a. its economic consequences or its denial of traditional guarantees of a fair trial.
    b. its unconstitutional goal of regulating imperial trade.
    c. its violation of the no-taxation-without-representation principle.
    d. all of the above

44. Which of the following men was *not* a British prime minister during the reign of George III?   **b**

    a. George Grenville
    b. Thomas Hutchinson
    c. the Marquis of Rockingham
    d. Frederick, Lord North

45. During the 1760s, British tax rates were   **c**

    a. considerably lower than the rates in the colonies.
    b. the second lowest in Europe.
    c. the second highest in Europe.
    d. the same as the rates in the colonies.

46. An important difference between the Sugar Act and the Stamp Act was that the   d
latter

    a. was merely a revision of a previously existing tax, so colonists could not object.

    b. instituted a tax that was to be paid mainly by merchants, shippers, and lawyers and would therefore not upset the average colonist.

    c. received united support from members of Parliament and therefore could be effectively enforced.

    d. was an internal tax that few colonists could escape rather than an external tax that fell mainly on merchants and ship captains.

47. The British claimed that Americans had virtual representation because   c
    SG

    a. the colonists were allowed to send delegates to the House of Commons.

    b. the colonies had their own assemblies.

    c. the members of Parliament represented all citizens of the British Empire.

    d. the colonists were represented in the Continental Congress.

48. Which of the following statements represents the conception of parliamentary   a
power held in the 1760s by most American colonists?

    a. Parliament had limited powers of legislation that included authority to regulate imperial trade but excluded the authority to tax the colonists.

    b. Parliament represented all citizens of the empire and therefore had the authority to legislate on all matters relevant to American colonists.

    c. Parliament included no Americans among its members and therefore had no authority to interfere with colonial trade.

    d. Because Parliament created the colonies, the colonial assemblies possessed no more power than Parliament permitted them.

49. American opposition to the Stamp Act took which of the following forms?   b

    a. street fighters who maimed or murdered anyone who supported the act

    b. primarily violence against property

    c. gangs of seamen who tarred and feathered stamp distributors

    d. a congress that, in the end, was able to protest the Stamp Act on only narrow economic grounds

50. In the face of the colonial reaction to the Stamp Act the British government   d

    a. revoked the act and slowly began to return its colonial policies to those of salutary neglect.

    b. reinforced all British garrisons in North America and prepared for a long conflict.

    c. concluded that the colonies were incapable of cooperating and that the next phase of imperial restructuring should begin.

    d. revoked the act but reaffirmed parliamentary power to legislate for the colonies in all cases.

51. The chief reason for Parliament's repeal of the Stamp Act and the Townshend c
duties was the   SG
    a. conviction that the colonists were on the verge of revolution.
    b. pleas of Burke and Pitt to conciliate with the colonists by recognizing their
       right to tax themselves.
    c. harmful effects of colonial boycotts and non-importation agreements on
       British business.
    d. expectation that the colonial assemblies would voluntarily vote for higher
       taxes.

52. The conflict over the Quartering Act demonstrated that   a
    a. there was strong anticolonial sentiment in the House of Commons and that
       Parliament would not hesitate to defend its sovereignty.
    b. there was a strong procolonial bloc in the House of Commons that was pre-
       pared to exert considerable pressure on the government to maintain good
       relations with the colonies.
    c. the British government was caught in a dilemma of wanting to permit con-
       tinued American self-governance but, at the same time, wanting to reassert at
       least the principle of parliamentary sovereignty.
    d. King George III was, in reality, the main force within the British government
       restraining the ministry of Lord North from imposing a tyranny on the
       colonies.

53. The Townshend Duties   b
    a. required that all legal documents and newspapers be printed on special
       watermarked paper.
    b. set only moderate tax rates that did not price goods out of the colonial
       market.
    c. imposed such heavy duties on imported goods that colonists could no longer
       afford to buy them.
    d. raised large amounts of revenue and helped to reduce the British treasury's
       serious deficit.

54. Who wrote twelve *Letters from a Farmer* arguing that Parliament could regulate d
    trade but could not tax for the purpose of raising revenue?
    a. Benjamin Franklin
    b. Patrick Henry
    c. James Otis
    d. John Dickinson

55. While condemning both taxation without representation and Parliament's   a
    attempts at making royal colonial officials financially independent of the legisla-
    ture, this document also acknowledged Parliament as the supreme legislative
    power in the empire:
    a. Samuel Adams's circular letter
    b. John Dickinson's *Letters from a Farmer*
    c. Thomas Jefferson's original draft of the Declaration of Independence
    d. Governor Thomas Hutchinson's secret letters

56. Which of the following would have been *most* important in influencing the opin-   b
    ion of the average colonial American on political issues of the day?

    a. political pamphlets
    b. sermons
    c. newspapers
    d. books

57. Which of the following is typical of the role that colonial women played during the   c
    Townshend crisis?

    a. remaining at home to ensure that family affairs continued to function in an
       orderly fashion
    b. providing refreshments at Sons of Liberty meetings
    c. organizing spinning bees
    d. encouraging the men to be moderate and peaceful

58. From the perspective of a member of the British government, which of the follow-   d
    ing was the *best* indication of the strength of colonial hostility to the Townshend
    duties?

    a. strident sermons urging congregations to stand up for God and liberty
    b. the increasing membership of the Sons of Liberty
    c. renewed non-importation agreements
    d. female participation in symbolic protests

59. According to the colonists, the American Board of Customs Commissioners   a

    a. pursued a program that was little more than a system of legalized piracy.
    b. should have been allowed to function only if the British government fur-
       nished the funds needed to pay the commissioners.
    c. offered a more efficient and equitable method of collecting customs because
       it was an American, rather than a British, commission.
    d. was hampered in defending merchant John Hancock because of British
       regulations.

60. Who was the prominent American whose experience with the customs commis-   b
    sioners forced many Americans to conclude that Parliament had no lawmaking
    authority over the colonies except on matters of imperial trade?

    a. Thomas Paine
    b. John Hancock
    c. Samuel Adams
    d. Thomas Hutchinson

61. Events in the late 1760s and early 1770s helped to bring about a new consensus in the colonies. What was that consensus?   c

    a. that the government could not tax the colonies because they were not represented in Parliament
    b. that the British constitution could be altered by the passage of new laws
    c. that Parliament had no lawmaking authority over the colonies except for the right to regulate imperial commerce
    d. that the American colonies would be free from tyranny only when they were independent of British rule

62. In the Boston Massacre,   d

    a. a large force of British troops ruthlessly fired on unarmed civilians, killing fifty.
    b. an unpopular customs informer killed two young boys when he fired birdshot at several children bombarding his house with rocks.
    c. a fictitious confrontation, invented by Samuel Adams, took place between British troops and Boston citizens.
    d. Bostonians hurled ice, rocks, and lumber at British soldiers, who then fired without orders and killed five citizens.

63. Which of the following was the attorney who defended the British soldiers accused of firing on the civilians in the Boston Massacre?   a

    a. John Adams
    b. Thomas Hutchinson
    c. Thomas Paine
    d. John Dickinson

64. The colonial divisiveness that existed in the early 1770s could be seen in   d

    a. guerrilla warfare in Vermont between settlers from New York and New Hampshire over Vermont.
    b. Pennsylvania's legal battles with Virginia and Connecticut.
    c. civil war in North Carolina between eastern and western factions of the state.
    d. all of the above

65. Samuel Adams was associated with all of the following *except*:   c
                                                                        SG
    a. drafting a "circular letter" to colonial legislatures condemning the Townshend duties
    b. starting committees of correspondence
    c. serving as the lawyer for the soldiers tried for shooting civilians in the Boston Massacre
    d. stirring up hatred of redcoats in his *Journal of the Times*

66. The colonists' first attempt at maintaining close and continuing cooperation over a wide area was   b

    a. the Stamp Act Manifesto.
    b. the committees of correspondence.
    c. the circular letter.
    d. the spinning bee network.

67. All of the following incidents helped to convince colonists that the British government was set on a course aimed at destroying fundamental freedoms *except*:

    a. Edmund Burke's proposals to Parliament in March 1775
    b. government reaction to the *Gaspee* incident
    c. the Hutchinson letters
    d. the Townshend duties

    a

68. In 1773, the British government passed the Tea Act, which

    a. raised import duties on tea and thereby caused the cost of tea to skyrocket.
    b. granted the British East India Company a monopoly on all tea sold in the colonies, thereby permitting the company to raise tea prices across the board.
    c. eliminated the additional import duties on tea and, as a result, significantly lowered the price of tea in the colonies.
    d. ended all tea monopolies, thereby opening up competition and putting American smugglers out of business.

    c

69. Americans objected to the Tea Act because

    a. it would raise the price they had to pay for tea.
    b. there was still a tax on tea and the customs duties collected on it would be used to pay the salaries of royal governors.
    c. it forced them to drink tea when they preferred coffee.
    d. it forced them to buy from the British East India Tea Company, which sold low-quality, overpriced tea.

    b
    SG

70. The Coercive Acts

    a. restructured the Massachusetts government.
    b. closed Boston harbor.
    c. permitted certain murderers to be tried in England.
    d. all of the above

    d

71. One of the reasons that American colonists objected to the Quebec Act was

    a. it made Roman Catholicism Quebec's official religion.
    b. it permitted criminal cases to be settled without the use of juries.
    c. it gave French-Canadians unrestricted entry into northern New York and New England.
    d. all of the above

    a

72. The purpose of the Continental Association was to

    a. abolish individual colonial governments and replace them with a unified colonial government under royal control.
    b. boycott all British goods and cease exporting almost all goods to Britain.
    c. provide a forum in which representatives of all the colonies would be able to share plans for resisting British oppression.
    d. devise a method of collecting all taxes until the former Massachusetts charter was restored.

    b

73. Which of the following is out of correct chronological order?   c

    a. First Continental Congress meets.
    b. Americans and British fight the Battle of Concord.
    c. Congress adopts the Declaration of Independence.
    d. Britain declares the colonies in rebellion.

74. Which of the following was *not* one of the demands of the Olive Branch Petition?   d

    a. that the government proclaim a cease-fire at Boston
    b. that the Intolerable Acts be repealed
    c. that negotiations be opened in order to establish guarantees of American rights
    d. that King George turn over the running of the colonies to his ministers

75. The mood of the people of Concord, Massachusetts, in April 1775, was one of   b
    PT

    a. unity.
    b. apathy.
    c. division.
    d. confusion.

76. The attitude of colonial Americans in 1775 concerning reconciliation with Britain can be seen in   d

    a. the Olive Branch Petition.
    b. the creation of the Continental Army.
    c. a sentimental attachment to the king.
    d. all of the above

77. In the Declaration of Independence, who did the Americans indict for "repeated injuries and usurpations"?   b

    a. Parliament, because of the oppressive legislation that it has passed over ten years
    b. King George III, because of the crown's apparent intention to establish despotism
    c. the king's ministers, because they had refused to compromise and had turned the king and Parliament against the colonies
    d. British merchants, because their drive for personal profits had caused them to ignore the greater good of the empire

---

ESSAY QUESTIONS

---

78. The American Revolution can be seen as a constitutional and legal crisis. Explain the constitutional and legal issues that led to revolution. Discuss the colonial and British views of, among other issues, the British constitution, colonial and parliamentary powers, representation, and the conception of the empire.

79. What does your text mean when it says, "Of all the world's colonial peoples, none became rebels more reluctantly than did Anglo-Americans in 1776."

80. Between 1689 and 1763 Britain and France and their respective allies fought four   SG
    wars for supremacy in Europe and control of India and North America. Discuss
    the impact of those wars on America and relations with Britain and its thirteen
    colonies.

81. What was meant by "salutary neglect"? Why did English imperial policy change
    course from the 1760s onward?

82. Taxation was the most visible issue leading to the American Revolution. Explain
    why. Were the American arguments valid? Discuss, among other issues, the
    twofold purpose of British taxation; internal and external taxes; and the Town-
    shend duties, the Sugar Act, and the Stamp Act.

83. The British government believed that it was being reasonable in its handling of the
    American colonies. Americans, on the other hand, came to fear that the British
    were attempting to establish tyranny in the New World. Who was right? To what
    extent were the two positions the result of Anglo-American misunderstanding?

84. From the late 1760s to the mid-1770s, an ideology of revolution began to evolve in
    the colonies. Explain the foundations of that ideology. Did the revolutionary ide-
    ology of common Americans differ from that of elite Americans? How did political
    ideology take on religious dimensions? What did Samuel Adams mean by his
    "Christian Sparta"?

85. Why did the British government institute the Stamp Act? How did the colonists
    react? Who were the leaders of the colonial response? Why did "respectable gen-
    tlemen" decide that they had to "keep an explosive situation from getting out of
    hand"?

86. During the two decades from 1754 to 1775, the American colonies moved from
    division to unity. Explain why that change occurred by comparing the accom-
    plishments of the Albany Congress, the Stamp Act Congress, and the First Conti-
    nental Congress.

87. What were the causes of the "Boston Tea Party"? How did the British government
    respond? Did the government overreact, or did it do what needed to be done?

MAP QUESTIONS

Choose the letter on the accompanying map of northeastern North America that correctly identifies each of the following:

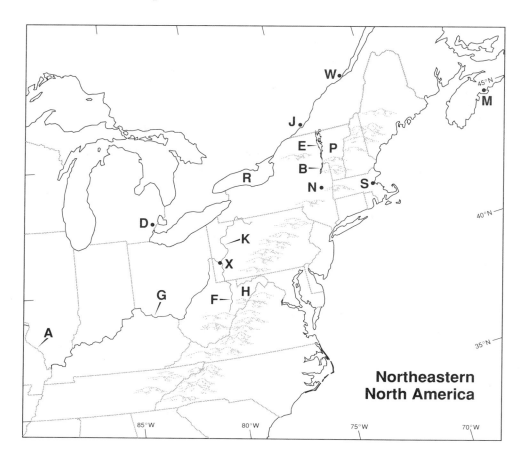

88. Boston, Massachusetts   S

89. Halifax, Nova Scotia   M

90. Quebec   W

91. Montreal   J

92. Albany, New York   N

93. Allegheny River   K

94. Monongahela River   F

95. Pittsburgh, Pennsylvania   X

96. Lake Ontario   R

97. Lake George   **B**

98. Lake Champlain   **E**

99. Appalachian Mountains   **H**

100. Detroit   **D**

101. Ohio River   **G**

102. Mississippi River   **A**

103. Vermont   **P**

CHAPTER 5

The Forge of Nationhood, 1776–1788

IDENTIFICATIONS

Identify the following. Be as specific as possible, and include names, dates, and relevant facts as appropriate. Be sure to explain the *significance* of the person or term.

1. George Washington

2. Henry Knox

3. Whigs and Tories, loyalists

4. Hessians

5. William and Richard Howe

6. Marquis de Lafayette

7. Battle of Saratoga, Barry St. Leger, John Burgoyne, Horatio Gates

8. Benjamin Franklin

9. Valley Forge

10. Frederick von Steuben

11. General Henry Clinton

12. Daniel Boone

13. George Rogers Clark

14. Joseph Brant

15. Lord Charles Cornwallis, Battle of Yorktown

16. General Nathaniel Greene

17. Peace of Paris

18. Mercy Otis Warren, *The Group*, Mary Wollstonecraft, *Vindication of the Rights of Women*

19. entails and primogeniture

20. Articles of Confederation

21. Ordinance of 1785, Northwest Ordinance

22. treaties of Fort Stanwix, Treaty of Fort McIntosh

23. Alexander McGillivray

24. Robert Morris, Newburgh Conspiracy

25. Alexander Hamilton, James Madison

26. Shays's Rebellion

27. Virginia Plan, New Jersey Plan, Connecticut Compromise

28. functional separation of powers, checks and balances, federalism

29. Federalists and Antifederalists

30. *The Federalist*

MULTIPLE-CHOICE QUESTIONS

Choose the answer that *best* completes the statement or answers the question.

31. American Tories believed that   a
    a. separation from Britain was an illegal act that would ignite an unnecessary war.
    b. Parliament had the right to tax the colonies.
    c. only independence could preserve the colonists' constitutional rights.
    d. the king, not Parliament, was responsible for the problems facing the colonies.

32. Which of the following was a loyalist stronghold during the Revolution?   b
    a. New England
    b. New York
    c. the South Carolina seacoast
    d. tidewater Virginia

33. Which of the following would be most likely to support the Revolution?   c
    a. a newcomer to the colonies
    b. a Catholic French-Canadian
    c. a member of the Virginia gentry
    d. a slave

34. Britain met its manpower needs during the War for Independence by   d
    a. raising the recruiting bonuses.
    b. lowering physical requirements.
    c. hiring foreign troops.
    d. all of the above

35. Which of the following was *not* one of Britain's difficulties during the War for   a
    Independence?
    a. a large but ill-trained army
    b. difficulty in supplying the army
    c. a navy weakened by budget cuts
    d. American privateers that seriously hampered Britain's merchant marine

36. The American army in the early years of the War for Independence can be charac-   b
    terized as
    a. a well-trained army with a strong tradition of bravery under fire.
    b. ill-fed, ill-clothed, and ill-trained.
    c. buoyed by a string of exhilarating victories.
    d. floundering because of a lack of effective or respected leaders.

37. During the first two years of the war, Americans were victorious at all of the fol-   c
    lowing battles *except*:
    a. Trenton
    b. Saratoga
    c. Long Island
    d. Princeton

38. What generally happened when the British evacuated areas they had previously   d
    occupied—such as New Jersey, New York, Georgia, and the Carolina?
    a. Local loyalists formed secret organizations to continue a guerrilla war against
       the rebels.
    b. State governments deported anyone shown to have assisted the redcoats dur-
       ing the occupation.
    c. Indians ravaged the communities that had been left without British
       protection.
    d. State militias ruthlessly pursued loyalists, forced many to flee, and coerced
       most into renouncing the crown.

39. At the Battle of Saratoga   a
    a. a British drive toward Albany was halted when General Burgoyne surren-
       dered 5,800 troops to General Gates.
    b. cooperation between General Washington's armies and the French fleet
       trapped General Cornwallis and forced him to surrender.
    c. General Washington was forced to retreat to New Jersey to escape defeat.
    d. fifty-nine cannons that Colonel Henry Knox brought overland from Fort
       Ticonderoga helped to save the day for the Americans.

40. The outcome of the Battle of Saratoga was important because   b
    a. it enabled the British to sever New England from the rest of the colonies.
    b. it convinced the French government to formally recognize the United States
       and go to war against Britain.
    c. it provided the beleaguered Americans with their first victory against the
       British since the beginning of the war.
    d. it convinced Lord North that, as he said, "It's all over," and that the Ameri-
       cans had won their independence.

41. Which of the following nations was an ally of the British during the American War   d
    for Independence?
    a. France
    b. the Dutch Republic
    c. Spain
    d. none of the above

42. Frederick von Steuben was   c
    a. the commander of the Hessian forces employed by the British during the War
       for Independence.
    b. the representative of Prussia at the Paris peace conference.
    c. the man who turned the American army into a formidable fighting force.
    d. the leader of the Antifederalist forces in Pennsylvania.

43. Why were the western Indians firm allies of the British during the American War   a
    for Independence?   PT
    a. White expansion into the Ohio Valley made the Indians distrust and resent
       the Americans.
    b. Indians saw comforting similarities between their tribal structure and the
       structure of the British government.
    c. The expansion of British natives into the Ohio Valley had created a strong
       bond of friendship between the Indians and the British.
    d. Most Indian chiefs believed that after the war the British would be less
       formidable adversaries than the Americans.

44. Which of the following is *not* true of the War for Independence as it was fought in   b
    the West?   PT
    a. It gave the United States a strong claim to the lands to the Mississippi River.
    b. It was fought between large British and American armies and determined the
       outcome of the war.
    c. It considerably reduced the Iroquois population.
    d. It left a legacy of bloodshed between whites and Indians.

45. British strategy after 1778 was to   c

    a. subdue New England by severing it from the other colonies, invading it from Quebec, and blockading it from the sea.
    b. capitalize on their relations with the native Americans in order to stabilize the backcountry and then press eastward toward the seacoast.
    c. seize key southern ports, enlist the aid of loyalist militiamen, and move northward to pacify one region after another.
    d. hang on until the Americans were worn down, out of supplies, and bankrupt.

46. Why does General Nathaniel Greene have a reputation for success despite losing   d
    three major battles between March and September 1781?

    a. His presence on Long Island was enough to convince the British to abandon New York.
    b. France's King Louis was impressed with the discipline and style of American troops and decided to aid the rebels in their struggle.
    c. He succeeded in harassing so many British merchant vessels that British merchants pressured their government to end the war.
    d. He sapped British strength and forced General Cornwallis to abandon the backcountry and lead his troops into Virginia.

47. Which of the following battles forced the British government to commence peace   a
    negotiations with the Americans?

    a. Yorktown
    b. Saratoga
    c. Brandywine Creek
    d. Camden

48. Which of the following was *not* one of the terms of the Peace of Paris?   b

    a. Loyalists were to be compensated for their property losses.
    b. East and west Florida were transferred from Spain to the United States.
    c. The United States received fishing rights off the Grand Banks of Canada.
    d. The British were to return slaves who had been confiscated by their troops.

49. Why did relations between the elites and the common people change as a result of   c
    the American Revolution?

    a. The distribution of wealth changed dramatically during the Revolutionary era.
    b. The new state constitutions radically democratized politics and reduced the power of the elites.
    c. The elites learned that they would have to treat the common people with respect in order to receive their support.
    d. The departure of the loyalists removed most of the pre-Revolutionary elite from the nation.

50. All of the following states ended slavery between 1777 and 1804 *except*:   d

    a. New York
    b. Pennsylvania
    c. New Jersey
    d. Maryland

51. In general, what approach to slavery did the Revolutionary generation favor?   a
    a. gradual steps to weaken the institution and bring about its eventual demise
    b. immediate abolition by state law
    c. support of slavery as the foundation of national prosperity
    d. deportation of most slaves to the West Indies

52. Which of the following was one of the ways the American Revolution affected   b
    blacks?
    a. States throughout the nation abolished slavery.
    b. Northern states granted free blacks the right to vote and repealed or stopped
       enforcing curfews.
    c. New England states took steps to ensure that revolutionary ideologies of
       freedom and equality applied to blacks as well as whites.
    d. all of the above

53. How did the Revolution affect American women?   c
    a. In half of the states they gained the right to vote.
    b. A widespread movement for female equality began as soon as the Constitu-
       tion was ratified.
    c. Their subordination became the subject of debate.
    d. all of the above

54. All of the following were true of the state constitutions adopted during the Revo-   d
    lution *except*:   SG
    a. they concentrated power in the popularly elected legislatures
    b. they all contained bills of rights
    c. they provided for weak executives and frequent elections
    d. they abolished property and tax-paying qualifications for voting

55. Which of the following was *not* one of the accepted traditions, practices, or   a
    assumptions that helped to shape American politics in the 1770s and 1780s?
    a. A strong executive branch was the best bulwark against a tyranny of the
       majority.
    b. Legislatures should have two houses to embody the distinctions between the
       elite and the common people.
    c. Voters could think and act independently only if they owned property.
    d. Elected representatives should exercise independent judgment in leading the
       people rather than simply carrying out the popular will.

56. In the late eighteenth century, what did many Americans think about political   b
parties?

    a. Political parties were necessary instruments for identifying and mobilizing public opinion.
    b. Political parties were factions—selfish groups that advanced their own interests at the expense of the public good.
    c. Political parities could function as the practical embodiment of different social classes and regions.
    d. Political parties would provide stability and a sense of tradition to a system that, otherwise, would unravel at the seams.

57. Who was the author of Virginia's Statute for Religious Freedom and bills abolish-   c
ing entails and primogeniture?   SG

    a. George Washington
    b. Richard Henry Lee
    c. Thomas Jefferson
    d. Patrick Henry

58. Which branch of state government lost the most power as a result of the political   d
changes that were instituted during the 1770s and 1780s?

    a. the judicial branch
    b. the assembly
    c. the upper house of the legislature
    d. the executive

59. For most American Whigs, what did the concept of "democracy" imply?   a

    a. either mob rule or concentration of power in the hands of the uneducated multitude
    b. government by capable leaders elected for their superior talents and wisdom
    c. a system that delicately balanced the interests of different classes to prevent any one group from gaining absolute power
    d. a system that was unworkable in a nation as geographically extensive and ethnically diverse as the United States

60. The state constitutions written in the 1780s differed from those composed in   b
1776–1777 in that

    a. the earlier constitutions granted much broader powers to the executive branch.
    b. in the later constitutions, power was more balanced among the branches of the government.
    c. the earlier constitutions granted women the right to vote, a right removed by the later constitutions.
    d. the later constitutions returned to the practice of single-house legislatures.

61. Of all the political innovations of the era of the American Revolution, which can be   c
    considered the most radical?
    a. the theory that power within a government had to be restrained through a series of checks and balances
    b. the realization that both houses of a bicameral legislature represented all the people, not just narrow classes
    c. the idea that political institutions should be judged by the standard of whether they served the public good rather than the interests of the powerful few
    d. the assertion that government was based on the consent of the governed and that revolution, therefore, was sometimes justifiable

62. The long delay in approval of the Articles of Confederation was primarily caused   a
    by   SG
    a. Maryland's demand that Virginia and New York give up their western land claims.
    b. fear that it created too strong a central government.
    c. bitterness between northern and southern states.
    d. feuding between loyalists and Whigs.

63. Which of the following was *not* one of the features or powers of government   d
    under the Articles of Confederation?
    a. a national congress in which each state had only one vote
    b. unanimous approval of the states required before Congress could enact any tax measure
    c. no congressional power to regulate interstate or foreign commerce
    d. a president elected by the state legislatures

64. The Northwest Ordinance did all of the following *except*:   d
                                                                  SG
    a. forbid slavery in the Northwest Territory
    b. permit the citizens of a territory to elect a legislature and make their own laws
    c. permit the citizens of a territory to write a state constitution and apply to Congress for admission as a new state
    d. remove native Americans and guarantee white settlers the right to buy land in the territory

65. The basic unit of settlement in the territory north of the Ohio River was estab-   b
    lished by the
    a. Articles of Confederation.
    b. Ordinance of 1785.
    c. Connecticut Compromise.
    d. Northwest Ordinance.

66. The British justified their refusal to evacuate their military forts in the Ohio Valley after the Revolution by pointing to America's failure to

    a. stop Indian attacks against Canada.
    b. pay for damage done to British shipping during the war.
    c. return or pay for loyalists' property and pay British creditors.
    d. allow British goods to enter the United States duty free.

    c
    SG

67. Problems facing the Confederation government included

    a. closing of West Indian trade to American merchants.
    b. an economic depression.
    c. continued British occupation of western forts.
    d. all of the above

    d

68. After the Peace of Paris, New Orleans was controlled by

    a. Spain.
    b. France.
    c. Britain.
    d. the United States.

    a

69. Robert Morris proposed to solve the nation's financial crisis by

    a. amending the Articles of Confederation to allow the national government to levy taxes without state approval.
    b. levying a national import duty to finance the congressional budget and to guarantee interest payments on the war debt.
    c. encouraging the army to mutiny and seize control of the national government.
    d. all of the above

    b

70. The conditions which led to Daniel Shays's Rebellion included

    a. economic recession.
    b. huge tax increases.
    c. farm foreclosures.
    d. all of the above

    d

71. What would an urban artisan, a merchant, a land speculator, and a western settler have had in common in 1787?

    a. They all benefited from the Confederation's decentralized authority and therefore stood to lose if the government were changed.
    b. They all tended to have local viewpoints and therefore were indifferent to national politics, specifically the debates over the Articles of Confederation.
    c. They all were dissatisfied with the Confederation and wanted a stronger national government that could protect their interests.
    d. They were the main groups represented at the Constitutional Convention.

    c

72. At the Constitutional Convention,   a
    a. every state but Rhode Island was represented.
    b. all thirteen states were represented.
    c. a bare majority of seven states attended.
    d. Rhode Island, North Carolina, and New York refused to attend until after the Constitution was drafted.

73. The delegates to the Constitutional Convention   b
    a. were dominated by the great farmers from the mid-Atlantic and southern states.
    b. tended to be wealthy lawyers in their thirties and forties.
    c. were predominantly America's "elder statesmen," the generation that had shaped the nation's destiny since the 1750s.
    d. were mainly merchants, shippers, and businessmen with a solidly commercial, international outlook.

74. The fundamental issue at the Constitutional Convention was   c
    a. whether the new national government should be more or less powerful than the Confederation government.
    b. whether or not slavery should be abolished.
    c. how to balance the conflicting interests of large and small states.
    d. none of the above

75. The proposal to create a bicameral national legislature, with representation based   d
    proportionally on each state's population, was known as the
    a. New Jersey Plan.
    b. Connecticut Plan.
    c. Three-fifths Plan.
    d. Virginia Plan.

76. The proposal to create a single-chamber congress in which each state had an equal   a
    vote was known as the
    a. New Jersey Plan.
    b. Connecticut Plan.
    c. Three-fifths Plan.
    d. Virginia Plan.

77. The compromise by which the new government was to have a bicameral legisla-   b
    ture, with an equal vote for each state in the upper house and proportional voting
    in the lower house, was known as the
    a. New Jersey Plan.
    b. Connecticut Plan.
    c. Three-fifths Plan.
    d. Virginia Plan.

78. Which of the following provisions of the Constitution represents an abandonment   c
    of one or more of the principles on which the Articles of Confederation had
    rested?

    a. The states had full freedom to act autonomously on purely internal matters.
    b. No one could interfere with the return of runaway slaves.
    c. Congress had the authority to levy and collect taxes, regulate commerce, and
       conduct diplomacy.
    d. none of the above

79. The relationship that the Constitution established between the national and state   d
    governments is known as

    a. functional separation of powers.
    b. bicameralism.
    c. virtual representation.
    d. federalism.

80. Which of the following was *not* one of the Constitution's provisions about slavery?   a

    a. Restrictions against slavery passed under the Confederation government were
       repealed.
    b. Three-fifths of all slaves would be counted for congressional representation.
    c. Individuals could not prevent the return of runaway slaves to another state.
    d. Congress could ban the importation of slaves after 1808.

81. One of the Antifederalists' key objections to the proposed Constitution was the   b

    a. existence of an independent federal judiciary.
    b. absence of a bill of rights.
    c. existence of a bicameral legislature.
    d. absence of checks on the power of the president.

82. The last state to ratify the Constitution was   c

    a. North Carolina.
    b. Virginia.
    c. Rhode Island.
    d. New York.

ESSAY QUESTIONS

83. Explain what the text means when it says that "it took the War for Independence
    to create American citizens." What did Americans learn about themselves? How
    did the war affect Americans' sense of nationhood?

84. Who were the loyalists, and why did they remain loyal? What were their beliefs?
    What happened to them? Were they treated justly?

85. What were the military advantages and disadvantages of the two sides in the War   PT
for Independence? What important military victories did each side win? Choose
two victories that can be considered turning points, and explain why. Compare
the war in the East with the war west of the Appalachians.

86. What were the terms of the Peace of Paris? Why did the United States receive as
much as it did? What problems did the peace treaty leave unresolved?

87. Discuss the impact that the American Revolution had on American social structure.
In what ways did "the Revolutionary era set in motion significant social changes"?
How did the war "subtly but fundamentally" democratize the political assump-
tions of Americans?

88. Compare the impact that the American Revolution had on blacks and women in
the United States. What specific changes occurred during the Revolutionary era,
and how did the events of the era lay the groundwork for future reforms?

89. Political thought in the Revolutionary era was marked by a dynamic interplay
between two impulses: traditional ideas and practices on one side, and republican
ideals on the other. Explain the interplay between these two impulses, and
demonstrate how they were manifested in the political institutions and innovations of the period.

90. Discuss the domestic and foreign difficulties the United States experienced under   SG
the Articles of Confederation. What were the accomplishments of the government
under the Articles?

91. What were the causes of Shays's Rebellion? What were the results? Was the rebellion justified? Was it a real threat? What side would you have been on, and why?

92. Compare the Federalist and Antifederalist positions on the ratification of the
Constitution. Which side would you have taken?

93. Why does the text say that in the Constitution there was "a complete abandonment of the principles on which the Articles of Confederation had rested." Why
does the text call the Constitution "an extraordinary document"?

MAP QUESTIONS

Choose the letter on the accompanying map of the mid-Atlantic states and Old Northwest that correctly identifies each of the following:

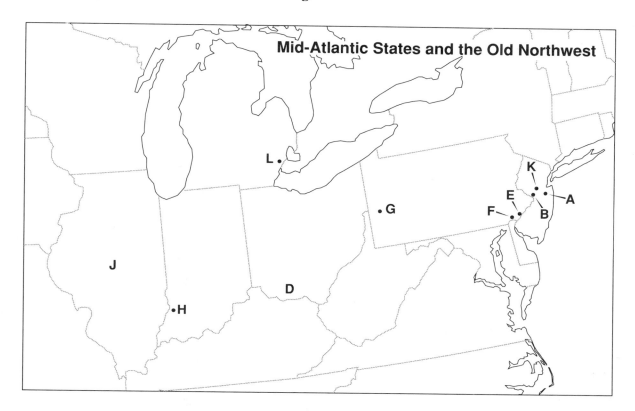

Mid-Atlantic States and the Old Northwest

94.	Princeton, New Jersey	**K**
95.	Trenton, New Jersey	**B**
96.	Philadelphia, Pennsylvania	**E**
97.	Brandywine Creek, Pennsylvania	**F**
98.	Monmouth Court House, New Jersey	**A**
99.	Fort Detroit	**L**
100.	Illinois	**J**
101.	Vincennes, Indiana	**H**
102.	Ohio River valley	**D**

Choose the letter on the accompanying map of the southern United States that correctly identifies each of the following:

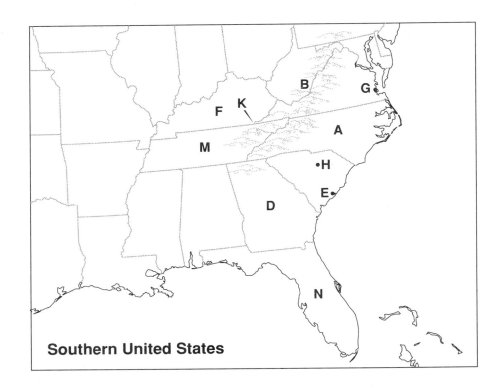

Southern United States

103. Appalachian Mountains   B

104. Kentucky   F

105. Tennessee   M

106. Cumberland Gap   K

107. Georgia   D

108. Charleston, South Carolina   E

109. Camden, South Carolina   H

110. Yorktown, Virginia   G

111. Florida   N

Choose the letter on the accompanying map of the Northeast that correctly identifies each of the following:

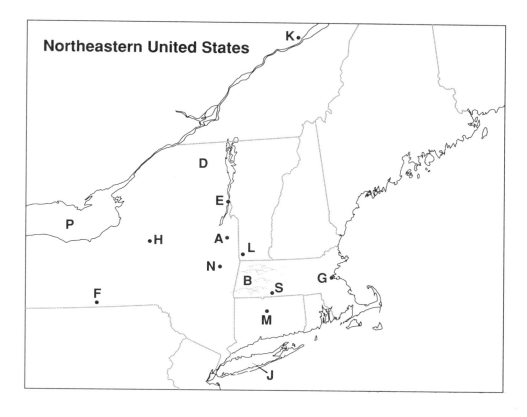

112. Berkshire Mountains   B

113. Ticonderoga   E

114. Boston   G

115. Quebec   K

116. Long Island   J

117. Saratoga   A

118. Bennington, Vermont   L

119. Springfield, Massachusetts   S

120. Fort Stanwix, New York   H

121. Albany, New York   N

122. Elmira, New York   F

123. Lake Ontario   P

CHAPTER 6

Launching the New Republic, 1789–1800

IDENTIFICATIONS

Identify the following. Be as specific as possible, and include names, dates, and relevant facts as appropriate. Be sure to explain the *significance* of the person or term.

1. Society for the Encouragement of Useful Manufactures

2. Stephen Girard   PT

3. mechanics

4. republican ideals, republican virtue

5. Judiciary Act of 1789

6. James Madison

7. Bill of Rights

8. *Chisholm* v. *Georgia*, *Hylton* v. *United States*, *Ware* v. *Hylton*

9. Eleventh Amendment

10. Alexander Hamilton

11. Report on Public Credit

12. Bank of the United States

13. Report on Manufactures

14. strict interpretation and loose interpretation of the Constitution

15. Whiskey Rebellion, Fries's Rebellion

16. Creek Indians and Ecunnaunuxulgee

17. Citizen Genêt

18. impressment

19. Jay's Treaty

20. Pinckney's Treaty, Treaty of San Lorenzo

21. Battle of Fallen Timbers, Treaty of Greenville

22. Federalists and Republicans

23. Washington's Farewell Address

24. XYZ Affair

25. Quasi-War with France

26. Alien and Sedition Acts

27. Virginia and Kentucky Resolutions

28. Handsome Lake

29. Fugitive Slave Law

30. Gabriel's Rebellion

MULTIPLE-CHOICE QUESTIONS

Choose the answer that *best* completes the statement or answers the question.

31. By 1789, Indian tribes in the Ohio Valley had   **a**
    a. formed a confederacy to resist the encroachment of white Americans.
    b. been either wiped out by federal troops or forced to relocate to Canada.
    c. accommodated themselves to white rule and had sworn allegiance to the Constitution.
    d. effectively halted further white settlement for the immediate future.

32. During the late 1780s, relations between whites and native Americans in the western American wilderness were characterized by   **b**
    a. religious conversion.
    b. death and destruction.
    c. a flourishing fur trade.
    d. accommodation through segregation.

33. In the late 1780s, why did many frontier folk feel that the United States government had forfeited their loyalty?   **d**
    a. The British still occupied seven western forts.
    b. Spain still prevented them from using New Orleans.
    c. Indians continued to raid white settlements.
    d. all of the above

34. Why did westerners feel special bitterness toward the British during the late 1780s?   c

    a. Westerners believed that the British wished to award loyalists tracts of western land.
    b. The federal government insisted that westerners pay a share of the debt owed to Britain.
    c. The British continued to occupy seven forts on American soil and backed the northwestern Indian confederacy.
    d. A large portion of westerners were former French-Canadians who had hated the British ever since the end of the Seven Years' War.

35. After the Revolutionary War, Virginia and North Carolina had rewarded veterans with   a

    a. western land.
    b. nothing.
    c. lavish pensions.
    d. the right to keep their uniforms.

36. In the late 1780s, the southern economy was becoming increasingly diversified with all of the following agricultural products *except*:   b

    a. indigo
    b. cotton
    c. hemp
    d. grain

37. If you had visited the United States in 1789, which state would you have found the *least* healthy economically?   c

    a. Pennsylvania
    b. Virginia
    c. Massachusetts
    d. New York

38. What was the condition of the American merchant marine and fishing fleet by 1789?   d

    a. They were flourishing because they had been released from the regulatory restrictions of the British Navigation Acts.
    b. The fishing fleet thrived because the right to fish off the Grand Banks had been guaranteed, but the merchant marine struggled because British sailors were no longer permitted to work on American vessels.
    c. The merchant marine expanded to meet the newly opened carrying trade to the British West Indies, but the fishing industry declined because Americans were eating more beef and less fish.
    d. Both struggled for existence because of the loss of the West Indian trade, high British customs fees, and other British restrictions.

39. Americans from which of the following regions preferred to resolve problems with   **a**
    Britain through peaceful accommodation rather than confrontation or war?
      a. New England
      b. the South
      c. the West
      d. none of the above

40. Which of the following best represents the kind of economy many northern busi-   **b**
    nessmen advocated after 1783?
      a. banking and commerce
      b. agriculture, banking, manufacturing, and commerce
      c. agriculture
      d. shipping and fishing

41. Which of the following was *not* one of the innovative business ventures that Amer-   **c**
    ican entrepreneurs began during the two decades after the American Revolution?
      a. private banks
      b. water-powered textile factory
      c. shipbuilding and global shipping
      d. association for trading government bonds

42. The economic environment of Philadelphia in the 1790s can be described as   **d**
      a. stagnant.
      b. traditional.
      c. stable.
      d. treacherous.

43. What lesson should a Philadelphia businessman in 1795 have learned from the   **a**
    career of Stephen Girard?   **PT**
      a. that great success would come only through a readiness to take risks in new
         kinds of business ventures
      b. that bankruptcy was the certain result of straying into new and untested
         business ventures.
      c. that great fortunes were to be made in fishing and commerce
      d. that immigrants would have little chance of breaking into Philadelphia's
         Quaker-dominated upper class.

44. If you lived in 1790 and called yourself a mechanic, what would you do for a   **b**
    living?
      a. maintain the carriages and carts of a large landholder
      b. manufacture goods by hand in a workshop
      c. repair sails on warships
      d. work at a loom in one of the new water-powered factories

45. Which of the following statements about mechanics is *not* true?   c
    a. They tended to follow in their fathers' occupational footsteps.
    b. Their wives and daughters often helped in the shop but rarely sought outside employment.
    c. They had supported the Articles of Confederation, advocated the removal of all restrictions on trade, and favored a weak and passive national government.
    d. They lived in close-knit neighborhoods with others of their trade and enjoyed drinking, marching, and mobbing.

46. Which of the following was *not* one of the first four cabinet departments in the   d
    Washington administration?
    a. State
    b. Treasury
    c. War
    d. Agriculture

47. Which of the following is an accurate description of George Washington's style of   a
    presidential leadership?
    a. He deferred to Congress on domestic issues, spoke publicly only on foreign relations and military affairs, and sought a wide range of opinions.
    b. He took a prominent role in guiding national opinion, saw himself as a creator of the legislative agenda, and fought bitterly with Congress over his initial domestic program.
    c. He surrounded himself with loyal Federalists, deferred to Alexander Hamilton on all issues, and preferred a merely ceremonial role in national affairs.
    d. He enjoyed the trappings of great power, strove to enhance the authority of the presidency, and conferred only with his vice president on most issues.

48. The Constitution said nothing about   c
    a. passing ex post facto laws.
    b. the existence of a vice president.
    c. the structure of the federal judicial system.
    d. the need for senatorial approval of presidential nominees.

49. The Bill of Rights did all the following *except*:   b
    a. guarantee personal liberties such as public debate, religious beliefs, and procedures for a fair trial
    b. specify explicit limits on federal power
    c. reserve to the people or the states powers not allocated to the federal government under the Constitution
    d. ensure the collective right of each state to maintain a militia free from federal interference

50. Which of the following represents an early Supreme Court decision that was over-   d
    turned through a constitutional amendment?

    a. that the Court had the right to determine the constitutionality of congres-
       sional statutes
    b. that state or federal legislation could not interfere with contracts
    c. that the Court had the right to determine the constitutionality of state laws
    d. that states could be sued in federal courts by nonresidents

51. Who took the lead in establishing the Washington administration's domestic   a
    priorities?

    a. Alexander Hamilton
    b. George Washington
    c. Thomas Jefferson
    d. John Adams

52. Hamilton's domestic program reflected his belief that   b

    a. the survival of the federal government depended on the republican virtues of
       the common people.
    b. the nation had to be industrially self-sufficient, and that the national govern-
       ment had to maintain authority over the states.
    c. America's best opportunity for economic survival lay in its traditional source
       of strength, agriculture.
    d. the states needed to reassert power over the national government, because
       individual self-sacrifice and virtue were most effective on the local level.

53. Hamilton wanted the federal government to take over in full the Revolutionary   c
    debt of the Continental Congress and the states because he believed that   SG

    a. this would cause a heavy loss to speculators in certificates.
    b. the payment of all such obligations was guaranteed in the Constitution.
    c. this would cause well-to-do creditors to favor the new federal government
       and the extension of its powers.
    d. the states unanimously favored such a policy.

54. Why did the southern states vote for Hamilton's plan to assume state debts?   d

    a. Most of them had been unable to pay off their debts and stood to gain from
       federal assumption of that debt.
    b. Most southern senators and congressmen had speculated in state bonds and
       would make large profits if they were repaid in full by the federal
       government.
    c. Southerners believed that a stronger union would benefit the South more
       than other sections of the nation.
    d. Northern representatives agreed to transfer the federal capital from Philadel-
       phia to a location on the Potomac River in Virginia.

55. All of the following statements about the national bank established during Washington's administration are correct *except*: **a**

    a. The majority of the stock was owned by the government and it was run by the government.
    b. The controversy over its establishment brought forth the first clear-cut statement of the strict versus loose interpretation of the Constitution.
    c. The notes it issued circulated as national currency.
    d. It served as a depository for government funds and could lend money to the United States government.

56. The main purpose of the tariff that Hamilton proposed in his Report on Manufactures was to **b**

    a. raise all the money the federal government needed to operate.
    b. protect and foster domestic manufacturing.
    c. punish the British for their discriminatory tariffs.
    d. raise the price of domestic products so that merchants and manufacturers, Hamilton's main supporters, would prosper.

57. The strongest argument against Hamilton's Bank of the United States was that **c**

    a. the Bank of England had undermined the integrity of the British government, and a national bank would undermine the integrity of the American government.
    b. the bank would accumulate immense wealth.
    c. the Constitution had given Congress no specific authorization to issue charters of incorporation.
    d. the nation should avoid commercial activity and should remain true to its agrarian roots.

58. Hamilton's contention that a federal activity could be unconstitutional only if the Constitution specifically forbade the government from engaging in that activity is known as **d**

    a. strict interpretation of the Constitution.
    b. federalism.
    c. republicanism.
    d. loose interpretation of the Constitution.

59. Political coalitions began to develop during Washington's first term over the issue of **a**

    a. Hamilton's financial program.
    b. the creation of the federal court system.
    c. interference with American shipping by France and Britain.
    d. Washington's successor.

60. The first significant challenge to the authority of the new federal government   **b**
    occurred
    a. on the high seas.
    b. in western Pennsylvania.
    c. in western Massachusetts.
    d. in New Orleans.

61. What did the Whiskey Rebellion demonstrate?   **c**
    a. that Americans faced a serious challenge from alcoholism
    b. that the young government had still not become strong enough to enforce its
       laws
    c. that dissent could be expressed only through the constitutional system of
       laws and elections, not through armed rebellion
    d. that sectionalism was stronger than nationalism

62. The Washington administration's policy of pacifying the northwestern and south-   **d**
    western Indian tribes to weaken their friendship with Britain and Spain
    a. was derailed by New Englanders who feared disrupting commercial relations
       with Britain.
    b. constituted the greatest diplomatic triumph of the administration.
    c. ended when France's revolutionary government sent Citizen Genêt to the
       frontier to recruit Indians for the French side.
    d. failed completely.

63. Which of the following accurately describes American opinion regarding the   **a**
    Anglo-French struggle after the French Revolution?
    a. New Englanders favored Britain because they believed that good relations
       with the British were essential to the region's prosperity.
    b. Southerners favored Britain because they believed that the British offered the
       best potential market for southern agricultural exports.
    c. New Englanders favored France because of the alliance signed during the
       American Revolution and because of their desire to see the French humiliate
       King George III.
    d. New Englanders, Southerners, and most residents of the Middle Atlantic
       states believed that the Washington administration's declaration of American
       neutrality was the only way to ensure the survival of their young republic.

64. How did the United States government respond to France's declaration of war on   **b**
    Britain in 1793?
    a. by declaring war against France
    b. by proclaiming neutrality
    c. by reaffirming the 1778 Franco-American alliance
    d. by suddenly seizing the western forts occupied by Britain

65. Citizen Genêt was

    a. one of the French representatives who had demanded a bribe in the XYZ Affair.
    b. the leader of a slave uprising on Saint Domingue in 1791.
    c. the French minister to the United States who was instructed to enlist American mercenaries to conquer Spanish territories and attack British shipping.
    d. the leader of the Creek Indians who signed a peace treaty with the United States permitting whites to occupy lands in the Georgia piedmont.

c

66. Which of the following was a British practice that damaged Anglo-American relations during the Washington administration?

    a. confiscating foreign ships trading with the French Caribbean islands
    b. forcibly enlisting American crewmen into the British navy
    c. building new forts on American soil
    d. all of the above

d

67. The Treaty of Greenville

    a. opened most of modern-day Ohio to white settlement and ended Indian hostilities there.
    b. opened New Orleans to American shippers and guaranteed American rights to use the Mississippi River.
    c. reopened the British West Indies to American commerce.
    d. released the United States from the obligations it had incurred in its 1778 alliance with France.

a

68. Which of the following was one of the accomplishments of Jay's Treaty?

    a. It ended the British practice of impressment.
    b. It arranged for withdrawal of British troops from American soil.
    c. It reopened the British West Indies trade to American ships.
    d. It settled the issue of compensation for slaves taken during the Revolution.

b

69. Which of the following treaties was an unqualified diplomatic triumph for the United States?

    a. Jay's Treaty
    b. Treaty of Greenville
    c. Pinckney's Treaty
    d. none of the above

c

70. How was the United States able to gain unrestricted access to the Mississippi River and New Orleans?

    a. by sending 3,000 regulars and Kentucky militiamen across the river into Spanish territory
    b. by signing an alliance with France against Spain
    c. by buying New Orleans from the French
    d. by negotiating a treaty with Spain

d

71. Who might have agreed with the statements that "the many do not think at all," and that democracy means "government by the passions of the multitude."   **a**
    a. Alexander Hamilton
    b. Thomas Jefferson
    c. Edmond Genêt
    d. Stephen Girard

72. Who might have agreed with the statement that "liberty is safe only if power is diffused among virtuous, independent citizens."   **b**
    a. John Adams
    b. Thomas Jefferson
    c. Alexander Hamilton
    d. Fisher Ames

73. All of the following might have belonged to one of the Democratic societies formed in the 1790s *except*:   **c**
    a. a planter
    b. an artisan
    c. a clergyman
    d. a sailor

74. What role did newspapers play in American politics during the mid and late 1790s?   **d**
    a. They declined in circulation and became mainly the means for the elite to communicate among themselves.
    b. They expanded in number and circulation and through their carefully reasoned articles and editorials helped to raise the quality of public discussion.
    c. They declined dramatically in influence because both Republicans and Federalists turned against their incessant fear-mongering and character assassination.
    d. They expanded in number and circulation and, regardless of political perspective, were often libelous and irresponsible.

75. What was the central charge that Republicans aimed at Federalists during the late 1790s?   **a**
    a. that Federalists had become a faction bent on enriching wealthy citizens at the taxpayers' expense and that they were scheming to introduce legal privilege, aristocracy, and monarchy
    b. that Federalists were free-thinking libertines who planned to eliminate religion in the United States
    c. that Federalists were plotting a reign of terror and eventually wished to turn the nation over to France
    d. that Federalists, by favoring an agrarian society, were out of touch with the economic forces transforming the nation

76. Who said the following about whom? ". . . treacherous in private friendship . . .   b
    and a hypocrite in public life, the world will be puzzled to decide whether you are
    an apostate or an imposter, whether you have abandoned good principles or ever
    had any."
    a. John Adams about Thomas Jefferson
    b. Thomas Paine about George Washington
    c. Thomas Jefferson about Alexander Hamilton
    d. Gabriel Prosser about Martha Washington

77. Who became a prime target for Republican recruiters preceding the presidential   c
    election of 1796?
    a. women
    b. merchants
    c. immigrants
    d. army veterans

78. All of the following statements about the XYZ Affair are correct *except*:   a
    a. Republican participation in it helped defeat Jefferson and elect Adams presi-   SG
       dent in 1796.
    b. It happened during Adams's administration.
    c. Taking advantage of the wave of anti-French feeling it generated, Congress
       enlarged the army and passed the Alien and Sedition Acts.
    d. It arose out of the French government's demand for a bribe as the price for
       negotiations.

79. The Sedition Act   d
    a. forbade any individual to oppose any law of the United States.
    b. made it illegal to speak, write, or print any statement about the president that
       would put him into disrepute.
    c. was designed to be in effect for only three years.
    d. all of the above

80. The Virginia and Kentucky Resolutions   d
    a. attacked the Alien and Sedition Acts.   SG
    b. were written by Madison and Jefferson.
    c. claimed the right of a state to protect its people from unconstitutional federal
       laws.
    d. all of the above

81. Which action of President Adams angered the "High Federalists"?   c
    a. his handling of the XYZ Affair   SG
    b. his signing of the Alien and Sedition Acts
    c. his decision to improve relations with France in 1799–1800
    d. his request for a larger army

82. During the early years of the United States, Indian tribes   b
    a. embraced Revolutionary ideology and began to assume roles of equality in white society.
    b. experienced a social and moral crisis.
    c. grew in power and strength.
    d. experienced a revival of their traditional cultures.

83. Beginning in the late 1790s, which of the following helped to shape the treatment   b
    of blacks?
    a. the decision to build the new national capital largely with slave labor
    b. the bloody slave revolt on Saint Domingue and the abortive slave insurrection in Virginia
    c. George Washington's freeing of his slaves at the end of his life
    d. all of the above

ESSAY QUESTIONS

84. The United States faced grave problems in 1789, but by 1800 most of them had been overcome. Explain those problems, how they were overcome, and at what cost.

85. How did the United States begin to change economically during its first two decades? Explain the roles of government policy and the individual in bringing about this transformation.

86. Describe life in America's cities in the 1790s. Discuss, in particular, urban life and   PT
    work as they were experienced by artisans, blacks, the middle class, women, and the new breed of businessman.

87. Describe and explain Alexander Hamilton's financial program and the assumptions on which it was based. What were the political and economic results of his program? Were the political results inevitable?

88. What were the causes and results of the Whiskey Rebellion? What was the significance? Did the government overreact? Compare the Whiskey Rebellion with Shays's Rebellion and Fries's Rebellion.

89. Discuss the hostile international environment that confronted the United States in its early years. How did the United States react? Compare the goals and accomplishments of Jay's Treaty and Pinckney's Treaty.

90. Examine the development of political parties in the United States during the 1790s. What were the causes and issues? What were the political philosophies of the Federalists and the Republicans?

91. What groups in the United States were pro-British during the 1790s, and what groups were pro-French. Why? Which nation would you have supported? Why?

92. What were the four laws that are generally called the Alien and Sedition Acts? Why were they passed, and what were their provisions? Evaluate their effect on national security and civil liberties. What was the reaction to them?

93. Discuss the deteriorating positions of African-Americans and native Americans in the post-Revolutionary period. How do you account for the deterioration? What were the major changes or events that marked the declining status of each group?

MAP QUESTIONS

Choose the letter on the accompanying map of the eastern United States that correctly identifies each of the following:

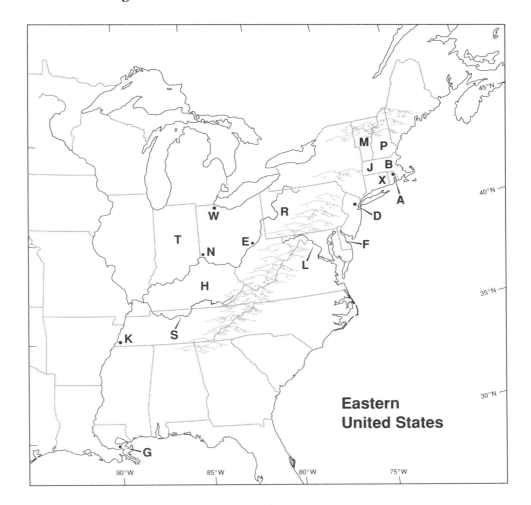

94. Marietta, Ohio   E

95. Cincinnati, Ohio   N

96. Cumberland River   S

97. Toledo, Ohio   W

98. Memphis, Tennessee   K

99. Kentucky   H

100. New Orleans   G

101. Pawtucket, Rhode Island   A

102. Paterson, New Jersey   D

104. Potomac River   L

105. western Pennsylvania   R

106. Vermont   M

CHAPTER 7

Jeffersonianism and the Era of Good Feelings

IDENTIFICATIONS

Identify the following. Be as specific as possible, and include names, dates, and relevant facts as appropriate. Be sure to explain the *significance* of the person or term.

1. Burr conspiracy

2. Albert Gallatin

3. Barbary pirates

4. Judiciary Act of 1801

5. midnight judges

6. John Marshall, *Marbury* v. *Madison*

7. Lewis and Clark expedition

8. Sacajawea

9. Twelfth Amendment to the Constitution

10. John Randolph and the Quids

11. Yazoo Land Compromise

12. British Orders in Council, Berlin and Milan Decrees

13. *Chesapeake* Affair

14. Non-Intercourse Acts, Macon's Bill No. 2, the Embargo

15. war hawks

16. Henry Clay and the American System

17. John C. Calhoun

18. Tecumseh and the Prophet

19. William Henry Harrison and the Battle of Tippecanoe

20. Oliver H. Perry and the Battle of Lake Erie (Put-in-Bay)

21. Treaty of Ghent

22. Andrew Jackson and the Battle of New Orleans

23. Hartford Convention

24. "Era of Good Feelings"

25. *Dartmouth College* v. *Woodward*

26. *McCulloch* v. *Maryland*

27. Missouri Compromise

28. John Quincy Adams

29. Rush-Bagot Treaty, British-American Convention, and Adams-Onís (Transcontinental) Treaty

30. Monroe Doctrine

MULTIPLE-CHOICE QUESTIONS

Choose the answer that *best* completes the statement or answers the question.

31. Which of the following describes American political consciousness at the opening of the nineteenth century?   **a**
    a. Most ordinary Americans were interested mainly in local issues and only occasionally in national issues.
    b. Who would be the next president was always the chief topic of conversation at pubs and taverns.
    c. Ordinary Americans longed for the pomp and ceremony of European politics.
    d. Because American politics was new, Americans wished to avoid political controversy on even minor questions.

32. Jefferson's political philosophy included a belief that   **c**
    a. people should learn to serve the government rather than expecting the government to serve the people.
    b. an established church was the best bulwark against corruption.
    c. freedom was threatened by a government that undermined popular liberty.
    d. to maintain order, a government had to levy substantial taxes and maintain a sizable standing army.

33. Thomas Jefferson favored sovereignty of state government over the federal government because he   c
    a. knew that the opposition Federalist party still dominated the federal government.
    b. wanted the states to be free to build new cities.
    c. believed that state government was responsive to popular will.
    d. believed that the federal government was not yet strong enough.

34. For Jefferson and others, "popular virtue" meant that   d
    a. citizens had the responsibility of leading moral lives.
    b. government had a popular mandate to enforce standards of behavior.
    c. the majority of citizens wished to be good.
    d. a citizen should be inclined to place the public good ahead of his own personal interests.

35. Who did Thomas Jefferson believe were the most vigilant and virtuous people?   b
    a. city dwellers
    b. farmers
    c. factory workers
    d. Indians

36. How did President Jefferson plan to reverse what he perceived to be a drift toward despotism in the 1790s?   a
    a. by reducing the need for taxes by eliminating the national debt
    b. by eliminating the opposition Federalist party
    c. by strengthening the army to stand guard against tyrants
    d. by sending cash payments to America's foreign foes

37. All the following were President Jefferson's ways of cutting federal expenses *except*:   d
    a. closing various American embassies in Europe
    b. reducing the size of the army
    c. reducing the federal debt
    d. bribing the Barbary pirates rather than fighting them

38. Why did President Jefferson advocate naval action against the Barbary pirates?   a
    a. He believed that waging war would be less expensive than paying tribute.
    b. He believed that Americans wanted war.
    c. He wanted to turn public attention away from domestic difficulties.
    d. He believed that American prestige in Europe needed a boost.

39. In President Jefferson's view, the Judiciary Act of 1801 demonstrated that   d
    a. the federal government already needed to be overhauled.
    b. the Republican party would be able to dominate all branches of the federal government.
    c. John Marshall had to be impeached.
    d. the Federalists were going to make the judiciary their stronghold.

40. The "midnight" judges were   **b**
    a. federal judges fired by President Jefferson late in the evening of his first day
       as president.
    b. judicial appointments made by President Adams in the last months of his
       presidency.
    c. judges requested by Adams to preside over night court.
    d. none of the above

41. Thomas Jefferson believed that an independent judiciary was   **d**
    a. a dangerous, undemocratic institution.
    b. a potential source of Republican patronage.
    c. a threat to the success of the Republican party.
    d. vital to the success of republican government.

42. What legal principle was established by the case of *Marbury* v. *Madison*?   **b**
    a. federal supremacy
    b. judicial review
    c. presidential succession
    d. territorial acquisition

43. The principles of the Monroe Doctrine included all the following *except*:   **c**
    a. The United States would abstain from European wars unless American inter-
       ests were involved.
    b. The New World was closed to future European colonization.
    c. The United States would never annex any part of Spain's former territories.
    d. none of the above

44. John Pickering and Samuel Chase were   **c**
    a. explorers of the Louisiana Territory.
    b. candidates for vice president.
    c. judges whose behavior had been outrageous.
    d. President Jefferson's choices for the Supreme Court.

45. Why did President Jefferson consider French ownership of Louisiana   **d**
    unacceptable?
    a. Ownership by a weaker nation than France offered more possibilities for the
       United States.
    b. The French might join forces with the British and endanger American
       security.
    c. If the French quarreled with the British, the United States might find itself
       caught in the middle.
    d. all of the above

46. Jefferson briefly hesitated about accepting Napoleon's offer to sell the Louisiana   c
    Territory to the United States because he   SG
    a. doubted that Congress would appropriate the $15 million that Napoleon was
       asking.
    b. knew that much of the territory was desert land, unsuitable for agriculture.
    c. believed in strict interpretation of the Constitution, and it did not specifically
       give the federal government the power to purchase large new territories.
    d. did not trust the sincerity of Napoleon's offer.

47. Why did Jefferson overcome his doubts about the constitutionality of the   c
    Louisiana Purchase?
    a. He found a passage in the Constitution that mentioned the purchase of
       territory.
    b. An amendment was ratified permitting territorial acquisition.
    c. He decided that a guarantee of land for American farmers was more impor-
       tant than a constitutional principle.
    d. all of the above

48. Why did Federalists oppose the Louisiana Purchase?   d
    a. They objected to the purchase of something that had been tainted by the
       French Revolution.
    b. They wished to be the party in power when territorial acquisitions were
       made.
    c. They believed that the Constitution had to be interpreted strictly.
    d. They believed that the purchase would lead to a decline in the relative impor-
       tance of their strongholds.

49. What was the *main* reason that President Jefferson authorized the Lewis and Clark   b
    expedition?
    a. to convince skeptics of the value of the territory
    b. to advance scientific knowledge
    c. to Christianize the Indians
    d. to promote American business

50. The Lewis and Clark expedition produced all the following *except*:   c
    a. new scientific information
    b. new geographic knowledge
    c. hostile relations with native Americans
    d. stimulation of interest in the West

51. By the terms of the Twelfth Amendment to the Constitution,   d
    a. there could be no more than two candidates for president and vice president.
    b. the vice president and president had to belong to the same political party.
    c. a tie in the vote for the presidency had to be settled in a second election.
    d. there had to be separate ballots in the electoral college for the presidency
       and vice presidency.

52. Aaron Burr's intrigues during the period 1804–1806 included all the following   **b**
except:
    a. a plot to form a pro-British northern confederacy
    b. a scheme to become vice president as a Federalist
    c. a duel that resulted in Alexander Hamilton's death
    d. a plot for a southwestern confederacy

53. The Yazoo Land Compromise involved a controversy over   **a**
    a. land that had been sold through the bribery of a state legislature.
    b. an attempt by President Jefferson to cash in on a vast real-estate development in Georgia.
    c. the discovery that much of the Yazoo territory had been incorrectly surveyed by Lewis and Clark.
    d. Aaron Burr's attempt to form an independent confederacy out of the lands of the Yazoos.

54. What was the basic conflict between President Jefferson and the Quids?   **c**
    a. Jefferson believed that John Randolph lacked the background necessary to lead the Republican party.
    b. The Quids believed that the United States should acquire no new territory.
    c. The Quids believed that Jefferson was not true to their party's "country" ideology.
    d. Jefferson thought that the Quids were too flexible and pragmatic.

55. The British Rule of 1756 said that   **c**
    a. in wartime, neutral nations were expected to pick up the trade formerly conducted by the belligerents.
    b. warfare would not extend to the high seas.
    c. trade closed in time of peace could not be opened in time of war.
    d. conditions of war would determine shipping rules.

56. The 1805 case involving the *Essex* declared that   **a**
    a. broken voyages were illegal.
    b. no restrictions on trade were permissible.
    c. England had to accept French supremacy on the ocean.
    d. none of the above

57. The practice of impressment involved   **d**
    a. attempts by the British to convince their opponents that they were wrong.
    b. seizure of American sailors who had defected to the French during the Napoleonic Wars.
    c. the French policy of forcing all nations to impress their soldiers into the French army.
    d. seizure of purported British sailors from American merchant ships, and pressing them into service.

58. The basic thrust of John Quincy Adams's foreign policy was to   d
    a. conquer commercial rivals by military means.
    b. militarize the Great Lakes for security.
    c. encourage European involvement in keeping peace in the Western Hemisphere.
    d. secure American borders and strengthen the peace with Great Britain.

59. The Embargo Act   **b**
    a. badly damaged the British economy.   SG
    b. stimulated the growth of manufacturing in the United States.
    c. convinced the French to drop their trade restrictions against the United States.
    d. was favored by New England but resisted in the South.

60. Which section of the United States most strongly opposed the embargo?   a
    a. New England
    b. the Southeast
    c. the mid-Atlantic states
    d. the Old Northwest

61. What were the terms of the Non-Intercourse Act?   **b**
    a. Premarital sex became a federal offense.
    b. America would trade with all nations except Britain and France and would restore trade with either nation if it ceased to violate neutral rights.
    c. America would refrain from trading with any nation that was at war.
    d. Britain and France would refrain from trading with the United States unless it observed proper neutrality.

62. Which of the following actions of the American government reopened trade with Britain and France and determined that if either nation repealed its restrictions the United States would halt all commerce with the other nation?   c
    a. the embargo
    b. the Non-Intercourse Act
    c. Macon's Bill No. 2
    d. the War Hawk Proviso

63. The war hawks were   d
    a. mostly from New England.
    b. eager for war against Napoleon in order to gain the Louisiana Territory.
    c. supporters of Jefferson and Madison's policy of economic coercion.
    d. Republicans from the West and South who wanted to take Canada from Britain and Florida from Spain.

64. The pressures for war mounting in backwoods sections of the United States can be seen in   **a**

    a. the episode involving Tecumseh and the Prophet.
    b. William Henry Harrison's selection as governor of the Indiana Territory.
    c. public opinion regarding the Orders in Council.
    d. Aaron Burr's plots.

65. The Shawnee Indians were defeated by William Henry Harrison's forces at the Battle of   **b**

    a. New Orleans.
    b. Tippecanoe.
    c. Lake Erie.
    d. Queenston.

66. What was the *main* source of votes in favor of war with Britain when Congress declared war in June 1812?   **a**

    a. Republicans in populous states like Pennsylvania, Maryland, and Virginia
    b. war hawks from western states
    c. New England
    d. New York and New Jersey

67. The United States went to war with Great Britain in 1812 for all the following reasons *except*:   **d**

    a. an economic recession that affected the South and West after 1808
    b. a conviction that British policy was damaging America's economy
    c. President Madison's belief that Britain wished to eliminate the United States as an economic rival
    d. pressure from New England merchants to protect their shipping

68. As a result of Captain Oliver Perry's victory at the Battle of Put-in-Bay (Lake Erie),   **c**

    a. the United States won the War of 1812.
    b. the British came to realize that Canada was indefensible and had to be abandoned.
    c. the British lost control of Lake Erie and therefore pulled back from Detroit.
    d. the American people turned to new political leadership in the next presidential election.

69. The Treaty of Ghent ending the War of 1812 included all the following provisions *except*:   **a**

    a. outlawing of the impressment of American sailors
    b. restoration of the status quo antebellum
    c. no territorial gain or loss for the United States
    d. referral of boundary issues to a joint commission

70. Which of the following was *not* proposed at the Hartford Convention?   d
    a. abolition of the Constitution's three-fifths clause
    b. a required two-thirds vote to declare war and admit new states
    c. a prohibition against two successive presidents from the same state
    d. the idea that New England should form an independent confederacy

71. During the Era of Good Feelings,   a
    a. the Federalist party disappeared, but the Republican party adopted some of its policies.   SG
    b. the United States won a war against England.
    c. sectional and partisan conflicts became more acute.
    d. President Monroe signed new treaties of alliance and friendship with Britain and France.

72. After the War of 1812, Henry Clay called for an "American System," by which he meant   d
    a. a system of high tariffs to keep out European products.
    b. a unique method of manufacturing that Europeans could not emulate.
    c. a new way of winning wars.
    d. internal improvements that would make the nation self-sufficient.

73. In *McCulloch* v. *Maryland*, the Supreme Court declared that   b
    a. Congress lacked the power to charter a national bank.
    b. a state cannot tax an agency of the federal government.
    c. the state of Maryland was superior to the United States.
    d. a college had a right to a charter.

74. Why did the Supreme Court decisions in *McCulloch* v. *Maryland* and *Dartmouth College* v. *Woodward* dismay Republicans?   a
    a. They saw the decisions as an attack on state and popular authority.
    b. They believed that the Court was giving away too much of its power.
    c. They feared that too many states would begin to interfere with corporations.
    d. all of the above

75. The Missouri Compromise included all the following provisions *except*:   a
    a. All children of Missouri slaves born after Missouri became a state would be emancipated at age twenty-five.   SG
    b. Maine was admitted to the Union as a free state.
    c. Slavery would be barred from the Louisiana Territory north of 36 degrees, 30 minutes latitude, except for Missouri.
    d. Missouri was admitted as a slave state.

ESSAY QUESTIONS

76. In what ways did Thomas Jefferson try to restore "republican simplicity" to the American government? Were his actions revolutionary, or was he simply refining previous policies?

77. What was Jefferson's philosophy of government? To what extent was he politically pragmatic and realistic? Did his philosophy and actions change from his first term in office to his second term?

78. What was Thomas Jefferson's attitude toward the judiciary? How did his actions demonstrate that attitude?

79. Why did the United States engage in a nearly disastrous war against the British SG from 1812 to 1814? What, if anything, did the United States gain from that war?

80. How does the situation depicted in the essay on Charles Bulfinch's Boston represent the changing nature of American politics in the opening decades of the nineteenth century?

81. To what extent was the "Era of Good Feelings" a period of political harmony, and to what extent were the good feelings actually "paper thin"?

82. What were the issues behind the Missouri Compromise? What were the terms of the compromise? What did the controversy reveal about the future of the United States?

83. How did slavery become the central issue in the sectionalism that had long been a hallmark of American politics and society?

84. What major political and diplomatic accomplishments can we credit to the leaders of the early republic? Why were domestic political developments fraught with dissension, while in foreign affairs a political consensus developed rather quickly?

85. What basic principles were enunciated in the Monroe Doctrine? Why was the doctrine proclaimed?

MAP QUESTIONS

Choose the letter on the accompanying map of North America that correctly identifies each of the following:

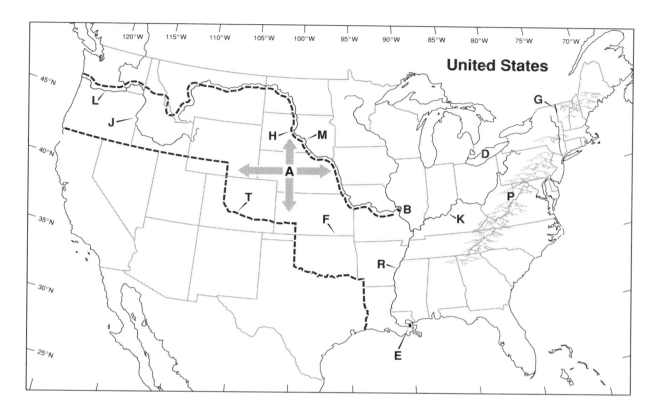

86. New Orleans   E

87. lands of the Louisiana Purchase   A

88. Appalachian Mountains   P

89. Mississippi River   R

90. Missouri River   M

91. Snake River   J

92. Columbia River   L

93. Ohio River   K

94. St. Louis, Missouri   B

95. Lake Erie   D

96. Lake Champlain   G

97. 36 degrees, 30 minutes latitude   F

98. route of the Lewis and Clark expedition   H

99. the boundaries established by the Adams-Onís (Transcontinental) Treaty   T

CHAPTER 8

The Transformation of American Society, 1815–1840

IDENTIFICATIONS

Identify the following. Be as specific as possible, and include names, dates, and relevant facts as appropriate. Be sure to explain the *significance* of the person or term.

1. the Panic of 1819

2. putting-out system

3. voluntary association

4. transportation revolution

5. mountain men

6. Five Civilized Tribes

7. Indian Removal Act

8. *Cherokee Nation* v. *Georgia* and *Worcester* v. *Georgia*

9. sea-island cotton and short-staple cotton

10. Eli Whitney and the cotton gin

11. subsistence farming and commercial farming

12. specie

13. Robert Fulton and *North River Steam-Boat* (*Clermont*)

14. *Gibbons* v. *Ogden*

15. Erie Canal

16. American system of manufacturing

17. Waltham and Lowell mills

18. separate spheres

19. *The Young Man's Guide* and *Letters to Mothers*

20. squatters

MULTIPLE-CHOICE QUESTIONS

Choose the answer that *best* completes the statement or answers the question.

21. One of the differences between easterners and residents of the frontier was that   a
    a. residents of the frontier had a looser attitude toward private property.
    b. easterners tended to be more politically active.
    c. easterners were more egalitarian.
    d. life on the frontier was more bountiful than life in the East.

22. Which of the following was *not* one of the developments that took place in the   c
    United States after the War of 1812?
    a. improvements in transportation
    b. growth of interregional trade and migration
    c. slowing of economic growth
    d. growth of towns

23. The direction of the population movement that took place between 1790 and   b
    1840 was
    a. from the North to the South.
    b. from the Atlantic coast to the areas between the Appalachians and the
       Mississippi.
    c. from New England to California.
    d. from the Old Northwest back to New England.

24. What do Vermont, Kentucky, Tennessee, Ohio, Louisiana, Indiana, Mississippi,   b
    Illinois, Alabama, Maine, and Missouri have in common?
    a. They were all slave states.
    b. They all became states between 1791 and 1821.
    c. They were all free states.
    d. Their economies were all based on fur trapping.

25. The "mountain men" of the West were   c
    a. farmers.
    b. family men.
    c. white fur trappers.
    d. mining engineers.

26. Which of the following is *not* a characteristic of the typical pioneer settlers?   d
    a. They migrated as families.
    b. They craved sociability.
    c. They sought stability and security.
    d. They were wild and restless individualists.

27. As pioneers moved westward between 1790 and 1820, where did they tend to settle?   d
    a. in large urban areas where jobs were available
    b. on lakes and ponds away from other human society
    c. along railroad lines where they could meet new people
    d. along rivers and with people from the same region back East

28. Which of the following were social activities in which a pioneer might engage?   d
    a. gander pulling and chicken plucking
    b. quilting, sewing, and carpet tacking
    c. dances and hoedowns
    d. all of the above

29. In a pioneer family   a
    a. a clear sexual division of labor usually existed.
    b. women were responsible for lighter and daintier household chores.
    c. social activities kept the sexes separated.
    d. none of the above

30. What did many easterners think of westerners?   b
    a. that westerners were more honest and hard-working than easterners
    b. that westerners were half-savage yokels
    c. that westerners were soft and decadent
    d. that westerners were "stuck up"

31. Military bounties awarded during the War of 1812 provided that   a
    a. soldiers would receive western land in exchange for military service.
    b. soldiers were paid cash bonuses for enlisting.
    c. soldiers were given cash bonuses for each new recruit they could find.
    d. soldiers were paid for each British soldier they captured.

32. What was the purpose of the National Road?   b
    a. to provide work for veterans of the War of 1812
    b. to facilitate westward migration
    c. to encourage a political alliance between Virginia and Illinois
    d. to enable the president to reach Washington easily

33. Which of the following did *not* stimulate westward settlement?   d
    a. military bounties
    b. building the National Road
    c. the growing strength of the federal government
    d. federal support of existing Indian settlements

34. Which group in American society did *not* benefit from the westward expansion that was encouraged by the federal government?   **c**   **PT**
    a. European immigrants
    b. military veterans
    c. native Americans
    d. whites from the eastern seaboard

35. What group do historians believe had the best school system west of the Mississippi in the 1840s?   **b**   **PT**
    a. the Spanish
    b. native Americans
    c. German immigrants
    d. Protestant missionaries

36. Which of the following is *not* true of the Cherokee Indians?   **b**
    a. They were one of the Five Civilized Tribes.
    b. They led the movement of Indians out of the South.
    c. They published their own newspaper.
    d. They engaged in agriculture.

37. President Andrew Jackson's policy toward the native Americans included   **c**
    a. an attempt to declare the Indians a separate nation.
    b. the establishment of government missions to each Indian tribe.
    c. a more coercive removal policy.
    d. a desire to bolster their culture.

38. What was the purpose of the Indian Removal Act of 1830?   **d**
    a. to eliminate barriers to Indian unity
    b. to encourage Georgia to establish Indian schools
    c. to remove Indians from the jurisdiction of the Supreme Court
    d. to facilitate white settlement on Indian lands

39. Which of the following is *not* a principle drawn from Chief Justice John Marshall's decisions on federal Indian policy?   **a**
    a. Native American tribes could have the status of a state or a foreign nation.
    b. As tribes, native Americans could not bring suit against the federal government.
    c. Native Americans were entitled to federal protection.
    d. Native Americans had a right to their land because of prolonged occupancy.

40. Which pair of Supreme Court cases dealt with federal Indian policy?   **c**
    a. *Fletcher* v. *Peck* and *Gibbons* v. *Ogden*
    b. *Dartmouth College* v. *Woodward* and *McCulloch* v. *Maryland*
    c. *Cherokee Nation* v. *Georgia* and *Worcester* v. *Georgia*
    d. *Marbury* v. *Madison* and *Worcester* v. *Georgia*

41. Which of the following did *not* contribute to rising farm prices after the War of   d
1812?

    a. increased wheat and corn exports to Europe
    b. new agricultural markets in the West Indies and South America
    c. increased demand in the eastern United States
    d. declining agricultural output in the West

42. A major agricultural product of the Old Northwest was   a

    a. wheat.
    b. cotton.
    c. apples.
    d. oranges.

43. A major agricultural product of the Old Southwest was   d

    a. wheat.
    b. apples.
    c. oranges.
    d. cotton.

44. Which of the following was most responsible for the spread of cotton growing   d
into the Old Southwest?   SG

    a. the discovery of methods for getting sea-island cotton to flourish in the interior uplands
    b. the removal of the Five Civilized Tribes
    c. the adoption of a homestead law making the land available free to qualified settlers
    d. Eli Whitney's invention of the cotton gin

45. Which of the following statements is the best description of federal land policy   a
from 1790 to 1820?

    a. Federalists encouraged land sales to speculators, while Republicans encouraged farmers to purchase federal land.
    b. A political consensus kept land policy above partisan or sectional politics.
    c. Federal land policy was consistent throughout the period.
    d. The federal government allowed the states total control over the distribution of public lands.

46. What role did squatters play in western land development?   b

    a. They tended to gobble up all available public land.
    b. They exerted a restraining influence on the land speculator.
    c. They lobbied for a stronger Indian removal policy.
    d. They brought about the Panic of 1819.

47. Americans drew the following conclusions from the Panic of 1819 *except*:   d

    a. Banks were to be distrusted.
    b. American industries had to be protected against foreign competition.
    c. Farmers had become dependent on businessmen.
    d. Speculators were the best protection against foreign competition.

48. Which of the following is *not* true of early American steamboat development?   **d**
    a. They became ornate and luxurious.
    b. They were prone to fires and collisions.
    c. They shortened travel time and extended the navigation season.
    d. They were subsidized by the federal government.

49. What was the first major canal project in the United States?   **d**
    a. the Blackstone Canal
    b. the Ohio Canal
    c. the Panama Canal
    d. the Erie Canal

50. What was one of the major changes that took place in American towns and cities   **b**
    between 1820 and 1860?
    a. Western towns declined as more people moved to farms.
    b. Towns grew rapidly, especially in the West.
    c. River cities rose to prominence while lake cities declined.
    d. Cities tended to grow up on the open plains of the West.

51. Which of the following did *not* stimulate American industrialization after the War   **c**
    of 1812?
    a. protective tariffs
    b. ending of European immigration
    c. improved transportation
    d. preference for factory-made products

52. Which of the following factors helped to make New England America's first indus-   **c**
    trial region?
    a. few rivers to interfere with transportation
    b. influx of foreign capital
    c. surplus of young women to work in the mills
    d. young men returning from fur trapping in the West

53. How would you describe working conditions in a Waltham or Lowell mill?   **d**
    a. Workers lived at home and commuted to work.
    b. Factories were clean, pleasant places in which to work.
    c. Families worked together in the mills.
    d. Unmarried women made up the bulk of the workers.

54. New York or Philadelphia artisans might have reacted to industrialization in all the   **b**
    following ways *except*:
    a. going to work in a factory
    b. forming a communal factory
    c. forming an organization to try to protect artisans' privileges
    d. going on strike

55. In antebellum America, the richest citizens   b
    a. usually didn't live in mansions because they didn't want to appear wealthy.
    b. usually started out with considerable wealth.
    c. usually didn't have much more wealth than the middle class.
    d. usually constituted about one-half of the population.

56. Which of the following was *not* one of the ways that free blacks in the antebellum   c
    North were treated?
    a. Their right to vote was generally restricted.
    b. They were either excluded from public school or forced to attend segregated
       schools.
    c. They were encouraged to migrate to other states or cities.
    d. They were forced into the least skilled jobs.

57. What was the economic status of most people in antebellum America?   c
    a. wealthy
    b. poor
    c. middling
    d. on the edge

58. One sign of how some antebellum Americans reacted to the economic changes   b
    that were taking place can be seen in
    a. the declining suicide rate.
    b. increasing consumption of liquor.
    c. declining church attendance.
    d. increasing patriotism.

59. What did the intense antebellum criticism of lawyers, physicians, ministers, and   c
    other professionals indicate about America?
    a. People no longer had need for doctors.
    b. People were becoming less religious.
    c. Americans were inclined to question authority.
    d. Professional corruption had reached new peaks.

60. Which of the following changes in marriage patterns did *not* occur in the antebel-   c
    lum period?
    a. romantic love having a greater role in marriage decisions
    b. more women marrying out of birth order
    c. fewer lengthy engagements
    d. more women choosing not to marry

61. The doctrine of "separate spheres" suggested that   b
    a. children and parents should not mingle.
    b. men were superior in worldly pursuits while women were superior for their
       moral influence.
    c. moral issues were to be determined by the church, while economic issues
       were to be determined by the family.
    d. all of the above

62. During the antebellum period, what happened to the birthrate among native-born   b
    white women?
    a. It was declining.
    b. It was rising.
    c. It remained the same.
    d. none of the above

63. Which of the following was a reason for the declining birthrate during the antebel-   a
    lum period?
    a. disease
    b. abstinence
    c. declining marital rates
    d. abortion

64. People who are in similar social positions tend to form relationships called   c
    a. vertical allegiances.
    b. voluntary allegiances.
    c. horizontal allegiances.
    d. democratic allegiances.

65. Andrew Jackson's remark "John Marshall has made his decision; now let him   c
    enforce it" refers to the president's intention to   SG
    a. destroy the National Bank despite the Supreme Court ruling upholding its
       constitutionality.
    b. use force, if necessary, to make South Carolina obey federal law that South
       Carolina thought was unconstitutional.
    c. move the Cherokees west of the Mississippi River regardless of Supreme
       Court rulings.
    d. disregard Chief Justice Marshall's ruling in *Gibbons* v. *Ogden*.

66. By 1840 about what portion of Americans lived between the Appalachian Moun-   b
    tains and the Mississippi River?   SG
    a. one-quarter
    b. one-third
    c. one-half
    d. two-thirds

67. All the following statements about the Erie Canal are correct *except*:   a
                                                                                      SG
    a. It and the National Road were the only major internal improvements financed
       by the federal government prior to the Civil War.
    b. It contributed to the decline in importance of Mississippi River cities such as
       New Orleans and St. Louis and the rise between 1830 and 1860 of lake cities
       such as Buffalo and Cleveland.
    c. It linked New York through inland waterways to Ohio and made the city a
       major outlet for midwestern produce.
    d. It sharply reduced shipping costs.

68. Which of the following statements about the professions in the late 1840s is correct?   c
    SG

    a. Lawyers, doctors, and clergymen were highly paid and respected.
    b. Women were entering the professions in significant numbers.
    c. No state required a person to have medical education or a license to be a doctor.
    d. Increasing numbers of doctors, lawyers, and ministers moved to the West because they were most needed and valued there.

ESSAY QUESTIONS

69. Discuss the importance of the following changes that had occurred in the United States by 1840: the rise of western agriculture, the changes in the nature of farming, the rise of industry, and the alterations in basic social relationships.

70. Compare and contrast the typical pioneer with the legendary "mountain men." How were western customs and society different from eastern customs and society?

71. Why did the federal government pursue a policy of Indian removals? Compare President Jackson's policy with those of previous administrations. Which Indian tribes in particular were affected? How had their lives changed by the 1840s?   PT

72. Compare and contrast Federalist and Republican land policies. How did squatters, speculators, and western farmers help to shape the course of western land development after the War of 1812?

73. Discuss the transportation revolution of the period 1815 to 1850. What changes took place? What was the impact of those changes on the country economically, politically, and socially?   SG

74. What were the causes and patterns of industrialization in the United States after the War of 1812? Why did industrialization begin in New England?

75. Describe working conditions in early American factories. Compare New York and Philadelphia factories with the Lowell and Waltham mills. How did workers react to the new factory system?

76. How did the changing economy affect the following groups in antebellum America: the rich and the poor, artisans, families, unmarried women, middling classes, merchants, and free northern blacks?

77. Major changes took place within the family unit during the antebellum period. Discuss those changes, with specific reference to relations between parents and children, and husbands and wives.

78. Why did horizontal allegiances develop in the period between 1815 and 1840? What functions did "voluntary associations" fulfill during that time?

MAP QUESTIONS

Choose the letter on the accompanying map of the eastern United States that correctly identifies each of the following:

Eastern United States

79. Erie Canal   K

80. Ohio Canal   A

81. Blackstone Canal   G

82. Main Line Canal   H

83. Miami Canal   B

84. Hudson River   J

85. Mississippi River   E

86. Coastal Road   D

87. National (Cumberland) Road   F

CHAPTER 9

Politics, Religion, and Reform in Antebellum America

IDENTIFICATIONS

Identify the following. Be as specific as possible, and include names, dates, and relevant facts as appropriate. Be sure to explain the *significance* of the person or term.

1. spoils system

2. nullification controversy

3. *South Carolina Exposition and Protest*

4. Tariff of Abominations

5. Nicholas Biddle and the Bank of the United States

6. pet banks

7. Locofocos

8. Whigs

9. Millerites

10. "log cabin" campaign

11. the second party system

12. Second Great Awakening

13. Burned-Over District

14. perfectionism

15. Unitarianism

16. Mormonism

17. Horace Mann

18. William Lloyd Garrison

19. Frederick Douglass and Sojourner Truth

20. Angelina and Sarah Grimké

21. gag rule

22. Elizabeth Cady Stanton

23. Seneca Falls Convention of 1848

24. Auburn System v. Pennsylvania System

25. Dorothea Dix

26. Robert Owen and New Harmony

MULTIPLE-CHOICE QUESTIONS

Choose the answer that *best* completes the statement or answers the question.

27. The Whig Party was made up of former Federalists and former Republicans who   c
    a. retained Jefferson's suspicion of a strong federal government.
    b. believed that westward expansion should end.
    c. believed that the national government should encourage economic development.
    d. refused to accept the new techniques of American politics.

28. Which of the following was *not* one of the forces of division within the Republican   d
    party in the early 1820s?
    a. industrialization in New England
    b. spread of cotton cultivation in the South
    c. westward expansion
    d. democratization of the political process

29. Which of the following was *not* part of the democratization of American politics in   c
    the antebellum period?
    a. decline of property requirements
    b. institution of written ballots
    c. elimination of the electoral college
    d. election rather than appointment of some offices

30. What happened to the American political system during the antebellum period?   c
    a. It collapsed.
    b. It fragmented into a multiple-party system.
    c. It became more democratic.
    d. It came under the control of a business elite.

31. Andrew Jackson's supporters charged that a "corrupt bargain" had been made by   a
    SG
    a. John Quincy Adams and Henry Clay to make Adams president and Clay secretary of state.
    b. Henry Clay and John C. Calhoun to undermine Jackson and secure passage of the Compromise of 1833.
    c. Henry Clay and Daniel Webster to secure recharter of the Second Bank of the United States.
    d. John C. Calhoun and John Quincy Adams to punish Jackson for his unauthorized raid on Spanish Florida.

32. One reason for Andrew Jackson's popularity was   d
    a. his military reputation.
    b. his slave holdings.
    c. his attitudes toward the native Americans.
    d. all of the above

33. Martin Van Buren's political machine in New York was known as   c
    a. Tammany Hall.
    b. the Whigs.
    c. the Albany Regency.
    d. the Latter-day Saints.

34. What did the presidential election of 1828 demonstrate?   c
    a. that supporters of common people would have difficulty being elected
    b. that first-term presidents usually can be reelected
    c. that the new political parties were strongly sectional in their sources of strength
    d. that New Englanders would never vote for a southerner for president

35. Removing officeholders of the rival political party and replacing them with members of your own party is called the   c
    a. just deserts system.
    b. rotating system.
    c. spoils system.
    d. rotten system.

36. Why did President Jackson veto the Maysville Road Bill?   b
    a. The bill did not provide enough money for his own state.
    b. He opposed federal funding of internal improvements.
    c. He preferred to support steamboat lines.
    d. The governor of Kentucky objected to the road.

37. Which section of the country tended to oppose tariffs?   c
    a. New England
    b. West
    c. South
    d. Middle Atlantic

38. The theory that the Union is a compact among the states and that a state has the right to override a federal law is known as

    a. statism.
    b. division.
    c. sectionalism.
    d. nullification

    d

39. The *South Carolina Exposition and Protest* was drawn up in opposition to the

    a. Missouri Compromise.
    b. spoils system.
    c. "Tariff of Abominations."
    d. Compromise of 1833.

    c
    SG

40. The Force Bill authorized President Jackson to

    a. use arms to collect customs duties.
    b. raise an army to put down an Indian insurrection.
    c. force the Congress to pass an acceptable tariff bill.
    d. appoint a secretary of the treasury who would do the president's bidding.

    a

41. The tariff controversy of the early 1830s showed that

    a. the nation was united in the pursuit of economic nationalism.
    b. Andrew Jackson was too stubborn to compromise on matters of high principle.
    c. the nation faced serious and growing sectional pressures in the years ahead.
    d. Henry Clay could never be elected president.

    c

42. What was one of the reasons why Andrew Jackson vetoed the rechartering of the Bank of the United States?

    a. The bank prevented state banks from lending money.
    b. It refused to accept deposits of federal revenue.
    c. It was a private monopoly run by a privileged few.
    d. Its president constantly meddled in national politics.

    c

43. The election campaign of 1832 is noteworthy because

    a. it was the first time no presidential candidate received a majority of the votes.
    b. it was the first time a president ran for reelection.
    c. it was the first time a vice president ran for reelection.
    d. it was the first time national nominating conventions chose the candidates.

    d

44. The term "pet banks" was applied to

    a. state banks that were preferred by Nicholas Biddle.
    b. branches of the Bank of the United States in states hostile to Andrew Jackson.
    c. state banks chosen by President Jackson to be depositories of federal money.
    d. foreign banks that lent capital to American mill owners.

    c

45. What did President Jackson do in his "war" on the Bank of the United States?   a
    a. removed federal deposits from the Bank of the United States and deposited them in state banks
    b. forced the nation to adopt a paper money system
    c. banned the use of specie in business transactions
    d. closed all branches of the Bank of the United States

46. The difference between "hard money" and "soft money" is   b
    a. hard money is difficult to acquire.
    b. hard money is gold or silver, while soft money is paper.
    c. soft money is issued for only a specified number of months.
    d. hard money has no value, while soft money increases in value.

47. The Locofocos of New York were   d
    a. a group of reformers who advocated insane asylums.
    b. a tribe of Indians who had come from Georgia.
    c. a group of Whigs who supported Martin Van Buren.
    d. a workers' party that advocated hard money.

48. Who was the main opposition to Andrew Jackson during his second term in office?   b
    a. Democratic party
    b. Whig party
    c. Republican party
    d. Federalist party

49. Which of the following groups would *not* have supported the Whig party during   c
    the Jacksonian era?
    a. southern advocates of nullification
    b. northern temperance reformers
    c. Irish immigrants
    d. Anti-Masons

50. The Specie Circular   b
    a. was designed to bolster the economy by encouraging speculation.
    b. said only specie was to be accepted in payment for public land.
    c. helped to prevent a depression in 1837.
    d. outlawed paper money.

51. Which of the following did *not* contribute to the depression of 1837?   a
    a. the Bank of the United States
    b. Jackson's use of state banks
    c. the Specie Circular
    d. British limitations on foreign investment

52. In the late 1830s and early 1840s, what group believed that the end of the world was imminent?   d

    a. Mormons
    b. Oneidans
    c. Reformers
    d. Millerites

53. Which political party had become the anti-bank, hard-money party by 1840?   d

    a. Whigs
    b. Republicans
    c. Millerites
    d. Democrats

54. What was the purpose of the Independent Treasury advocated by President Van Buren?   c

    a. It would allow banks to operate with less government interference.
    b. It would abolish state banks.
    c. It would help to keep federal money out of the grasp of business corporations.
    d. It would determine which state banks would receive federal deposits.

55. Why did Vice President Martin Van Buren lose the presidential election of 1840?   d

    a. the economic depression
    b. the military record of his opponent
    c. his sluggish campaigning
    d. all of the above

56. What was the *main* cause of the great increase in the popular vote between the 1836 and 1840 presidential elections?   c

    a. lower suffrage requirements
    b. population growth
    c. higher percentage of eligible voters actually voting
    d. increased immigration

57. The period of revivalism that swept the nation in the early years of the nineteenth century is known as   d

    a. the Camp Meeting Era.
    b. the Great National Circuit Ride.
    c. the Methodist Rebirth.
    d. the Second Great Awakening.

58. The belief that people can live without sin was called   a

    a. Perfectionism.
    b. Mormonism.
    c. Revivalism.
    d. Protestantism.

59. Which sect believed that Jesus was not divine but merely an exemplary human being?   c

    a. Mormons
    b. Revivalists
    c. Unitarians
    d. Perfectionists

60. Why can Mormonism be described as ''pushing against the currents of American religion and society''?   d

    a. It rejected the Bible as the only source of revelation.
    b. It embraced polygyny.
    c. It emphasized economic cooperation rather than competitiveness.
    d. all of the above

61. Which of the following was one of the unique tenets of the Shakers?   c

    a. materialism was the surest route to heaven
    b. absolute immobility was necessary for religious ecstasy
    c. at the Second Coming, Jesus would take the form of Mother Ann Lee
    d. men could have multiple wives

62. Which of the following was a reform movement of the antebellum period?   d

    a. abolition
    b. temperance
    c. public education
    d. all of the above

63. Why did temperance reformers make one of their main targets the moderate drinkers among the laboring classes?   b

    a. These drinkers were not supporting local tavernkeepers.
    b. Drinking interfered with the orderly and steady habits required by the new factory system.
    c. Reformers hated factory workers.
    d. Taverns prevented workers from relaxing.

64. The goals of the school reform movement in the antebellum period included   d

    a. classifying pupils by age and attainment.
    b. making attendance compulsory.
    c. spreading uniform cultural values.
    d. all of the above

65. Who was the most famous and controversial white abolitionist?   a

    a. William Lloyd Garrison
    b. Frederick Douglass
    c. John C. Calhoun
    d. Horace Mann

66. What did most white abolitionists want?   c

    a. immediate emancipation
    b. colonization of freed slaves in Africa
    c. legal but not necessarily social equality
    d. use of federal force to end slave uprisings

67. The "gag rule" was repealed in 1845 largely because of the efforts of   c
                                                                               SG
    a. Theodore Weld.
    b. Horace Mann.
    c. John Quincy Adams.
    d. Andrew Jackson.

68. The Seneca Falls Declaration of Sentiments called for   b
                                                                               SG
    a. state tax support for public schools.
    b. equal rights for women.
    c. immediate abolition of slavery.
    d. humane treatment of the mentally ill and the establishment of insane asylums
       for their care.

69. What was one of the major reasons for the changing attitude toward poverty,   c
    crime, and insanity in the early nineteenth century?

    a. Factory owners wanted deviants locked up.
    b. There were no longer enough jails to hold all the criminals.
    c. Americans began to believe that human nature could be improved.
    d. Americans began to believe that penitentiaries, workhouses, and insane asy-
       lums were counterproductive.

70. All of the following were founded as utopian communities *except*   d
                                                                               SG
    a. New Harmony, Indiana.
    b. Oneida, New York.
    c. Brook Farm, Massachusetts.
    d. Rochester, New York.

71. Most founders of utopian communities believed that   a

    a. if social arrangements could be perfected, the ills of society could be
       eliminated.
    b. if men and women lived together without being married, the population
       would decline.
    c. if perfect communities were created, the government would be forced to
       abolish slavery.
    d. if the natural defects of human society could be outlawed, men and women
       could live in harmony.

ESSAY QUESTIONS

72. Discuss how economic changes, political and social reforms, and religious movements began to remake American society during the antebellum years.

73. What was the "second party system"? Why did it arise? In what ways was it markedly different from the political system of the era of the nation's founders?

74. How did politics in the antebellum period become more democratic? Discuss the political careers of John Quincy Adams, Andrew Jackson, and Martin Van Buren to demonstrate the new political winds that were blowing across the nation.

75. Sectional controversy began to grow during the 1820s and 1830s. Discuss how the following issues aroused sectional differences: internal improvements, protective tariffs, and nullification.

76. What were the reasons for the controversy over the Bank of the United States? Explain both the pro-bank and anti-bank positions. What does the controversy reveal about the American economy, attitudes about business and banking, and the relationship between the economy and the political system?

77. What were the causes and consequences of the Panic of 1837?

78. Discuss the American religious movements that developed during the antebellum period. In what sense might it be said that American religion became "democratized" during these years?   PT

79. What was the connection between the religious and reform movements of the antebellum period? Use Rochester, New York, as one of your examples.

80. How did the women's rights movement evolve out of other reform movements, especially the abolition movement? Why did the women's rights movement make only slow advances?

81. In what ways did American attitudes toward poverty, crime, and insanity change during the first half of the nineteenth century? Why did those changes occur, and what were the results of such changing attitudes?

MAP QUESTIONS

Choose the letter on the accompanying map of the United States that correctly identifies each of the following:

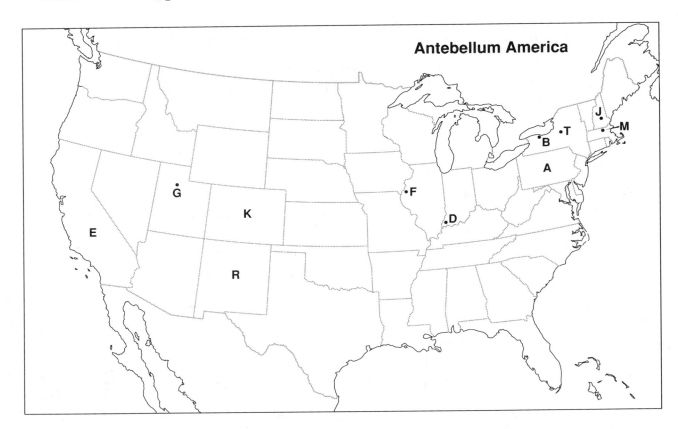

Antebellum America

82. Rochester, New York   B

83. Salt Lake City, Utah   PT

                                        G

84. New Harmony, Indiana   D

85. Oneida, New York   T

86. Nauvoo, Illinois   F

87. Canterbury, New Hampshire   J

88. Brook Farm, Massachusetts   M

CHAPTER 10

The Old South and Slavery, 1800–1860

IDENTIFICATIONS

Identify the following. Be as specific as possible, and include names, dates, and relevant facts as appropriate. Be sure to explain the *significance* of the person or term.

1. Nat Turner Rebellion

2. Upper South and Lower South

3. J. D. B. De Bow

4. Tredegar Iron Works

5. yeomen

6. people of the pine barrens

7. Hinton R. Helper

8. James Henry Hammond and George Fitzhugh

9. southern code of honor

10. plantation system

11. kinship ties and networks

12. Gabriel Prosser

13. Denmark Vesey

14. Underground Railroad

15. pidgin

16. Frederick Douglass

17. Harriet Tubman

18. George Fitzhugh

19. the proslavery argument

20. free southern blacks

MULTIPLE-CHOICE QUESTIONS

Choose the answer that *best* completes the statement or answers the question.

21. Compared with the North, the Old South had a higher   **c**
    a. literacy rate.
    b. proportion of its people living in cities.
    c. murder rate.
    d. proportion of its white population working for other whites.

22. Which of the following is a crop that was *not* associated with the Old South?   **c**
    a. cotton
    b. rice
    c. wheat
    d. tobacco

23. Which of the following was *not* one of the reasons that cotton became "king" in   **d**
    the South?
    a. It could be grown profitably on any scale, not just on large plantations.
    b. Southern climate was suited to cotton cultivation.
    c. It was convenient to grow corn with cotton.
    d. It required the use of slaves.

24. Which of the following accurately describes the Upper South and the Lower   **b**
    South?
    a. The Upper South depended entirely on cotton, while the Lower South had a
       diversified economy.
    b. Both sections aggressively advocated secession.
    c. After about 1830, both were united in their defense of slavery.
    d. The Upper South tended to identify more with the North than with the Lower
       South.

25. One of the ways in which the North and the South were different was   **c**
    a. the North was more rural.
    b. southern industry was growing more rapidly.
    c. southern factories were smaller and more closely tied to agriculture.
    d. all of the above

26. Factories developed slowly in the South for all the following reasons *except*:   d
    a. slave discipline was difficult to maintain in a factory system
    b. the economic rewards of agriculture were more certain
    c. industrialization might have disrupted the traditional southern social structure
    d. southerners had no source of capital

27. Southern education lagged behind northern education because   b
    a. the South had no money for schools.
    b. southerners were indifferent to public schools.
    c. there were too many children to be educated.
    d. slaves demanded to be educated along with whites.

28. By 1860 what percentage of white southern families owned slaves?   a
    a. 25%
    b. 50%
    c. 75%
    d. 100%

29. What was the largest group of southern whites in the antebellum period?   c
    a. planters
    b. small slaveholders
    c. nonslaveholding yeomen
    d. people of the pine barrens

30. How many slaves would half of all slaveowning families have owned?   b
    a. 50
    b. fewer than 5
    c. 100 or more
    d. 25–50

31. Life for most plantation mistresses was marked by   a
    a. isolation, drudgery, and humiliation.
    b. an endless round of social balls and soirees.
    c. frequent trips to town to buy new gowns.
    d. secret abolitionist activity.

32. The typical southern yeoman hoped for   a
    a. self-sufficiency with a modest profit.
    b. profit more than self-sufficiency.
    c. large numbers of slaves.
    d. a chance to move to the city.

33. The people of the pine barrens were   b
    a. lazy and shiftless.
    b. independent and somewhat self-sufficient.
    c. prosperous slaveowners.
    d. leaders of southern society.

34. How would you describe antebellum southern politics?   **c**
    a. Serious and divisive issues caused fragmentation.
    b. Only the Democratic party had any support in the South.
    c. An underlying political unity reigned despite conflicts.
    d. The political structure was controlled by one social group.

35. In 1857 a book calling upon nonslaveowning whites of the South to abolish   **b**
    slavery in their own interest was published by   **SG**
    a. James Henry Hammond.
    b. Hinton R. Helper.
    c. George Fitzhugh.
    d. Gabriel Prosser.

36. Why did nonslaveholding southerners support the slave system?   **d**
    a. Some hoped to become slaveholders.
    b. They accepted the racist assumptions of slavery.
    c. They feared what freed slaves might do.
    d. all of the above

37. All of the following are true of the proslavery argument *except*:   **a**
    a. it emphasized the economic profitability of slavery   **SG**
    b. it was developed by southern intellectuals like James Henry Hammond and George Fitzhugh
    c. it claimed that southern slaves were better cared for than northern factory workers
    d. it pointed out that the great civilizations of the past such as ancient Greece and Rome depended on slave labor

38. What shaped relations among whites in the Old South?   **a**
    a. a complex code of honor
    b. a federal code of laws
    c. an ancient list of dos and don'ts
    d. a historic code of morality

39. One of the few groups in the Old South to speak against the dueling, brawling,   **c**
    and drinking of southern society was
    a. the people of the pine barrens.
    b. plantation mistresses.
    c. evangelical churches.
    d. lawyers of the Lower South.

40. How had the American slave population changed by about 1830?   **c**
    a. It had declined.
    b. It had become largely African-born.
    c. It had increased dramatically.
    d. It had become predominantly male.

41. Which statement best describes the work of plantation slaves?   b
    a. They were usually supervised in the field by the plantation master.
    b. They worked long hours throughout the year and were subject to brutal discipline.
    c. Males and females were separated when they worked in the field.
    d. All plantation slaves were employed in unskilled field work.

42. One of the hallmarks of the West African cultures from which many American   a
    slaves had originated was
    a. broad kinship ties.
    b. loose standards of morality.
    c. no knowledge of relatives.
    d. an overriding parent-child bond.

43. Which of the following is an accurate description of the typical slave diet?   c
    a. Slaves usually suffered from malnutrition.
    b. They ate better than whites during the summer, but worse during the winter.
    c. It was unbalanced but with plenty of food.
    d. It was vegetarian.

44. What were typical slave mortality rates?   b
    a. lower than those for whites
    b. higher than those for whites
    c. the same as those for whites
    d. none of the above

45. Why were some slaves allowed to work in towns or cities?   d
    a. Slaveowners needed the extra income.
    b. Slaveowners usually didn't have enough work for them to do on the plantation.
    c. Southern reformers wanted slaves to learn new skills for later in life.
    d. The southern economy suffered from a perennial shortage of white labor.

46. Where did over half of all free blacks in the Lower South live?   a
    a. in rural areas
    b. in cities
    c. on plantations
    d. in small coastal villages

47. Which profession was open to free blacks in the Old South?   d
    a. carpentry
    b. barrel making
    c. barbering
    d. all of the above

48. Why did the growth rate of the free black population in the South slow after 1810?　　**a**

    a. Fewer southern whites were freeing their slaves.
    b. The number of births was declining.
    c. Plantation conditions for slaves were improving.
    d. Blacks began to view freedom as too dangerous.

49. Which of the following was a common form of slave resistance?　　**c**

    a. frequent armed uprisings
    b. escape to freedom in the North
    c. work stoppages, arson, theft, or negligence
    d. refusal to marry

50. All the following probably explain the rarity of slave revolts in the Old South　　**d**
    except:　　**SG**

    a. blacks were outnumbered by whites almost everywhere in the South
    b. blacks in revolt had no allies
    c. whites had all the guns and soldiers
    d. blacks had strong bonds of loyalty to masters who treated them fairly

51. Who was the leader of a slave uprising?　　**b**

    a. Hinton R. Helper
    b. Nat Turner
    c. James Henry Hammond
    d. George Fitzhugh

52. Which of the following is an accurate statement about slave uprisings in the ante-　　**c**
    bellum South?

    a. They occurred frequently.
    b. They were infrequent but usually bloody.
    c. There were only three, and only one resulted in white deaths.
    d. Slaveowners had no fear of them.

53. What lesson did white southerners learn from the Nat Turner rebellion?　　**b**

    a. that gradual emancipation was inevitable
    b. that slave insurrection was an ever-present threat
    c. that slaves should not be allowed to work in cities
    d. that slaves should not be allowed to read the Bible

54. What was the pattern followed by most runaway slaves?　　**b**

    a. They escaped to the North on the Underground Railroad.
    b. They remained in the South.
    c. They relocated with the help of northern abolitionists.
    d. They were recaptured and beaten to death.

55. Which was the most common reaction of blacks to slavery?　　**c**

    a. suicide
    b. armed rebellion
    c. furtive resistance
    d. escape to the North

56. In order for a slave culture to develop in the United States, what was the first   b
    prerequisite?

    a. a breakdown of the slave family
    b. Afro-American religion and a common slave language
    c. renewed importation of additional slaves from Africa
    d. a rediscovery of African music

57. Pidgin was   b

    a. the language forced upon the slaves by their white masters.
    b. the language of American-born slaves.
    c. the area in Africa where most slaves originated.
    d. the secret tongue used in slave resistance.

58. Why was pidgin indispensable for slaves?   b

    a. It enabled them to work in shops or mills.
    b. It allowed them to communicate and develop a culture.
    c. It helped them to keep secrets from their masters.
    d. It distinguished them from free urban blacks.

59. Southern evangelical churches generally preached against all of the following   a
    except: SG

    a. slavery
    b. gambling
    c. dueling
    d. drinking

60. A comparison of southern white and black religion in the antebellum period   c
    reveals

    a. whites and blacks attended separate churches.
    b. black spirituals and white hymns were virtually identical in purpose and
       meaning.
    c. white ministers usually reminded slaves that spiritual equality was not the
       same as civil equality.
    d. whites placed greater emphasis on religion than did blacks.

61. What was the religion of the majority of slaves when they were transported from   c
    Africa to the United States?

    a. Catholic
    b. Moslem
    c. a variety of native religions
    d. Protestant

62. What were the most interracial institutions in the Old South?   c

    a. grammar schools
    b. voluntary organizations
    c. churches
    d. colleges

63. Music and dance enabled slaves to   **d**
    a. demonstrate religious beliefs.
    b. lessen the tedium of work.
    c. express the sorrows of slavery.
    d. all of the above

64. Which of the following is *not* a reason why the Upper South tended to identify   **c**
    with the Lower South rather than with the North?
    a. The settlers in the Lower South had come from the Upper South.
    b. Abolitionist criticism drew southerners together.
    c. Railroads linked Upper and Lower South.
    d. The Upper and Lower South were tied economically.

65. What was the status of the black slave family?   **b**
    a. Children and mothers were kept together.
    b. It had no legal status.
    c. It was the same as that of free white families.
    d. Extended families spanning several generations were common.

ESSAY QUESTIONS

66. Explain the southern proslavery argument, and account for why it continued despite abolitionist criticism. Why did southerners increasingly defend slavery as a positive good rather than simply a necessary evil? Why did southern pro-emancipation sentiment decline?

67. Explain how the southern economy revived, and the southern slave population nearly doubled, in the antebellum period.

68. North and South during the antebellum period were often seen as two distinct nations, having very little in common. To what extent was that true? Compare the social, economic, and political structures of the two sections. How did northerners and southerners differ over industrialization and education?

69. In what sense was the Old South a "land of extremes"? In what ways was the antebellum South a surprisingly violent society?

70. Compare and contrast the four major southern white social groups in terms of economic goals, attitudes toward slavery, and political aspirations.

71. Describe life for the planter and plantation mistress on a large antebellum plantation. What were the economic challenges that faced the large planters?

72. Compare and contrast the Upper South with the Lower South. In what ways were they similar and different? Why, despite their significant differences, did they possess a basic political unity that was destined to put them in political opposition to the North?

73. Describe daily life for a typical plantation slave. What were the characteristics of the slave's health and diet, and the nature and structure of the slave family? How much practical freedom did a slave enjoy?

74. Explain why there were so few slave uprisings in the antebellum South, and why the Nat Turner rebellion had such a devastating impact on the southern outlook.

75. In what sense can it be said that Christianity changed slave culture *and* that slavery altered southern Christianity?

MAP QUESTIONS

Choose the letter on the accompanying map of the South that correctly identifies each of the following:

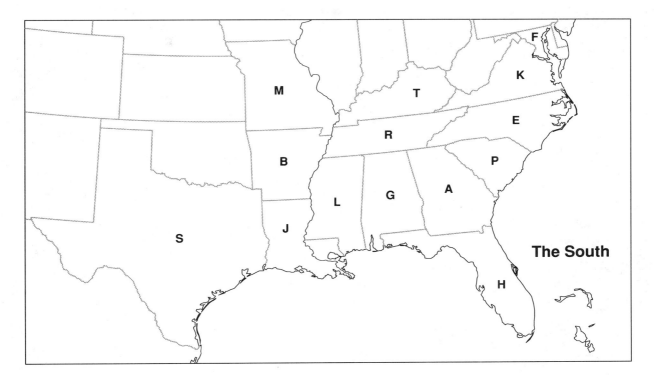

The South

76. Maryland   **F**

77. Virginia   **K**

78. Kentucky   **T**

79. Missouri   **M**

80. Arkansas   **B**

81. Tennessee   R

82. North Carolina   E

83. South Carolina   P

84. Georgia   A

85. Alabama   G

86. Mississippi   L

87. Louisiana   J

88. Florida   H

89. Texas   S

On the accompanying map of the South, draw in lines to indicate the following:

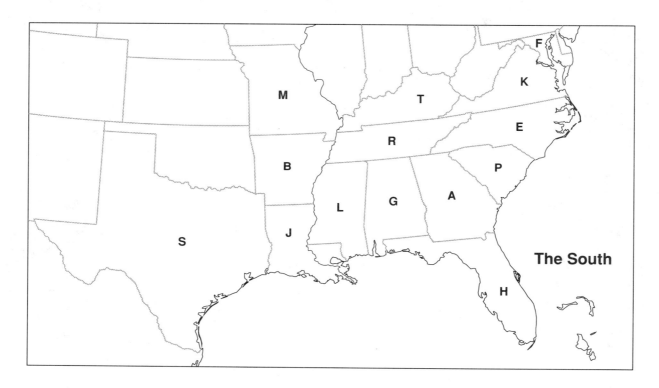

90. the dividing line between the Upper South and the Lower South

91. Tidewater, Virginia

92. Mississippi River

CHAPTER 11

Life, Leisure, and Culture, 1840–1860

IDENTIFICATIONS

Identify the following. Be as specific as possible, and include names, dates, and relevant facts as appropriate. Be sure to explain the *significance* of the person or term.

1. Cyrus McCormick's reaper

2. American system of manufacturing

3. contagion and miasm theories

4. nitrous oxide and ether

5. hydropathy

6. Sylvester Graham

7. phrenology

8. James Gordon Bennett and the penny press

9. P. T. Barnum's American Museum

10. Astor Place riot

11. minstrel shows

12. Emerson's "The American Scholar"

13. American Renaissance

14. James Fenimore Cooper's Leatherstocking Tales

15. Henry David Thoreau's *Walden*

16. Walt Whitman's *Leaves of Grass*

17. Nathaniel Hawthorne

18. Hudson River school

19. Frederick Law Olmsted   PT

20. lyceum lectures and the American Art Union

MULTIPLE-CHOICE QUESTIONS

Choose the answer that *best* completes the statement or answers the question.

21. The 1840s and 1850s in the United States were characterized by all the following   **b**
    except: **SG**
    a. heightened literary and artistic output and inventiveness
    b. advances in medical knowledge that lessened the danger and frequency of
       epidemics
    c. improvements in transportation and increases in productivity that raised the
       standard of living for the middle class
    d. building of municipal waterworks in many of the big cities to supply the
       needs of urban dwellers

22. Which of the following statements best captures the attitude of antebellum Ameri-   **d**
    cans about technology?
    a. They believed that technology was democratic and would help everyone.
    b. They believed that technology was a progressive force for positive change.
    c. They believed that technology would help to make up for a labor shortage.
    d. all of the above

23. Which antebellum innovation did *not* help to transform American life?   **c**
    a. cotton gin
    b. interchangeable parts
    c. telephone
    d. sewing machine

24. Why was the reaper a significant innovation?   **b**
    a. It created more agricultural jobs.
    b. It saved time and labor.
    c. It mechanized southern agriculture.
    d. It encouraged the development of a corn crop.

25. What was one of the advantages of the "American system" of manufacturing?   **d**
    a. Inventors would have more time to develop their inventions slowly.
    b. Manufacturers would have a convenient way of excluding outside investors.
    c. Foreigners would have no way of copying American machines.
    d. Damaged parts could be replaced easily.

26. Before the Civil War, European and American railroads differed in that   c
    a. European trains were designed for comfort.
    b. American trains ran on time.
    c. American trains had only one class for white travelers.
    d. European railroads were financed by the government.

27. Which of the following statements accurately describes railroads in the United   a
    States in 1860?
    a. The United States had more track than the rest of the world combined.
    b. American railroads lacked government support and therefore lagged behind
       the rest of the world.
    c. Railroad owners faced financial difficulties because they could not compete
       with canals.
    d. The railroads brought about the decline of the once great city of Chicago.

28. American railroads contributed to all of the following *except*:   c
    a. the rise of Chicago
    b. the forging of east-west agricultural ties
    c. the rise of new southern cotton-growing areas
    d. the stimulation of midwestern settlement

29. Which of the following is usually considered the first "big business" in the United   d
    States?
    a. steamshipping
    b. armaments manufacturing
    c. canals
    d. railroads

30. How was the building of the railroads in the Unites States financed?   d
    a. by state and local governments
    b. by the federal government
    c. by private investors
    d. all of the above

31. What impact did technological changes have on the American worker before the   c
    Civil War?
    a. Prices of many commodities rose.
    b. Hourly wages rose.
    c. The purchasing power of the average worker rose.
    d. Annual income declined.

32. Which of the following is an accurate statement about the standard of living of an   a
    antebellum urban family?
    a. Two-thirds of family income was spent on food and rent.
    b. Families were able to save for future retirement.
    c. Only the male head of the household had to work.
    d. all of the above

33. What statement best describes life for the average American farm worker in the antebellum period?   **a**
    a. Most workers founds it difficult to raise enough capital to buy a farm.
    b. Most agricultural workers eventually owned their own farms.
    c. Unlike urban workers, agricultural workers tended to have consistent employment throughout the year.
    d. Compared with urban workers, farm workers placed greater emphasis on education for their children.

34. An urban middle-class home in the 1850s would have been likely to have all of the following *except*:   **b**
    SG
    a. several floors
    b. indoor faucets supplying hot and cold running water
    c. conspicuously ornamented furniture
    d. a coal-burning stove for cooking and heating

35. What type of urban housing developed during the early nineteenth century?   **c**
    a. unattached frame houses
    b. one-story brick houses
    c. row houses
    d. garden apartments

36. What was one of the results of rising land values in the early-nineteenth-century American city?   **a**
    a. Renting became more common.
    b. Homeownership became more common.
    c. Fewer people occupied each row house.
    d. Tenements were replaced with lavish mansions.

37. How did home furniture change during the antebellum period?   **c**
    a. Furniture came to reflect an informal style of life.
    b. Furniture became "democratized" as rich and poor were more likely to buy the same types.
    c. Furniture became more ornate and heavily upholstered.
    d. The upper classes distinguished themselves from the rising middle class through ornate furniture.

38. What advance in heating and cooking occurred in antebellum America?   **d**
    a. acceptance of the open-hearth method of cooking
    b. central heating in tenement buildings
    c. decline of natural gas stoves
    d. introduction of the cast-iron stove

39. In the decades before the Civil War, what changes took place to influence the diet   c
of the average urban dweller?
    a. Affordable fresh fruit became available to all city dwellers.
    b. The consumption of salt pork declined.
    c. More fresh produce and fish became available.
    d. Most families purchased ice boxes for food storage.

40. What caused nationwide epidemics in the United States during the antebellum   d
period?
    a. Municipal health boards were powerless.
    b. People distrusted physicians.
    c. Doctors didn't understand the causes of disease.
    d. all of the above

41. What medical development greatly advanced the image of surgeons and the suc-   a
cess of health care in the decades before the Civil War?
    a. development of anesthesia
    b. discovery of the cause of epidemics
    c. realization of the importance of cleanliness
    d. all of the above

42. Which of the following was *not* a popular health movement in antebellum   c
America?
    a. hydropathy
    b. vegetarianism
    c. epidemiology
    d. phrenology

43. Who was Sylvester Graham?   a
    a. a prominent health food advocate
    b. the manager of a popular hydropathic sanatorium
    c. the nation's leading phrenologist
    d. the founder of a utopian community

44. The belief that bumps on the skull reveal an individual's personality is called   b
    a. hydropathy.
    b. phrenology.
    c. miasm.
    d. Grahamism.

45. Phrenology was popular in antebellum America for all of the following reasons   a
except:
    a. it required sacrifice and abstinence
    b. it was a way to assess strangers
    c. it held out a promise of human betterment
    d. it was inexpensive

46. The majority of the novel-reading public in the United States in 1860 was   c

    a. men.
    b. reformers.
    c. women.
    d. factory workers.

47. What was one of the changes that transformed American newspapers in the   d
    decades before the Civil War?

    a. Publishers had to increase the price in order to maintain a profit.
    b. Fewer newspapers were printed because Americans turned to other sources
       of information.
    c. Most of them became semi-official organs of national political parties.
    d. They began to print "human-interest" stories rather than just political and
       commercial news.

48. An American publisher who helped to transform newspapers and create the mod-   a
    ern concept of news and news reporting was

    a. James Gordon Bennett.
    b. Susan Warner.
    c. Phineas T. Barnum.
    d. Edwin Forrest.

49. Novels were very popular among American women in the antebellum period for   c
    all of the following reasons *except* that

    a. they were often extremely sentimental.
    b. they were inexpensive.
    c. they taught women to depend upon strong males.
    d. they taught women that they could overcome adversity.

50. At a typical antebellum theater   d

    a. lawyers were welcomed, but prostitutes were excluded.
    b. there were very few seats, and most of them were expensive.
    c. classical Greek drama was usually performed.
    d. audiences were rowdy.

51. Who was the most popular dramatist in antebellum America?   b

    a. Edwin Forrest
    b. William Shakespeare
    c. Stephen Foster
    d. Lydia Sigourney

52. How did the popular minstrel show help to shape public perceptions of blacks   c
during the antebellum period?

   a. The minstrel show accustomed white Americans to seeing blacks in public roles.

   b. The minstrel show helped to convince northerners that slavery should be abolished.

   c. The minstrel show reinforced stereotypes of the black as stupid and clumsy.

   d. none of the above

53. Who was the most famous impresario in nineteenth-century America?   b

   a. Robert Bonner

   b. Phineas T. Barnum

   c. Tom Thumb

   d. James G. Bennett

54. Why was P. T. Barnum a phenomenal success?   d

   a. He had a genius for publicity.

   b. He provided safe family entertainment.

   c. He tapped the public's curiosity about natural wonders.

   d. all of the above

55. Which of the following statements about transcendentalism is *incorrect*?   c
SG

   a. It was an American form of romanticism.

   b. It claimed that knowledge of God and truth were inborn in each individual.

   c. It claimed that great literature must conform to universal standards of form and beauty.

   d. It claimed that a new democratic republic could produce art and literature as great as that of the old traditional societies of Europe.

56. What was the subject of Ralph Waldo Emerson's 1837 address, "The American   b
Scholar"?

   a. Americans should improve their literature by emulating European forms.

   b. Americans should work for cultural autonomy.

   c. American literature should conform to universal standards of beauty and taste.

   d. Americans had to turn away from scholarship and concentrate on farming.

57. All of the following were prominent New England writers identified with the   d
American Renaissance *except*:

   a. Nathaniel Hawthorne

   b. Ralph Waldo Emerson

   c. Henry David Thoreau

   d. William Gilmore Simms

58. Which writer introduced into fiction the American frontiersman and the theme of conflict between civilization and primitive life in the wilderness? **c** SG
    a. Herman Melville
    b. Edgar Allan Poe
    c. James Fenimore Cooper
    d. Nathaniel Hawthorne

59. Which of the following writers defended the right to disobey unjust laws, criticized the materialism of American society, and doubted the beneficial effects of technological advances? **b** SG
    a. Walt Whitman
    b. Henry David Thoreau
    c. John Greenleaf Whittier
    d. James Fenimore Cooper

60. How did the writings of Emerson, Thoreau, and Whitman differ from those of Hawthorne, Poe, and Melville? **b**
    a. Emerson, Thoreau, and Whitman wrote only novels.
    b. Hawthorne, Poe, and Melville had a pessimistic view of human nature.
    c. Emerson, Thoreau, and Whitman celebrated the aggressiveness of their countrymen.
    d. Hawthorne, Poe, and Melville wrote mainly about European themes and experiences.

61. During the pre–Civil War decades American painters preferred to paint **d**
    a. historical topics.
    b. portraits.
    c. mythological tales.
    d. landscapes.

62. Why did movements for rural cemeteries and urban parks develop during the antebellum period? **a**
    a. a fear that urban and industrial growth was destroying natural resources
    b. a desire to meet the working-class demand for a quiet place to relax
    c. a hope of taming the undeveloped areas that still remained within city borders
    d. a need to find a use for undeveloped city land

63. What did Frederick Law Olmsted wish to create with his design for Central Park? **d** PT
    a. an idealized version of nature
    b. a harmonious meeting place for all classes
    c. a work of art
    d. all of the above

64. What were the goals of the Hudson River school of painters?   b
    a. to depict natural scenes with photographic accuracy
    b. to preserve a record of a disappearing wilderness
    c. to depict scenes of ruined castles and crumbling temples
    d. none of the above

65. What was one of the purposes of the lyceum lectures?   b
    a. to introduce controversial topics
    b. to spread and popularize knowledge
    c. to teach Americans how to paint
    d. to stimulate interest in gambling

ESSAY QUESTIONS

66. Why did antebellum Americans equate material, cultural, and moral progress, and how did they associate "progress" with "technology"? Give examples—including attitudes toward the railroad—that demonstrate this antebellum American outlook on life.

67. What innovations took place in American agriculture in the decades before the Civil War? What were the reasons for those innovations?

68. What was the "American system of manufacturing"? Why did it intrigue Europeans? What were its advantages?

69. How did railroads grow in the decades before the Civil War? What impact did they have on the economic development of the antebellum United States? In what sense were railroads the nation's first "big business"?

70. How did technology help to improve the quality of life for the antebellum American? Who benefited the most, and who benefited the least, and why did the gap between some classes widen? Discuss especially the impact of house construction, furniture, heating, diet, water and sanitation, disease and health.

71. Compare and contrast rural life with urban life in antebellum America. What factors shaped the differences? Were those differences widening or narrowing during the period?

72. What were the conditions of public health in antebellum America, and how did government policy and law, medical knowledge, popular health movements, and scientific fads contribute?

73. Why did many antebellum Americans turn to practical or popular science? How does that interest demonstrate a basic American optimism about life and society?

74. Explain how technology made entertainment a democratic commodity and a profitable business during the antebellum period. Discuss both the public and the private forms of entertainment available to working-class, middle-class, and upper-class Americans of the period.

75. In what ways did antebellum Americans express a growing sense of nationalism through their literature and art? What were the major literary and artistic achievements of the period?

MAP QUESTIONS

On the accompanying map of the eastern United States, trace the 1860 routes of the following railroads:

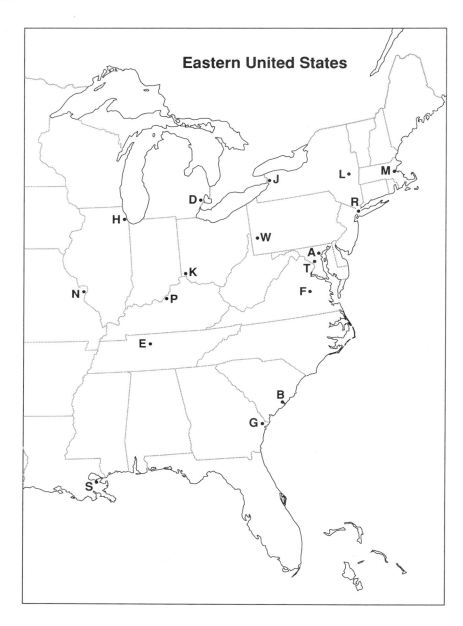

Eastern United States

76. New York Central Railroad

77. Erie Railroad

78. Pennsylvania Railroad

79. Baltimore and Ohio Railroad

80. Illinois Central Railroad

Choose the letter on the accompanying map of the eastern United States that correctly identifies each of the following:

81. Nashville, Tennessee   E

82. Savannah, Georgia   G

83. Chicago, Illinois   H

84. Buffalo, New York   J

85. Pittsburgh, Pennsylvania   W

86. Baltimore, Maryland   A

87. Detroit, Michigan   D

88. St. Louis, Missouri   N

89. Albany, New York   L

90. Washington, D.C.   T

91. Richmond, Virginia   F

92. Louisville, Kentucky   P

93. New Orleans, Louisiana   S

94. Cincinnati, Ohio   K

95. Charleston, South Carolina   B

96. New York, New York   R

97. Boston, Massachusetts   M

CHAPTER 12

Immigration, Expansion, and Sectional Conflict, 1840–1848

IDENTIFICATIONS

Identify the following. Be as specific as possible, and include names, dates, and relevant facts as appropriate. Be sure to explain the *significance* of the person or term.

1. *Commonwealth* v. *Hunt*

2. nativism

3. Maria Monk's *Awful Disclosures*

4. George Henry Evans's National Reform Association

5. Bible Riots

6. presidios

7. Stephen F. Austin

8. Antonio Lopez de Santa Anna

9. the Alamo

10. the overland trail

11. Webster-Ashburton Treaty

12. James K. Polk

13. "reannexation" of Texas

14. Manifest Destiny

15. Zachary Taylor

16. Battle of Buena Vista

17. Treaty of Guadalupe Hidalgo

18. Wilmot Proviso

19. squatter sovereignty

20. The Hounds

MULTIPLE-CHOICE QUESTIONS

Choose the answer that *best* completes the statement or answers the question.

21. In 1860 what groups accounted for three-fourths of all foreign-born Americans?   **a**
    a. Irish and Germans
    b. Irish and English
    c. Germans and Dutch
    d. Swiss and Norwegians

22. The main reason most European immigrants came to the United States between   **c**
    1815 and 1860 was
    a. religious freedom.
    b. reform urges.
    c. economic advancement.
    d. European military upheavals.

23. Emigrants from Europe to America encountered all of the following *except*:   **b**
    a. dishonest hucksters who cheated them
    b. separation from their countrymen after they reached America
    c. frustrations over the difficulties of American farming
    d. a terrifying ocean voyage

24. Where did German and Irish immigrants tend to settle in the United States?   **d**
    a. farms
    b. lakeside villages
    c. the Far West
    d. cities

25. Which statement best describes the Germans who came to the United States   **c**
    before 1860?
    a. They were largely of urban working-class background.
    b. They were mainly Catholics drawn from the poorer classes.
    c. They were diverse, hard-working, and clannish.
    d. They were largely free-thinking radicals and political.

26. How did the Irish and German immigrants of the 1840s differ from each other?   **b**
    a. The Germans were usually Catholic, while the Irish were both Catholic and Protestant.
    b. Most Irish immigrants were unskilled poor, while many German immigrants were well-to-do professionals.
    c. Most German immigrants were single women, while most Irish immigrants came as married couples.
    d. all of the above

27. In the case of *Commonwealth* v. *Hunt*, the Massachusetts Supreme Court ruled that   **b**
    SG
    a. slavery was unconstitutional in Massachusetts.
    b. labor unions were not necessarily illegal combinations or monopolies.
    c. Massachusetts tax money could not be used to support an unjust war against Mexico.
    d. segregated schools for blacks in Massachusetts did not violate the U.S. Constitution.

28. Anti-Catholic sentiment in the United States in the 1830s and 1840s was based on all of the following reasons *except*:   **c**
    a. the Irish taking jobs away from native workers
    b. reports of Catholic conspiracies to take over the country
    c. the Irish being identified with radical abolitionist activity
    d. tales of torture and immorality within Catholic convents

29. What was the response of American workers to the economic difficulties of the 1830s and 1840s?   **d**
    a. attacks on Irish Catholic immigrants
    b. strikes for wage increases
    c. plans to establish rural republican townships
    d. all of the above

30. Irish and German immigrants generally favored the Democratic over the Whig party for all of the following reasons *except*:   **b**
    SG
    a. perceptions of the Democrats as more sympathetic to common people
    b. perceptions of the Democrats as more opposed to slavery than the Whigs
    c. identification of the Whigs with temperance reform and anti-Catholicism
    d. the Democrats' image as antiprivilege and anti-aristocratic

31. In the 1820s, "California bank notes" referred to   **b**
    a. gold coins.
    b. cattle hides.
    c. letters of credit.
    d. Mexican silver pesos.

32. In the 1820s and 1830s, what kind of relationship did Americans have with the   c
people and lands of the Far West?
    a. a relationship marred by nativist harassment of Catholic Mexicans
    b. a general lack of interest and lack of contact
    c. Contact limited to traders and trappers but was beneficial to Americans
    d. frequent contact that resulted in border clashes

33. Presidios were   d
    SG
    a. agents who contracted with the Mexican government to bring American set-
    tlers into Texas.
    b. Mexicans who owned huge ranches worked by enslaved Indians.
    c. Franciscan priests who endeavored to convert the Indians to Christianity.
    d. forts constructed by the Spanish to protect their missions in the Southwest.

34. Why were there so few Mexican immigrants in the New Mexico, California, and   b
Texas territories by the 1830s?
    a. The areas had no natural resources worth exploiting.
    b. The areas were generally lawless regions wracked by Indian terrorism.
    c. Evangelical Protestant missionaries had taken over the old Spanish missions.
    d. The Mexican army dominated the area with its frontier fighting.

35. By 1830 Americans migrated to Mexico for all of the following reasons *except*:   a
    a. to convert Catholic Mexicans to Protestantism
    b. to find new land for cotton cultivation
    c. to escape creditors
    d. because they had agent contracts

36. What was the cause of the increasingly tense relations between the Mexican gov-   d
ernment and the American residents in Texas after 1830?
    a. the instability of Mexican politics
    b. attempts by the Mexican government to prohibit importation of slaves
    c. increasing American immigration
    d. all of the above

37. Which one of the following was a result of the late 1840s California gold rush?   d
    a. In one year alone, 100,000 newcomers arrived in California.
    b. Construction boomed in clipper ships like the *Flying Cloud*.
    c. The issue of slavery in the Mexican Cession was pushed to the forefront of
    national politics.
    d. all of the above

38. Which statement accurately describes travel to Oregon or California on the over-   d
    land trails during the 1840s?
    a. The route was well mapped out and well surveyed.
    b. By this period the route detoured around any formidable barriers.
    c. Emigrant families traveled alone in single wagons so that they would not be
       slowed by the needs of other families.
    d. Emigrants usually maintained their family units and cooperated closely with
       other families on the journey.

39. Along the overland trail, how did the duties and responsibilities of men and   c
    women compare?
    a. Because of a lack of women, men had to take on many tasks formerly handled
       by their wives.
    b. Men usually sheltered their wives from almost all work.
    c. The sexual division of labor that existed back home was usually maintained
       along the trail.
    d. Men and women shared equally in all tasks in a spirit of democratic
       cooperation.

40. The Indians whom white emigrants encountered along the overland trail com-   b
    monly acted in all of the following ways *except*:
    a. they were guides, couriers, and provisioners
    b. they frequently attacked white wagon trains
    c. they collected tolls for passage over crude bridges
    d. they pilfered from emigrant wagon trains

41. The Whig political program in 1840 included   d
    a. a high protective tariff.
    b. passage of an independent treasury act.
    c. annexation of Texas.
    d. government-financed internal improvements.

42. Why was John Tyler's ascendancy to the presidency a disaster for the Whig party?   d
    a. He was a former Democrat.
    b. He was a states' rights advocate.
    c. He vetoed bank and tariff bills that were central to the Whig program.
    d. all of the above

43. Which of the following was *not* one of the reasons why some antislavery north-   b
    erners believed there was a southern conspiracy to extend slavery into the
    Southwest?
    a. Texas was being settled by slaveholders.
    b. Abolitionists had uncovered a plot by southerners to invade Mexico and re-
       institute slavery.
    c. Slaveholder Andrew Jackson had accepted southern participation in the Bat-
       tle of San Jacinto.
    d. There was southern talk of creating four or five slave states out of the Texas
       Territory.

44. The Senate rejected the treaty annexing Texas drawn up by Secretary of State Calhoun because **a**
SG

    a. he defended annexation as a way to protect and defend slavery.
    b. the Texans were not yet ready to give up their independence and join the United States.
    c. the British threatened to break off diplomatic relations if the United States took the territory without compensating them.
    d. Mexico threatened to declare war if the United States stole its province.

45. What was one of the reasons that "dark horse" James K. Polk won the presidency in 1844? **c**

    a. Polk came out strongly against a protective tariff.
    b. The Whig party appeared to be the party of immigration and alcohol.
    c. Polk convinced many northerners that annexation of Texas would be in their best interest.
    d. He received an overwhelming popular vote.

46. In the 1840s, which of the following groups was *not* likely to support territorial expansion? **b**

    a. Irish immigrants
    b. members of the Whig party
    c. poor urban laborers
    d. southern slaveholders

47. By the mid-1840s, what reason might many Americans have given to support territorial expansion? **d**

    a. Expansion would keep blacks and racial tensions out of the North.
    b. It was America's destiny to possess the entire continent, from the Atlantic to the Pacific.
    c. Territorial expansion would help to maintain the agricultural heritage of America.
    d. all of the above

48. For an antebellum American, the phrase "Manifest Destiny" meant **a**

    a. God had ordained that the United States would eventually and inevitably come into possession of the entire continent.
    b. God had ordained that the southern system of slavery should eventually expand to all the territories on the Pacific coast.
    c. the Democratic party was destined to become the dominant national political party.
    d. it was obvious that the United States would, in future decades, dominate the trading routes to China.

49. What were President James K. Polk's objectives in Oregon? **a**

    a. division of the territory at the 49th parallel
    b. war with Britain to acquire the territory to 54° 40′
    c. division of the territory along the Columbia River
    d. peaceful, joint Anglo-American occupation of the territory

50. All of the following were background causes of the Mexican War *except*:   **b**
    a. Mexico had failed to pay $2 million in debts owed to American citizens
    b. northerners feared that the Mexican government would try to expand north-ward and extend the slave system
    c. Americans loathed Mexicans
    d. Mexicans feared the United States would expand slavery into Mexico

51. What did President James K. Polk want from Mexico in 1845 and 1846?   **c**
    a. a peaceful agreement like the Oregon compromise
    b. Mexican recognition of an independent Texas with a southern border at the Nueces River
    c. acquisition from Mexico of California and New Mexico
    d. all of the above

52. In the United States, opposition to the Mexican War included all of the following reasons *except*:   **a**
    a. Mexico's army was four times the size of American forces and would there-fore be unbeatable
    b. the war was being fought over territory that the United States had never claimed
    c. the president had undercut congressional authority by announcing that he war already existed
    d. a mere border incident was being used as an excuse to provoke a war to acquire more slave territory

53. What happened to the Mexican armies in the Mexican War?   **c**
    a. They collapsed instantly in the face of a massive American offensive.
    b. They were able to hold off the American advance for nine months because they had four times as many troops as the Americans.
    c. They fought bravely and stubbornly, but unsuccessfully.
    d. They offered little resistance, because most Mexican soldiers were hired mercenaries.

54. In the Mexican War, the United States was victorious in virtually all its encounters with Mexican forces for all of the following reasons *except*:   **c**
    a. Santa Anna's nearly unbroken series of military miscalculations
    b. the United States' superior weapons and supplies
    c. American army doctors' cure for yellow fever, which decimated the Mexican troops
    d. the American ability to organize massive military movements

55. Which of the following was one of the terms of the Treaty of Guadalupe Hidalgo?   **a**
    a. The United States government agreed to pay American citizens' claims against Mexico.
    b. Mexico agreed to cede Texas and California, but was allowed to lease New Mexico for twenty-five years.
    c. Mexico was to pay an indemnity of $15 million for war damages.
    d. all of the above

56. What military leader in the Mexican War became a national hero?   **a**
    a. Zachary Taylor
    b. Winfield Scott
    c. Robert E. Lee
    d. John C. Frémont

57. After the Mexican War, American opinion on the extension of slavery into the new   **c**
    territories included all of the following *except*:
    a. the Missouri Compromise, which applied to the new territories, settled the
       issue
    b. slavery should not be permitted in the new territories because it would deter
       free laborers from settling there
    c. the best way to stabilize and Americanize the new territories was to move
       black slaves to the area immediately
    d. slavery should not be permitted in any of the new territories because it was
       immoral

58. The Wilmot Proviso was   **a**
    a. a stipulation that slavery be prohibited in any territory acquired in the nego-
       tiations with Mexico.
    b. a legislative amendment that said that the United States should acquire only
       Texas as a result of the Mexican War.
    c. a plea to apply the terms of the Missouri Compromise to any territory
       acquired from Mexico.
    d. a request to outlaw slavery in Texas if the United States won the Mexican War.

59. Why did John C. Calhoun believe that the federal government had no power to   **c**
    prohibit slavery in the Mexican Cession?
    a. He said that no federal rules or regulations had ever addressed the issue of
       slavery in American territories.
    b. He believed that free states already had enough territory.
    c. He believed that slaves were property, and the Constitution protected the
       right to property.
    d. He argued that the resolution by congressman David Wilmot had specifically
       settled the issue.

60. From the point of view of the Whig party in 1848, why was Zachary Taylor an ideal   **d**
    candidate for president?
    a. He was a Louisiana slaveholder, and would therefore appeal to the South.
    b. He would have broad national appeal because he was a Mexican War hero.
    c. He had no connection to Clay's American System, which the party was trying
       to abandon.
    d. all of the above

61. The term "squatter" or "popular sovereignty" referred to

    a. allowing residents of a territory to decide whether or not to permit slavery.
    b. extending the right to vote to all male settlers in the Far West.
    c. deciding the ownership of a territory by vote of its residents.
    d. the right of the native Indian peoples to hold on to the lands they were already cultivating.

    d
    SG

62. Which of the following was *not* one of the groups that formed the 1848 Free-Soil party and nominated Martin Van Buren for president?

    a. former supporters of John C. Calhoun
    b. New York Democrats who favored the Wilmot Proviso
    c. former Liberty party abolitionists
    d. antislavery "Conscience" Whigs

    a

63. What happened to the San Francisco economy during the early years of the gold rush?

    a. The city experienced a steady economic boom.
    b. City businessmen and investors were able to become rich on iron and flour exports.
    c. Because of overpopulation, businessmen could pay starvation wages to the men who drove carts, unloaded ships, or built houses.
    d. There were wild gyrations of commodity prices, and real-estate prices soared.

    d
    PT

64. Which of the following is an accurate statement about the population of gold rush San Francisco?

    a. There were approximately six times as many females as males in San Francisco.
    b. Italians composed the largest group of foreign-born residents of San Francisco.
    c. Because of the need for menial labor, the city's black population was proportionally large.
    d. Only St. Louis and Milwaukee had a higher proportion of foreign-born residents.

    d
    PT

65. What were some of the characteristics of society in gold rush San Francisco, a city that grew very rapidly?

    a. San Francisco was a model western city in that it was able to eradicate most of the tensions and undemocratic traditions of older eastern cities.
    b. Because of the fluidity of city life, the population was able to avoid serious religious and ethnic tensions.
    c. Because of the economic opportunities presented by the gold rush, violence and crime were rare.
    d. City politics were shaped by strong regional and ethnic antagonisms.

    d
    PT

ESSAY QUESTIONS

66. Discuss emigration to the antebellum United States. Why did people leave Europe and come to the United States? What were their experiences both en route and once they arrived? Where did they settle, and why? What hardships did they encounter? Compare especially the experiences of the Germans and the Irish.

67. Why did antebellum immigrant groups come to identify themselves with the Democratic party? How did Democratic ideology appear to address the needs of immigrants? How, in turn, did immigrant groups help the Democrats? Discuss this relationship on both the local and the national levels.

68. What was the extent of American economic contact with the Mexican lands in the first three decades of the nineteenth century? Why and how did these contacts change? What were the political ramifications of the change?

69. Why did Americans migrate westward to Mexico, California, and Oregon after 1815? Where did they come from? What were their experiences along the overland trail, and how did those experiences compare with the myths and publicity that originally motivated them? Compare the experiences of white women, white men, and native Americans.

70. During the 1830s and 1840s, the slavery and expansion issues became intertwined. Explain how and why that occurred.

71. Why did the idea of territorial expansion—America's "Manifest Destiny"—become a cause that cut across virtually all regional, political, and class lines?

72. Compare American acquisition of Oregon with the Mexican Cession. Discuss reasons and issues, methods, justification for acquisition, and opposition to acquisition. In what ways were the acquisitions similar, and in what ways different?

73. Why did the United States win the Mexican War? Why was the victory a surprise to many European governments?

74. What was the impact of the Mexican War on the following elements of antebellum American national life: territorial expansion, nationalism, politics, and sectionalism?

75. How and why did the racial, ethnic, and sectional divisions in the United States deepen during the 1840s?

MAP QUESTIONS

Choose the letter on the accompanying map of the western United States that correctly identifies each of the following:

Western United States and Mexico

76. St. Louis, Missouri   D

77. Independence, Missouri   H

78. Leavenworth, Kansas   L

79. San Francisco, California   R

80. San Diego, California   G

81. Astoria, Oregon   K

82. Mexico City, Mexico   M

83. Matamoros, Mexico   B

84. Monterrey, Mexico   F

85. Vera Cruz, Mexico   J

86. Buena Vista, Mexico   A

87. Santa Fe, New Mexico   E

Choose the letter on the accompanying map of the western United States that correctly identifies each of the following:

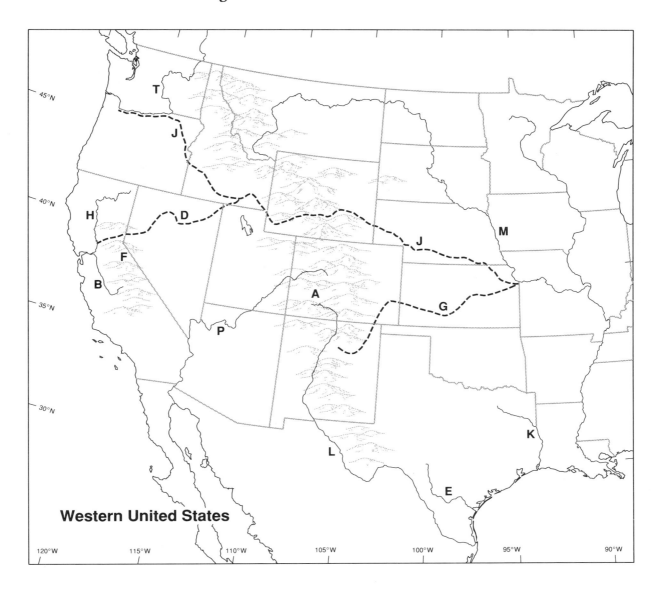

88. Rocky Mountains   **A**

89. Sierra Nevada range   **F**

90. Sabine River   **K**

91. Columbia River   **T**

92. Rio Grande   L

93. Nueces River   E

94. San Joaquin River   B

95. Sacramento River   H

96. California Trail   D

97. Oregon Trail   J

98. Santa Fe Trail   G

Choose the letter on the accompanying map of the western United States that correctly identifies each of the following:

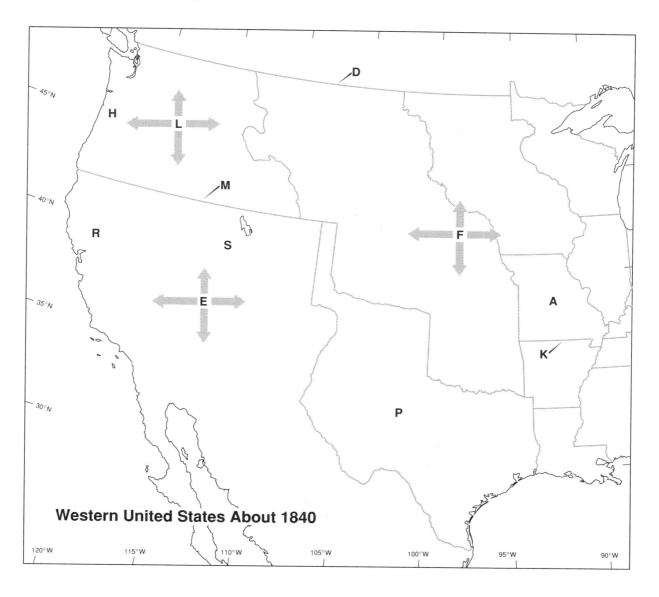

Western United States About 1840

99. 49th parallel   D

100. 42nd parallel   M

101. 36° 30′ latitude   K

102. Great Plains   F

103. Oregon Territory

104. Mexican Cession

105. Sacramento Valley

106. Texas

107. Willamette Valley, Oregon

108. Great Salt Desert

L

E

R

P

H

S

CHAPTER 13

From Compromise to Secession, 1850–1861

IDENTIFICATIONS

Identify the following. Be as specific as possible, and include names, dates, and relevant facts as appropriate. Be sure to explain the *significance* of the person or term.

1. William H. Seward

2. Henry Clay's Omnibus Bill

3. Daniel Webster

4. Fugitive Slave Act

5. Millard Fillmore

6. personal-liberty laws

7. Harriet Beecher Stowe's *Uncle Tom's Cabin*

8. Franklin Pierce

9. American or Know-Nothing party

10. Republican party

11. Conscience Whigs and Cotton Whigs

12. Kansas-Nebraska Act

13. Stephen A. Douglas

14. doctrines of "free soil" and "free labor"

15. Gadsden Purchase

16. Ostend Manifesto

17. William Walker

18. filibusters

19. "Bleeding Kansas"

20. John Brown, Pottawatomie Creek, and Harpers Ferry

21. "Beecher's Bibles"

22. Charles Sumner and Preston Brooks

23. James Buchanan

24. *Dred Scott* decision

25. Lecompton Constitution

26. Lincoln-Douglas debates

27. Freeport doctrine

28. Crittenden plan of compromise

29. Fort Sumter

MULTIPLE-CHOICE QUESTIONS

Choose the answer that *best* completes the statement or answers the question.

30. Why were northerners interested in both the economic development and the extension of slavery into western territories?   a
    a. They believed that slavery in the western territories would force free workers to compete with slaves for jobs.
    b. They believed that slavery would help to bring about early economic development in the western territories.
    c. They believed that a state with slavery would also be a state that favored low taxes and an unregulated business environment.
    d. all of the above

31. Which of the following best describes the image of the "good society" held by northerners or southerners?   c
    a. Northerners believed that in the "good society" all workers adhered to established standards of morality.
    b. Southerners believed that in the "good society" the federal government supported research into the genetic differences between blacks and whites.
    c. Northerners believed that in the "good society" individuals could achieve self-sufficiency as farmers, artisans, or shopkeepers.
    d. Southerners believed that in the "good society" slaves would gradually be relieved of their menial tasks and educated to take on more important jobs.

32. The issues behind the Compromise of 1850 included all of the following *except*:   **b**
    a. enforcement of the Fugitive Slave Act
    b. the ruling in the *Dred Scott* case
    c. the policy regarding slavery in the territories
    d. sale of slaves in the District of Columbia

33. One of Zachary Taylor's views on the slavery issue was that   **c**
    a. the South should modernize by eliminating slavery.
    b. California and New Mexico were well-suited to slavery and would do well to encourage the system within their borders.
    c. the states, rather than Congress, should make the decisions about the extension of slavery.
    d. slavery was an immoral system.

34. What was the cornerstone of the southern defense of slavery?   **d**
    a. Slavery was a humane and socially beneficial system for millions of black Americans.
    b. The future of American economic development depended upon the maintenance of the southern slave system.
    c. It had been good enough for the Founding Fathers, and so it should be good enough for the generation of the 1850s.
    d. It was up to *states* to deal with slavery because there was nothing in the Constitution to forbid it.

35. Henry Clay's "Omnibus Bill" included all of the following provisions *except*:   **a**
    a. abolition of slavery in states west of the Mississippi
    b. abolition of the slave trade in the District of Columbia
    c. a new fugitive slave law
    d. federal assumption of the Texas debt

36. All of the following contributed to passage of the Compromise of 1850 *except*:   **d**
    SG
    a. moderates' control of the Nashville Convention, indicating the South's willingness to compromise
    b. the death of President Taylor, who had opposed the compromise, and his replacement by Millard Fillmore, who supported it
    c. Stephen Douglas's division of Henry Clay's Omnibus Bill into separate parts that were easier to pass than one combined bill
    d. the dying John C. Calhoun's appeal to southerners to accept the compromise as an alternative to civil war

37. The failure of the Compromise of 1850 to bridge the underlying differences   d
    regarding slavery could be seen in the fact that
    a. each bill was opposed by the majority of congressmen in one section or the
       other, and passed only with the support of a determined minority who
       favored compromise.
    b. most southern congressmen voted against the admission of California and
       the abolition of the slave trade in the District of Columbia.
    c. most northern congressmen voted against the Fugitive Slave Bill and popular
       sovereignty for New Mexico and Utah.
    d. all of the above

38. A provision of the Fugitive Slave Act was that   a
    a. alleged fugitive slaves had no right to a jury trial.
    b. alleged fugitive slaves had to take the witness stand in their own defense.
    c. alleged fugitive slaves would be returned to slavery if the claimant presented
       at least six witnesses.
    d. slaves who had escaped prior to the signing of the Treaty of Guadalupe
       Hidalgo were exempt from capture.

39. What was the reaction of many northerners to the Fugitive Slave Act of 1850? b
    a. They joined with southerners to prevent runaway slaves from escaping to
       Canada.
    b. They became more vehement abolitionists.
    c. They began campaigns to repeal the old "personal-liberty laws" that had been
       passed under the Articles of Confederation.
    d. They built special jails to accommodate slaves captured on northern soil.

40. "Personal-liberty laws" were   a
    a. state laws aimed at hampering enforcement of the Fugitive Slave Act.   SG
    b. federal laws guaranteeing the right of slaveholders to protection of their slave
       property.
    c. state laws prohibiting blacks, free or slave, from entering a state.
    d. federal laws guaranteeing that states would not deny any person life, liberty,
       or property without due process of law.

41. What was the significance of Harriet Beecher Stowe's *Uncle Tom's Cabin*?   c
    a. It contradicted prevailing stereotypes that described dark-skinned blacks as
       docile and submissive and light-skinned blacks as aggressive and intelligent.
    b. By presenting a dynamic slave society, the book challenged the common
       notion that slavery tore apart the black family.
    c. It provoked a more aggressive anti-southern and antislavery position in those
       who were uncertain on the slavery issue.
    d. all of the above

42. In the presidential election of 1852   a
    a. the Whig party lost much support in the South and began to break up.
    b. Franklin Pierce won with virtually no opposition.
    c. Whig candidate Winfield Scott won by vigorously endorsing the Compromise of 1850.
    d. Franklin Pierce refused to run for reelection.

43. Which of the following is one of the reasons that the Whig party began to disinte-   b
    grate and decline in the 1850s?
    a. The Whigs introduced a policy of low tariffs at a time when most Americans favored a high protective tariff.
    b. They suffered an internal, north-south split over the slavery issue.
    c. Whig support of unlimited immigration was unpopular among urban workers.
    d. all of the above

44. The "Cotton Whigs" were   c
    a. members of the Whig party whose major interest was in federal subsidies for cotton growers.
    b. northern politicians who believed that the best way to eliminate slavery was to support the development of the English cotton industry.
    c. an alliance between the "lords of the loom" and "lords of the lash."
    d. politicians who wore old-fashioned hairpieces to demonstrate their support for a return to traditional values.

45. Stephen Douglas's motives in sponsoring the Kansas-Nebraska Act included   d
    a. preserving the Union by enabling the Midwest to hold the balance of political power.
    b. uniting the Democratic party around a single issue.
    c. encouraging construction of a railroad from Chicago to the West.
    d. all of the above

46. Which of the following is *not* true about the Kansas-Nebraska Act?   a
    a. It rendered the terms of the Compromise of 1850 void.
    b. It superseded the Missouri Compromise.
    c. It split the Nebraska Territory into Kansas and Nebraska.
    d. It applied the principle of popular sovereignty to Nebraska and Kansas.

47. Which of the following was *not* a free-soil position on slavery?   b
    a. Free-soilers objected to slavery because of their racist hatred of blacks.
    b. Free-soilers believed that American slavery had natural geographic limits beyond which it would not spread.
    c. Free-soilers believed that the presence of slavery impeded the progress of white civilization.
    d. Free-soilers thought that slavery should be abolished simply because it was immoral.

48. The Gadsden Purchase was   c
    a. the symbolic first land sale in the new Kansas Territory.
    b. James Gadsden's purchase of supplies for an unofficial military expedition to Honduras.
    c. a small strip of land in southern Arizona and New Mexico purchased for a railroad line.
    d. a plan to purchase Cuba from Spain for a maximum price of $25 million.

49. The Ostend Manifesto pertained to   a
                                                                                     SG
    a. Cuba.
    b. California.
    c. Mexico.
    d. Florida.

50. In the 1850s, the filibusters   d
    a. talked unceasingly in Congress to prevent the passage of any antislavery legislation.
    b. spoke on behalf of the Ostend Manifesto.
    c. led bands of proslavery "ruffians" into Kansas to vote illegally for a proslavery state legislature.
    d. organized unofficial military expeditions to Central America.

51. The final blow to the Whig party was the   b
    a. Ostend Manifesto.
    b. Kansas-Nebraska Act.
    c. Compromise of 1850.
    d. Lecompton Constitution.

52. The success of the Know-Nothings suggested that   d
    a. the voters of the Northeast were looking for alternatives to the two main political parties.
    b. there was significant nativist sentiment in the Northeast.
    c. there was significant antislavery sentiment in the Northeast.
    d. all of the above

53. The Know-Nothing party declined rapidly for all of the following reasons *except*:   c
    a. the party's split into northern and southern factions in the 1856 presidential campaign
    b. the Know-Nothings' failure to deliver on their program, once they gained political office
    c. the party's radical policy of open membership and public meetings
    d. the party's difficulty reconciling its antislavery attitudes with its anti-Catholic impulses

54. The new Republican party derived support from all of the following groups   a
    except:
    a. former cotton Whigs
    b. former northern Whigs
    c. former Know-Nothings
    d. former northern Democrats

55. The main issue unifying the otherwise diverse elements of the new Republican   b
    party was
    a. national economic policy relating to the tariff, banking, and internal
       improvements.
    b. "Bleeding Kansas."
    c. abolitionism.
    d. nativism.

56. "Bleeding Kansas" was brought about because   d
    a. proslavery forces stole the election for the state legislature.
    b. antislavery forces took up "Beecher's Bibles."
    c. John Brown led a brutal murder of five proslavery men.
    d. all of the above

57. The situation in Kansas in the mid-1850s demonstrated that   a
    a. popular sovereignty institutionalized the divisions over slavery rather than
       resolved them.
    b. extremist actions by fanatics like John Brown were irrelevant to the debate
       over slavery.
    c. the solution to the slavery controversy would be found once the morality of
       slavery had been determined.
    d. only in the United States Senate could men of vision continue to discuss the
       problem of slavery dispassionately.

58. As a result of the 1856 presidential election,   c
    a. the American party established itself as a new and powerful political force.
    b. the Democratic party declined as a major force in American politics.
    c. a sectional party came close to capturing the presidency.
    d. none of the above

59. James Buchanan's position on slavery was that   d
    a. it was less important than the preservation of the Union.
    b. it should be preserved in the current slave states but prohibited from the
       territories.
    c. it was an issue the legislature—not the courts—had to settle.
    d. it was wrong, but the federal government had no right to interfere with it.

60. The *Dred Scott* decision declared that Congress could *not*   **c**
    SG
    a. admit new slave states.
    b. prohibit slaveholders from taking slaves into northern states.
    c. bar slavery in the territories.
    d. pass a fugitive slave law.

61. The Lecompton Constitution   **a**
    a. protected the property rights of Kansas slaveholders and provided for a referendum on the admission of more slaves.
    b. outlawed slavery in Kansas and petitioned Congress for statehood.
    c. rejected the Kansas-Nebraska Act and proclaimed the *Dred Scott* decision to be the state's new guideline on slavery.
    d. was adopted by a convention that was boycotted by proslavery forces who believed it would be rigged by free-soilers.

62. In the course of his campaign against Stephen Douglas in 1858, Abraham Lincoln   **d**
    declared that
    a. Congress had no constitutional authority to abolish slavery in the South.
    b. social and political equality between blacks and whites was not desirable.
    c. the *Dred Scott* decision rendered popular sovereignty "as thin as soup boiled from the shadow of a dead pigeon."
    d. all of the above

63. According to Stephen Douglas's "Freeport doctrine,"   **c**
    a. a territorial legislature could not prohibit slavery because the legislature was created by Congress, which itself could not prohibit slavery.
    b. the *Dred Scott* decision had been superseded by the Kansas-Nebraska Act.
    c. popular sovereignty and the *Dred Scott* decision were compatible because states could *in effect* exclude slavery by refusing to protect the property of slaveowners.
    d. a house divided against itself could not stand.

64. As a result of the 1858 Illinois senatorial election,   **a**
    a. Stephen Douglas lost crucial political support in the southern states.
    b. Abraham Lincoln's political career went into temporary eclipse.
    c. Abraham Lincoln became the new Republican senator from Illinois.
    d. the Democratic party was able to solidify its dominance of national politics.

65. As a result of John Brown's raid at Harpers Ferry,   **b**
    a. southerners realized that extremists like John Brown had no ties to northern abolitionists.
    b. both northern abolitionists and southern fire-eaters were incensed.
    c. southern slaveowners were convinced that a slave uprising could never be successful.
    d. northern moderates formed vigilante committees to ensure civil peace in the southern states.

66. After the mid-1850s, southerners began to speak increasingly of secession for all of   c
the following reasons *except*:

    a. southerners' interpretation of the actions and words of northerners as declarations of war on the South
    b. southerners' belief that northerners were treating the South as an inferior section of the country
    c. the long-time popularity in the South of sentiments for independence
    d. southerners' thinking that the North had deserted the fundamental principles of the Union

67. Which statement best describes the Republican party position in the election of   c
1860?   SG

    a. There should be immediate emancipation of slaves in the South.
    b. A program of gradual compensated emancipation should be started.
    c. There should be no further extension of slavery into the territories.
    d. The principle of popular sovereignty should be honestly applied in the remaining territories.

68. In the 1860 presidential election, the Republican party adopted an economic program that included all the following features *except*:   d

    a. federal aid for internal improvements
    b. a protective tariff
    c. free 160-acre homesteads for settlers on publicly owned land
    d. retraining of former slaves to prepare them for the work force

69. Which 1860 presidential candidate is correctly paired with his position on slavery?   b

    a. Bell: The South had a constitutional right to slavery, but Congress should prohibit its extension.
    b. Breckenridge: Congress had to protect slavery in any territory that contained slaves.
    c. Lincoln: Popular sovereignty should determine the status of slavery in the territories.
    d. Douglas: Preservation of the Union was more important than extension of slavery.

70. Although the states of the Lower South had seceded by February 1, 1861, why   d
were the states of the Upper South more reluctant to secede?

    a. They had more vital economic ties to the North.
    b. They knew that if war came they would end up being the battleground.
    c. They doubted that their sizable nonslaveholding population would accept secession.
    d. all of the above

71. Which statement is an element of the compromise proposed by John Crittenden?   a
    a. There should be a constitutional amendment to prohibit federal interference with southern slavery.
    b. There should be another constitutional amendment declaring the Kansas-Nebraska Act as the guide for future slavery extension.
    c. Southerners would have to accept the personal economic loss if one of their slaves ran away.
    d. The principle of popular sovereignty should be applied to states' personal-liberty laws.

72. After the 1860 presidential election, Republicans rejected any further compromise on the slavery issue because   b
    a. they believed that war was the only method left to settle the issue.
    b. they believed that moderate southerners would soon regain control, and that compromise on matters of basic principle was tantamount to surrender.
    c. they believed that the nation was better off split in half because it obviously couldn't exist half slave and half free.
    d. they felt that the issue had already been settled by the election of 1860.

73. In his first two months as president, Lincoln   c
    a. devised a scheme to reunify the nation by provoking a war with France and Spain.
    b. abandoned any attempt to defend federal forts located in the seceded states.
    c. appealed for 75,000 militiamen to suppress an insurrection in the Lower South.
    d. declared war on the Confederate States of America.

74. The states of the Upper South joined the Confederacy only when   d
    a. Richmond was designated the capital of the Confederacy.
    b. Lincoln had announced his intention of appointing William Seward as secretary of state.
    c. the Crittenden compromises had been rejected.
    d. Lincoln proclaimed that an insurrection existed in the Lower South.

ESSAY QUESTIONS

---

75. In 1858, William Seward spoke of an "irrepressible conflict" between slavery and freedom, and Abraham Lincoln announced that the nation could not be "permanently half-slave and half-free." Both were suggesting that conflict and disunion over the slavery issue were inevitable. Were they right? Was a peaceful, nonpartisan solution impossible? Was a policy of moderation doomed to fail? Would it have made much difference whether the nation was led by moderates or fanatics?

76. What were the major issues discussed in the Lincoln-Douglas debates? On what issues did the two candidates agree, and on what issues did they disagree? In what sense did the debates summarize the controversy to date, and in what sense did they point to the future of the controversy?

77. On one level, the slavery issue was a debate over legal and constitutional issues. At the same time force and violence—the opposite of law—played a profound role in shaping the debate. Discuss both statements with special reference to the 1850s.

78. Discuss the Compromise of 1850 in terms of background issues, the elements of the proposed compromise, and the arguments for and against—especially those of Calhoun, Clay, and Webster. Who benefited and who suffered from the compromise? In what sense did it fail to resolve the issue, and in what ways did it actually intensify the argument during the next decade? Was it important to reach a compromise in 1850? What were the alternatives?

79. Why did the Fugitive Slave Act arouse strong emotions in both the North and the South? How did the act strike at the heart of the southern view of property rights and northern attitudes about the morality of slavery? Why did the act "radicalize" many conservative northerners on the slavery issue?

80. What were the issues behind the Kansas-Nebraska Act? How did political pressures shape the bill? Why did a seemingly uncontroversial issue—the advance of midwestern settlement—become such a heated sectional issue?

81. Trace the growth of free-soil sentiment in the antebellum United States. In what sense was the "free-soil" movement a mixture of moral vision, racism, and economic goals?

82. American politics underwent dramatic changes in the 1850s. Account for the decline of the Whig party, the rise and fall of the Know-Nothings, and the emergence of the Republican party.

83. The gap that had long existed between the North and the South widened during the 1850s, in part because of the perceptions that each section had of the other. To northerners, the slave power was bent on the extension of slavery over the entire nation, while to southerners the North was under the influence of demented leaders bent on abolition and civil war. Explain how these two views evolved. Was there any way that they could have been avoided?

84. Repeated sectional compromises, in 1820, 1833, and 1850, held the Union SG together and averted civil war. Why did compromise fail in 1860–1861?

MAP QUESTIONS

Choose the letter on the accompanying map of the United States in 1860 that correctly identifies each of the following:

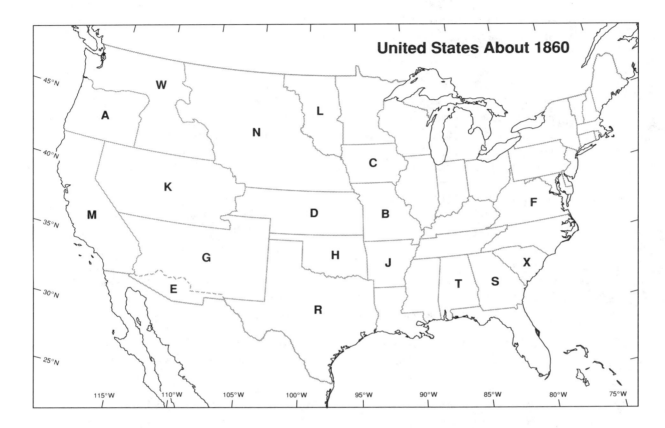

85. Missouri   B

86. Kansas Territory   D

87. Nebraska Territory   N

88. New Mexico Territory   G

89. Utah Territory   K

90. California   M

91. area of the Gadsden Purchase   E

92. South Carolina   X

93. Alabama   T

94. Indian Territory   **H**

95. Washington Territory   **W**

96. Utah Territory   **K**

97. Oregon   **A**

98. Texas   **R**

CHAPTER 14

Reforging the Union: Civil War, 1861–1865

IDENTIFICATIONS

Identify the following. Be as specific as possible, and include names, dates, and relevant facts as appropriate. Be sure to explain the *significance* of the person or term.

1. ironclads

2. 20-Negro law

3. bounty jumpers

4. "rich man's war and poor man's fight"

5. greenbacks

6. National Bank Act

7. *Ex parte* Merryman

8. Enfield and Springfield rifles

9. Anaconda plan

10. First Battle of Bull Run (First Manassas)

11. George B. McClellan

12. Peninsula Campaign

13. Thomas "Stonewall" Jackson

14. Robert E. Lee

15. Battle of Antietam

16. Ulysses S. Grant

17. Battle of Shiloh

18. William T. Sherman

19. *Trent* affair

20. *Florida*, *Alabama*, and the Laird "rams"

21. "cotton diplomacy"

22. Emancipation Proclamation and the Confiscation Act

23. Battle of Gettysburg

24. Homestead Act

25. Morrill Land Grant Act

26. Copperheads and Clement Vallandigham

27. *Ex parte* Milligan

28. New York City draft riots, 1863

MULTIPLE-CHOICE QUESTIONS

Choose the answer that *best* completes the statement or answers the question.

29. Which of the following was *not* one of the reasons why both the North and the   **a**
    South were unprepared for war?
    a. No one in either section had expected hostilities.
    b. Neither the North nor the South had the necessary tax structure to finance the war.
    c. Northerners were uncertain about Lincoln's ability to lead the nation.
    d. The South had poor railroads and virtually no navy.

30. Initially, what method did both the North and the South use to raise their armies?   **c**
    a. national conscription
    b. calling up state militias
    c. local rallies to sign up volunteers
    d. none of the above

31. Conscription was   **d**
    a. unnecessary during the Civil War.
    b. already in place nationally when the Civil War began.
    c. instituted first by the Union.
    d. instituted first by the Confederacy.

32. Who was exempted from conscription during the Civil War?   a

    a. northerners who paid the government $300 and southerners who owned at least twenty slaves
    b. northerners who had a widowed mother to support and southerners who owned no slaves
    c. northerners and southerners who could not afford the $300 conscription fee
    d. northerners and southerners who objected to war on moral grounds

33. During the Civil War, most of the soldiers in both the Union and Confederate   b
    armies were

    a. conscripts.
    b. volunteers.
    c. convicts.
    d. political appointees.

34. How did the Confederacy provide for its ordnance needs during the Civil War?   d

    a. munitions captured on the battlefield
    b. government-owned factories and private firms
    c. imports from Europe
    d. all of the above

35. What was most difficult for the North and the South to supply to their armies dur-   c
    ing the war?

    a. both North and South: munitions
    b. North: food and clothing; South: soldiers
    c. North: soldiers; South: food and clothing
    d. North: food and clothing; South: munitions

36. Of all the methods the northern and southern governments used to finance the   d
    war, which was the most effective in raising revenue?

    a. income taxes
    b. property taxes
    c. government war bonds
    d. printing paper money

37. What happened to consumer prices during the Civil War?   a

    a. The North had an inflation rate of 80%, while the South had an inflation rate of 9,000%.
    b. Prices remained relatively stable in both the North and the South because of government controls.
    c. The South experienced a drastic downward spiral of deflation, while northern prices skyrocketed.
    d. Both the northern and southern economies suffered from crippling declines in prices and wages.

38. The National Bank Act of 1863   **b**
    a. created a national bank in each Confederate state.
    b. established criteria by which a bank could get a federal charter and issue national bank notes.
    c. declared that it was a conflict of interest, and therefore illegal, for federally chartered banks to purchase federal war bonds.
    d. tied the value of Confederate currency to the price of cotton on the European market.

39. Why was the Union more politically cohesive than the Confederacy?   **c**
    a. There was little political dissent in the North because northerners were united in a crusade against slavery.
    b. The multiplicity of political parties in the South made Confederate party politics vicious and divisive.
    c. The presence of a vocal and politically powerful opposition in the North forced the Republicans to unite behind their leader.
    d. The South had no tradition of vigorous politics or strong political leadership.

40. Which border state is correctly matched with its reason for refusing to join the Confederacy?   **d**
    a. Delaware: It was mainly a nonslaveholding state that had no desire to be part of a slave Confederacy.
    b. Missouri: The citizens of this slave state were united in their loyalty to the Union and in their belief that an independent slave confederacy could not survive.
    c. Virginia: The nonslaveholding eastern part of the state refused to secede with the western part—which named itself West Virginia when it joined the Confederacy.
    d. Kentucky: It had a Unionist legislature whose resolve was strengthened by the presence of Grant's troops across the river in Illinois.

41. In the case of *Ex parte* Merryman   **a**
    a. the Supreme Court ruled that President Lincoln had exceeded his authority in suspending habeas corpus in Maryland.
    b. President Lincoln agreed to abide by Supreme Court decisions on questions of presidential power.
    c. the Supreme Court ruled that in wartime the president had the authority to banish anyone making treasonable statements.
    d. the Supreme Court ruled that civilians could not be tried by military tribunals when the civil courts were open.

42. The Civil War can be considered the first modern war for all of the following reasons *except*:   **b**
    a. its extensive reliance on technology such as the telegraph, iron-plated warships, and mass-produced weapons
    b. vastly improved military tactics and fighting conditions for the soldiers
    c. extensive army and navy cooperation in planning and executing the war
    d. made large-scale use of trench warfare by armies on both sides

43. The South was superior to the North in which of the following?   **d**

    a. population
    b. firearm production
    c. farm acreage
    d. none of the above

44. The development of the rifle was important because   **a**

    a. it enabled generals to rely less on cavalry.
    b. it permitted more effective use of the bayonet.
    c. it eliminated the value of trenches in defensive action.
    d. it invalidated traditional military tactics.

45. The purpose of the Anaconda plan was to   **b**

    a. elect George B. McClellan, nicknamed "Anaconda," as an antiwar candidate in 1864.
    b. seal off the Confederacy along the Mississippi and the coast through a blockade.
    c. seal off the Union along the Ohio River and along the Atlantic coast.
    d. infiltrate the South in a "snake-like" fashion and incite antisecession sentiment.

46. George B. McClellan was   **d**

    a. a Union general.
    b. a proslavery Democrat.
    c. a candidate for president.
    d. all of the above

47. Which of the following is *not* associated with the Peninsula Campaign of 1862?   **c**

    a. massive movement of Union troops by water
    b. aiming for the Confederate capital rather than the Confederate army
    c. the Union generals' boldness and willingness to accept casualties
    d. a virtual slaughter of Confederates

48. The Battle of Antietam in September 1862   **b**

    a. was a strategic victory for the South because General Grant called off his invasion of Richmond.
    b. encouraged Lincoln to issue the Emancipation Proclamation.
    c. encouraged Great Britain and France to recognize the Confederacy as an independent nation.
    d. a and c

49. During the first two years of the conflict, the Civil War in the East was marked by   **a**

    a. a stalemate.
    b. decisive victories for the Union.
    c. decisive victories for the Confederacy.
    d. b and c

50. Which of the following is *not* true regarding naval activity during the Civil War?   **b**

    a. The Confederacy achieved its greatest successes in commerce raiding—harassing and destroying Union merchant shipping.
    b. The Union used its superior navy to impose a watertight blockade of the southern coast and prevent virtually all blockade runners from making it through.
    c. The Union had overwhelming naval superiority throughout the entire war and bolstered its fleet with tugs, whalers, and ferries.
    d. During the war, the world's first engagement between two ironclad warships took place.

51. The Confederacy failed to receive diplomatic recognition by England or France for all of the following reasons *except*:   **c**

    a. Lincoln's Emancipation Proclamation, which dampened Europe's enthusiasm for Confederate recognition
    b. the British awareness that their true diplomatic interest lay in supporting the Union blockade, in principle
    c. the skillful diplomacy of the Union, which avoided diplomatic conflicts and tension with both England and France
    d. England's alternative sources of cotton

52. Why did the Confederacy expect assistance, or at least diplomatic recognition, from France or Great Britain?   **d**

    a. The French and British upper classes were thought to be sympathetic to the South.
    b. A permanent division of the United States would benefit European colonial designs in the Western Hemisphere.
    c. Britain depended on the South for four-fifths of its cotton.
    d. all of the above

53. President Lincoln initially preferred a cautious approach to the confiscation of rebel property for all the following reasons *except*:   **a**

    a. lack of sentiment in the Republican party for wholesale confiscation
    b. the loyalty to the Union of four slave states
    c. the opposition of many northern proslavery Democrats to making the war a crusade against southern social institutions
    d. Lincoln's belief that southerners were still United States citizens and therefore entitled to the constitutional protection of property

54. The Emancipation Proclamation   **b**

    a. freed the slaves and abolished slavery in all the states of the Union and the Confederacy.
    b. freed slaves only in areas in rebellion against the United States but not in areas that remained loyal.
    c. was formulated by the Radical Republicans and issued by Lincoln despite his strong personal objections.
    d. convinced England and France to enter the war on behalf of the Union in order to win the crusade against slavery.

55. President Lincoln issued the Emancipation Proclamation for all of the following   c
    reasons *except*:

    a. desire to injure the Confederacy, threaten its property, heighten its dread,
       sap its morale, and hasten its demise
    b. to gain the support of European liberals who wanted a crusade against
       slavery
    c. his acceptance of the Radicals' conviction that the constitutional protection of
       property rights was, under the circumstances, no longer relevant
    d. his intention to steal the political initiative from the Radical Republicans in
       Congress

56. Slaves during the Civil War   c
                                     SG
    a. mostly remained loyal to their masters and the South.
    b. often served as officers in the Union army over other blacks.
    c. ran to Union lines when they could and worked for or fought for the North.
    d. were never allowed to enlist as soldiers in either the Union or the Confeder-
       ate army.

57. During the Civil War, northern black leaders such as Frederick Douglass worked as   d
    army recruiting agents because they believed that

    a. it was the best way to prevent blacks from being drafted.
    b. blacks were more resistant to the diseases that ravaged white soldiers in the
       garrisons.
    c. blacks would get to see their loved ones in the South only by fighting for the
       Union.
    d. black participation in the army would be a step toward black citizenship.

58. Which of the following describes the experience of black soldiers in the Union   d
    army?

    a. They were more likely than whites to be killed or wounded in battle.
    b. They were usually treated as prisoners of war when captured by Confederate
       troops.
    c. From the start, Congress mandated that black soldiers be paid the same as
       white soldiers.
    d. none of the above

59. Northern uncertainty over what policy to follow regarding education, jobs, and   b
    land for the freedman is most clearly represented by the situation in   PT

    a. Andersonville Prison.
    b. the South Carolina Sea Islands.
    c. Appomattox Court House.
    d. New York City in 1863.

60. Union capture of Vicksburg and Port Hudson was strategically important because   **d**

    SG

    a. it opened the way to Richmond.
    b. it completed Union control over the Atlantic coast.
    c. it gave Lincoln the victories he was waiting for to issue the Emancipation Proclamation.
    d. it gave the North control over the whole Mississippi River.

61. The Republican administration in Washington sponsored all of the following economic measures during the Civil War *except*:   **a**

    a. institution of a free-trade policy of low tariffs
    b. development of a transcontinental railroad
    c. creation of a national banking system
    d. granting of free public land to western settlers

62. How did the Civil War affect ordinary workers in the North?   **a**

    a. Most suffered from higher prices, increased taxes, and lagging wages.
    b. Setbacks in the clothing industry caused large numbers of garment workers and seamstresses to lose their jobs.
    c. Because of general prosperity, a smaller proportion of women had to work outside the home.
    d. Because of the wartime emergency, national unions were able to win sizable wage increases for many workers.

63. One of the features of the southern economy during the Civil War was   **c**

    a. burgeoning food supplies.
    b. rapid and extensive railroad growth.
    c. flourishing trade with the North.
    d. an end to industrial growth.

64. What happened to southern agriculture during the Civil War?   **d**

    a. Wheat, corn, and cotton production declined.
    b. Planters continued to plant cotton rather than grow food.
    c. There was a serious shortage of agricultural workers.
    d. all of the above

65. How did the Union and Confederate governments compare in their handling of dissent?   **b**

    a. Since both governments originated from the same political tradition, they both viewed dissent the same way.
    b. Abraham Lincoln was far less hesitant about imposing martial law and suspending the fundamental right of habeas corpus than was Jefferson Davis.
    c. Compared with Jefferson Davis, Abraham Lincoln had greater faith in democracy and therefore thought that dissent was a beneficial part of the political process.
    d. The Confederate government was prepared to act swiftly and harshly to stamp out dissent, which it equated with treason.

66. The Supreme Court ruled in *Ex parte* Milligan that
    a. civilians could not be tried by military tribunals when the civil courts were open.
    b. Lincoln had no constitutional right to free slaves in the Confederacy.
    c. the Union had no right to confiscate the property of rebel leaders.
    d. Congress rather than the president had the right to direct reconstruction of the South.

    a
    SG

67. Which of the following is an accurate generalization about health and sanitation at the Civil War battlefront?
    a. Neither the Union nor the Confederate government devoted much energy to sanitary measures in hospitals.
    b. Because of the large number of volunteer nurses in northern hospitals, army camps were free from typhoid, malaria, diarrhea, and dysentery.
    c. Although the ratio of disease to battle deaths was much better than during the Mexican War, two-thirds of deaths came from disease rather than battle wounds.
    d. none of the above

    c

68. Which of the following statements about women in the Civil War is correct?
    a. Women were *not* allowed to enter army camps to nurse soldiers.
    b. Women came to hold about one-third of the industrial jobs in the North.
    c. Loyal Unionist women were allowed to vote and run for political office.
    d. Northern missionary and freedmen's aid societies refused to use women volunteers.

    b
    SG

69. Which of the following Union military objectives proved the hardest and took the longest to accomplish?
    a. taking Richmond
    b. gaining control of the Mississippi River
    c. taking New Orleans
    d. seizing the islands off the South's Atlantic coast in order to strengthen the blockade

    a
    SG

70. The *most* important factor in Abraham Lincoln's 1864 reelection victory was
    a. his furlough of Union soldiers so that they could vote for him.
    b. the fall of Atlanta in September 1864.
    c. the lack of any organized political opposition.
    d. the split between Lincoln and the Radicals over plans for post-war reconstruction.

    b

71. In 1864, General Sherman pursued a policy of mass destruction as he moved his army through the South because
    a. he was a ruthless and heartless military leader.
    b. he had lost control over his troops.
    c. he wanted to break the South's will and its ability to resist.
    d. he had been ordered to do so by President Lincoln.

    c

72. Which person is correctly paired with his plan or technique for military victory?   **d**
    a. McClellan: surround the Confederacy and choke it into submission
    b. Winfield Scott: simultaneous, coordinated attacks on several fronts
    c. Lincoln: a bloodless defeat followed by a negotiated peace that would leave slavery intact
    d. Sherman: "total war"

73. Which group of battles is correctly identified as Union or Confederate victories?   **b**
    a. Confederate victories: Chancellorsville, Chickamauga, and Antietam
    b. Union victories: Antietam, Gettysburg, and Vicksburg
    c. Confederate victories: Shiloh, New Orleans, and Fredericksburg
    d. Union victories: Vicksburg, Shiloh, and Chickamauga

ESSAY QUESTIONS

74. What was the Union's most important military victory? What was the Confederacy's? Describe the circumstances, the military leaders, and their strategies. Why did the victorious army win? Why, in each instance, was the victory important?

75. Discuss the expectations of Union and Confederate soldiers at the beginning of the war and the realities that they faced on the battlefield.

76. How did the Civil War affect each of the following: northern factory workers, southern plantation workers, northern industrialists, southern planters, and northern and southern women.

77. The Civil War raised the hopes of several groups in American society that their grievances might be addressed in the near future. Explain why this was so, with specific reference to blacks and women.

78. Compare the approaches of the Union and the Confederacy in dealing with the following wartime challenges: manning and supplying their armies, public finance, and political dissent.

79. Why did the South lose the Civil War, and why did the North win? Why did the war last four years? Discuss the following for both the North and the South: war goals, economic strengths and weaknesses, public finance, military and naval strengths and weaknesses, relations with the rest of the world, and political systems.

80. Discuss Abraham Lincoln as president. What was his style of leadership? Was he, as his critics charged, a yokel? Was he a conservative or a radical? What, especially, were his attitudes toward slavery and the Union?

81. Compare and contrast the economic impact of the Civil War on the Union and on the Confederacy.   SG

82. In 1861, President Lincoln asserted that he had no intention of interfering with slavery where it already existed. Two years later, however, he changed his position and issued the Emancipation Proclamation. Why? What were the practical and the ideological considerations? What did the proclamation do, and what did it *not* do? Should and could Lincoln have gone further?

83. Radical Republicans viewed the Civil War as a second American Revolution. What did they mean? Were they correct?

MAP QUESTIONS

Choose the letter on the accompanying map of the United States that correctly identifies each of the following:

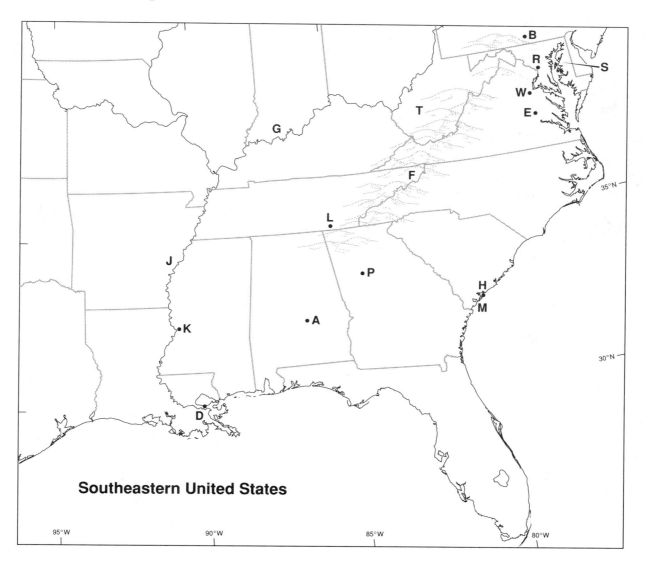

Southeastern United States

84. Appalachian Mountains   F

85. Mississippi River   J

86. Montgomery, Alabama   A

87. Richmond, Virginia   E

88. Washington, D.C.   R

89. Gettysburg, Pennsylvania   B

90. Atlanta, Georgia   P

91. Maryland   S

92. Ohio River   G

93. West Virginia   T

94. Sea Islands   M

95. Fredericksburg, Virginia   W

96. Vicksburg, Mississippi   K

97. Chattanooga, Tennessee   L

98. Charleston, South Carolina   H

99. New Orleans, Louisiana   D

CHAPTER 15

The Crises of Reconstruction, 1865–1877

IDENTIFICATIONS

Identify the following. Be as specific as possible, and include names, dates, and relevant facts as appropriate. Be sure to explain the *significance* of the person or term.

1. Radical Republicans

2. Charles Sumner

3. Thaddeus Stevens

4. "10 percent plan"

5. Wade-Davis bill

6. Andrew Johnson

7. black codes

8. Freedmen's Bureau

9. Civil Rights Act of 1866

10. Joint Committee on Reconstruction

11. "swing around the circle" (1866 congressional elections)

12. Reconstruction Act of 1867

13. Tenure of Office Act

14. "Reconstruction amendments"

15. scalawags and carpetbaggers

16. Ku Klux Klan

17. Enforcement Acts

18. freedmen's schools

19. sharecropping system

20. crop-lien system

21. Grantism

22. Horace Greeley and the Liberal Republicans

23. Panic of 1873

24. sound money vs. easy money debate

25. *Slaughterhouse* cases

26. redemption

27. Compromise of 1877

MULTIPLE-CHOICE QUESTIONS

Choose the answer the *best* completes the statement or answers the question.

28. The *most* important issue facing the nation in the post–Civil War era was   a
    a. the future of the freedmen.
    b. the future of the southern economy.
    c. the building of the transcontinental railroad.
    d. the refinancing of southern war debts.

29. In the three years immediately following the Civil War,   b
    a. President Johnson exiled, imprisoned, or executed many former Confederate leaders.
    b. intense and unparalleled political conflicts dominated the national scene.
    c. demobilized Confederate soldiers continued armed resistance to federal occupation forces.
    d. freedmen took revenge on their former owners and the rest of the white community.

30. Which of the following was *not* a feature of Lincoln's "10 percent plan"?   c
    a. State governments could be formed when at least 10 percent of those who had voted in 1860 had sworn allegiance to the Union and accepted emancipation.
    b. Confederate officials and army and naval officers needed presidential pardons before they could participate in the new governments.
    c. Southern plantations were to be confiscated and divided among the blacks who had formerly worked there as slaves.
    d. Freedmen were excluded from participation because they had not been voters in 1860.

31. The Wade-Davis bill   d
    a. failed to provide for black suffrage.
    b. was pocket-vetoed by President Lincoln.
    c. provided that each former Confederate state would be ruled by a military governor.
    d. all of the above

32. Which statement is *not* true about Andrew Johnson?   b

                                                                                          SG
    a. He wanted to exclude the planters from political leadership in the South but then undermined his intention by granting so many pardons to planters.
    b. He cared deeply about obtaining just treatment for the freedmen.
    c. He was a lifelong Democrat with no interest in building the strength of the Republican party.
    d. He vetoed all of the congressional reconstruction acts, only to have Congress override his vetoes.

33. The key difference between the Lincoln and Johnson plans for reconstruction was   a
    that, unlike Lincoln's plan, Johnson's plan
    a. barred from political participation any ex-Confederate with taxable property worth $20,000 or more.
    b. excluded freedmen from participating in the new reconstruction governments.
    c. required that southerners take oaths of allegiance to the United States.
    d. confiscated all property of all southerners.

34. The Thirteenth Amendment to the Constitution   b
    a. declared secession illegal.
    b. abolished slavery.
    c. guaranteed freedmen the right to vote.
    d. declared former slaves to be citizens.

35. By the end of 1865, under President Johnson's reconstruction policies,   c
    a. all southern states had ratified the Thirteenth Amendment and repudiated their Confederate debts.
    b. most southern states had passed special industrial codes to help the freedmen become economically independent.
    c. former Confederate congressmen, state officials, and generals had been elected to serve in Congress.
    d. the southern states had been divided into a series of military districts.

36. The black codes   d

                                                                                          SG
    a. were imposed by Congress on the ex-Confederate states.
    b. guaranteed such basic liberties as freedom of movement and employment, the right to testify in court, and the use of all public facilities.
    c. were seen by Thaddeus Stevens and other Radical Republicans as a necessary legal step to help blacks make the transition from slavery to freedom.
    d. were laws passed by the Johnson government in the South to keep blacks as a semi-free, cheap labor force.

37. What brought the Radical and moderate Republicans together in an alliance   a
    against President Johnson?

    a. the president's vetoes of the Freedmen's Bureau bill and the Civil Rights Act
       of 1866
    b. realization by congressional Republicans that Johnson was delaying readmis-
       sion of the former Confederate states
    c. the president's proposal for an agency that would provide relief, rations, and
       medical care for impoverished southerners
    d. a desire to send a message to northern Democrats that they could work
       together to rebuild the South

38. The Fourteenth Amendment to the Constitution included all of the following pro-   b
    visions *except*:

    a. citizenship in both the nation and their states for all persons born or natural-
       ized in the United States
    b. guaranteed right to vote for male blacks and loss of representation in
       Congress for states that denied them suffrage
    c. disqualification from state and national office of all prewar officeholders
    d. explicit repudiation of the Confederate debt

39. According to the Reconstruction Act of 1867, all of the following had to occur so   d
    that former Confederate states could be readmitted to the Union *except*:

    a. new constitutions by southern states, approved by Congress, granting black
       suffrage
    b. ratification of the Fourteenth Amendment by southern states and incorpora-
       tion of the amendment into the federal Constitution
    c. election of delegates to state constitutional conventions by southern black
       voters and whites not disqualified by the Fourteenth Amendment
    d. plans devised by southern state legislatures to finance veterans' benefits for
       former Confederate soldiers

40. Which of the following is *not* true about the Radical Republicans?   c

    a. They favored black suffrage and federal support for public schools.
    b. They wanted to crush the planter aristocracy and revolutionize southern
       institutions, habits, and manners.
    c. They believed that through intermarriage a true biracial society could be
       established in the South.
    d. They believed that Congress rather than the president should direct
       reconstruction.

41. As a result of the impeachment and trial of President Andrew Johnson,   **a**
    a. a precedent was established against the impeachment of presidents solely on political grounds.
    b. Johnson was acquitted and emerged triumphant in his battle with the Radicals in Congress.
    c. the president was convicted, dismissed from office, and replaced with Ben Wade.
    d. Republicans and Democrats in Congress at last found a cause around which they all could rally.

42. The Fifteenth Amendment   **b**
    a. defines citizenship and requires states to extend to all persons equal protec-   **SG**
    tion under the law.
    b. states that no one shall be denied the right to vote because of race, color, or previous condition of servitude.
    c. extends the suffrage to all citizens over twenty-one years of age.
    d. gives Congress the power to deny seats in the House to states that do not allow black men to vote.

43. Why did the battle over black suffrage ultimately divide the women's rights   **c**
    movement?
    a. A large part of the women's rights movement did not believe that a constitutional amendment was necessary in order to gain the vote.
    b. Half of the movement advocated focusing on the rights of black women, while the other half emphasized that first priority should be on the rights of black men.
    c. Some advocates of women's rights refused to support black suffrage without attendant women suffrage.
    d. The women's rights movement had always avoided the debate over slavery, and many now feared being drawn into the new debate over black rights.

44. The unique achievement of congressional Reconstruction was that   **d**
    a. the Republicans were able to establish a permanent political base in previously hostile territory.
    b. it was accomplished without the use of military force.
    c. the former ruling elite transformed its attitudes about race relations.
    d. former slaves participated in the new governments.

45. In the Republican reconstruction governments of the South the group that held   **b**
    the most political offices was the   **SG**
    a. carpetbaggers.
    b. scalawags.
    c. blacks.
    d. planter elite.

46. Which of the following descriptions best fits the carpetbaggers?   **a**
    a. former Union soldiers who hoped to buy land, open factories, build rail-roads, or enjoy a warmer climate
    b. northerners who went South seeking wealth and power, and who came with so few possessions that they could be stuffed into traveling bags made of carpet material
    c. predominantly poor and ignorant white southerners who sought to profit from Republican rule
    d. uneducated freedmen who moved to northern cities for better economic opportunity, and who took with them only what they could fit in a traveling bag

47. The scalawags were   **d**
    a. former slaveholders who opposed the reconstruction governments.
    b. advocates of black rights and black suffrage in the reconstructed southern states.
    c. black southerners who opposed the Republican program of national banking and high protective tariffs.
    d. none of the above

48. During Reconstruction, what group was the backbone of the Republican party in the South, providing eight out of ten Republican votes?   **c**
    a. scalawags
    b. carpetbaggers
    c. freedmen
    d. none of the above

49. What role did blacks have in the southern governments established under congressional Reconstruction?   **a**
    a. There were no black governors and only two black senators.
    b. Blacks held most of the political offices.
    c. Blacks formed a majority in most of the state legislatures.
    d. Blacks rarely filled any important positions in state government.

50. The accomplishments of the new government established under congressional Reconstruction included all of the following *except*:   **b**
    a. creation of public school systems and the institution of ambitious programs of public works
    b. land confiscation and more equitable redistribution
    c. expansion of state bureaucracies and increased salaries for state employees
    d. increased state debts and taxes

51. To meet the challenge of Republican congressional Reconstruction, Democratic political action included all of the following *except*:   **c**
    a. support for dissident Republican factions
    b. vigilante efforts to reduce black votes
    c. rallies to raise support for a renewed attempt at secession
    d. publicity campaigns to demean the new state constitutions

52. The Ku Klux Klan was   d
    a. a secret social club.
    b. a terrorist organization.
    c. an arm of the southern Democratic party.
    d. all of the above

53. Which of the following was *not* one of the effects of emancipation on the black   a
    family in the years after the Civil War?
    a. The majority became single-parent families as men left their wives and set out
       on new careers.
    b. Many blacks legalized marriages that had been formed under slavery.
    c. Black men often asserted themselves as heads of households by demanding
       that their wives wait on them.
    d. Black women temporarily withdrew from the work force.

54. Who was the main pillar of authority in the southern black community after the   b
    Civil War?
    a. the local public school teacher
    b. the minister of the black church
    c. the local justice of the peace
    d. the head of the county Democratic party

55. Why was a more strenuous effort not made to combat racial segregation in the   d
    south during Reconstruction?
    a. White southerners said integration would lead to intermarriage.
    b. Elite blacks such as teachers, ministers, and politicians depended on separate
       black institutions for their own power.
    c. Rural blacks just wanted land, they didn't want to mix with whites.
    d. all of the above

56. Which of the following was *not* one of the reasons why only a small proportion of   c
    blacks were able to own their own farms by the end of Reconstruction?
    a. Most lacked the capital to buy the land and equipment.
    b. White southerners didn't want to sell their land to blacks.
    c. Southern industrialists needed laborers to work in their new urban factories.
    d. Southern planters needed a source of labor to work on their plantations.

57. The southern sharecropping system that developed after the Civil War   b
    a. meant that the former southern planter elite would eventually be displaced   PT
       by a Jeffersonian aristocracy of small farmers.
    b. allowed freedmen day-to-day control over the land but kept them from own-
       ing it and often led to deep indebtedness.
    c. was forced on former slaves, who preferred to be able to work the land for
       wages.
    d. was usually pointed to by southerners as proof that the old slave plantation
       system was the only one that could be economically viable.

58. The sharecropping and crop-lien systems that developed in the post–Civil War South **a** **SG**

    a. contributed to soil depletion, agricultural backwardness, and southern poverty.
    b. reduced the portion of southern land owned and controlled by the planter elite.
    c. forced most black people out of agriculture and into southern cities.
    d. tied white planters and black tenants together economically, but had no effect on white small farmers.

59. Ulysses S. Grant's election in 1868 suggested that **c**

    a. Reconstruction was not popular anywhere in the country.
    b. sound money was the first priority for most voters.
    c. the Republicans needed the newly enfranchised southern freedmen to ensure national victories.
    d. American voters were tired of corruption in government.

60. Which of the following is *not* associated with "Grantism"? **d**

    a. Jay Gould
    b. whiskey ring
    c. Crédit Mobilier
    d. Seward's Ice Box

61. In the 1872 election, the Liberal Republicans disagreed with Grant and the "regular" Republicans on all of the following issues *except*: **a**

    a. the desirability of Charles Sumner's nomination
    b. civil-service reform
    c. free trade
    d. the end of military reconstruction

62. In the 1870s, the "money question" referred to the problem of **b**

    a. how to balance the federal budget without raising taxes.
    b. how to repay the federal debt and whether or not to issue more paper money.
    c. whether paper money should be green or yellow.
    d. whether or not Jim Fisk should go to jail for attempting to corner the gold market.

63. Why did the Republican party in the 1870s try increasingly to downplay reconstruction and focus on northern issues? **d**

    a. For economic reasons: the depression, the money question, and the desire to do business with the South
    b. For political reasons: realization that they had to change their political strategy in order to win
    c. For legal reasons: Supreme Court decisions that weakened or dismantled much of the Reconstruction machinery
    d. all of the above

64. What doctrine did the Supreme Court enunciate in the *Slaughterhouse* cases of   c
1873?

   a. Where civil courts were functioning, civilians could not be tried by military courts or commissions.

   b. Congress had the power to ensure each state a republican form of government.

   c. The federal government was obliged to protect only basic rights of national citizenship, and it did not have to protect such rights against state violation.

   d. The Fifteenth Amendment did not confer the right of suffrage upon anyone.

65. All of the following usually accompanied redemption *except*:   a

   a. returning greenbacks and receiving gold coin in exchange

   b. revising tax systems to relieve landowners of large tax burdens

   c. dismantling social programs

   d. legally restricting the actions of freedmen

66. In order to convince southern Democrats to accept the election of Rutherford B.   b
Hayes as president, Republican backers of Hayes promised all of the following   SG
except:

   a. to remove the remaining federal troops from the South and allow the Democrats to take over the last of the Republican Reconstruction governments

   b. to recognize and have the federal government help pay off the Confederate war debt

   c. to give more federal patronage to southern Democrats

   d. to give federal aid to building railroads and other internal improvements in the South

67. All of the following were considered Radical Republicans *except*:   c

   a. Charles Sumner

   b. Thaddeus Stevens

   c. Horatio Seymour

   d. Edwin Stanton

68. Which of the following Reconstruction laws is correctly paired with one of its pro-   d
visions?

   a. Civil Rights Act of 1866: required military commanders to initiate voter enrollment

   b. Army Appropriations Act: expanded the powers of military commanders in the South

   c. Supplementary Freedman's Bureau Act: prohibited the president from removing federal officials without consent of the Senate

   d. Reconstruction Act of 1867: invalidated state governments formed under Lincoln and Johnson

69. Which of the following statements accurately describes the rights of suffrage   a
    enjoyed by blacks in the United States in 1868?
    a. Black voting had been rejected by much of the North.
    b. Northern states led the way in demonstrating the advantages of black
       suffrage.
    c. Despite attempts by Congress, southern states refused to enfranchise black
       men prior to readmission to the Union.
    d. Northern states had instituted suffrage for black men *and* women, while
       southern states had enfranchised only black men.

70. During Reconstruction, southern black education   b
    a. was a national priority.
    b. advanced but remained quite limited.
    c. made rapid strides toward integration.
    d. focused exclusively on the elementary level.

71. In the former Confederate states, Republican rule   c
    a. was permanently established through the new state constitutions approved
       by Congress.
    b. in most states lasted until the Democrats were able to recapture the White
       House in 1884.
    c. lasted a maximum of about eight years, but in most states much less.
    d. lasted no more than two years anywhere in the South.

72. Over the years, Reconstruction has been viewed as   d
    a. a failed experiment of excessive radical rule, dominated by carpetbaggers,
       scalawags, and Radical Republicans.
    b. a democratic experiment that failed to ensure civil rights through property
       reforms and military force.
    c. the federal government's failure to fulfill its own goals and create a biracial
       democracy in the South.
    d. all of the above

ESSAY QUESTIONS

73. Explain the three major plans for reconstruction: Lincoln's "10 percent plan," the
    Wade-Davis plan, and Andrew Johnson's plan. Compare the political, social, and
    economic goals of presidential Reconstruction with those of congressional Recon-
    struction. Compare the methods and accomplishments of presidential and con-
    gressional Reconstruction.

74. Explain how and why the debate over reconstruction was, in part, a debate
    between Congress and the president over which branch had the authority to
    shape and direct reconstruction.

75. Reconstruction was brought about through a series of legal and constitutional changes—the "Reconstruction amendments" and other national legislation, for example. At the same time, legal and constitutional issues had much to do with the unmaking or ending of Reconstruction. Explain.

76. Who were the Radical Republicans and what were their goals? What actions did they take to try to achieve their goals? Were they successful? Could they have been *more* "radical"?

77. Why did basic land reform never come about in the South? Was land reform necessary to make reconstruction a success? Why or why not?

78. What were the circumstances surrounding the impeachment and trial of President Andrew Johnson? Why was he impeached? Why was he acquitted? What precedents were established in the process?

79. Explain why and how political, legal, economic and financial, ideological, and personal factors contributed to the end of Reconstruction in the South. Why did the Republican government in Washington fail to continue a military presence in the South?

80. What was the impact of emancipation on the freedman? Discuss family, jobs, education, politics, and religious and social institutions. Did emancipation affect all freedmen in the same way? How did black females fare as free citizens?

81. How did southern agriculture change during Reconstruction? Were southern agriculture and agricultural workers better or worse off after the Civil War than before?

82. Discuss the Grant administration. What were its policies on reconstruction and SG the freedmen? What was meant by "Grantism" and Grant's "Great Barbecue"? What successes and failures did the administration have in foreign policy? Why did Liberal Republicans break with Grant?

Final Examination Questions for Prologue and Chapters 1–15

IDENTIFICATIONS

Identify the following. Be as specific as possible, and include names, dates, and relevant facts as appropriate. Be sure to explain the *significance* of the person or term.

1. tidewater region

2. Pueblo culture

3. nuclear and extended families

4. Captain John Smith

5. John Winthrop

6. Bacon's Rebellion

7. the Navigation Acts

8. the Great Awakening

9. Pontiac's Rebellion

10. Coercive Acts, Quebec Act, Intolerable Acts

11. Ordinance of 1785, Northwest Ordinance

12. Virginia Plan, New Jersey Plan

13. Alexander Hamilton

14. Virginia and Kentucky Resolutions

15. John Marshall, *Marbury* v. *Madison*

16. Monroe Doctrine

17. transportation revolution

18. separate spheres

19. Seneca Falls Convention of 1848

20. Frederick Douglass, Sojourner Truth

21. Nat Turner rebellion

22. James Henry Hammond and George Fitzhugh

23. American system of manufacturing

24. American Renaissance

25. nativism

26. Manifest Destiny

27. *Dred Scott* decision

28. the doctrines of "free soil" and "free labor"

29. Battle of Antietam

30. *Florida*, *Alabama*, and the Laird rams

31. black codes

32. scalawags and carpetbaggers

MULTIPLE-CHOICE QUESTIONS

Choose the answer that *best* completes the statement or answers the question.

33. Which of the following most influenced the development of antebellum southern culture and economy?   a
    a. the fall line
    b. slash-and-burn techniques of the Indians
    c. the path of the retreating ice cap
    d. early colonial French culture

34. From the earliest European settlements through the end of the Civil War, relations   b
    between whites and native Americans were marked by all of the following *except*:
    a. mass removals of tribes from one region to another
    b. a movement to create a separate native American homeland on a Pacific island
    c. political and military alliances between native Americans and whites
    d. widespread efforts at Christianizing the native Americans

35. Which of the following American wars resulted in the highest ratio of casualties to the nation's population?   c
    a. War for Independence
    b. Mexican War
    c. Civil War
    d. War of 1812

36. Which of the following presidents served two terms in office?   d
    a. Abraham Lincoln
    b. John Adams
    c. John Quincy Adams
    d. James Monroe

37. For which of the following American political leaders would the concept of "union" *not* have been a preeminent concern?   a
    a. John C. Breckenridge
    b. James Madison
    c. Abraham Lincoln
    d. Henry Clay

38. An American living in the years between the ratification of the Constitution and the beginning of the Civil War might have spoken all of the following words with great reverence *except*:   d
    a. liberty
    b. union
    c. constitution
    d. equality

39. The sectionalism inherent in American society and politics was evident in all of the following *except*:   b
    a. the Constitutional Convention
    b. the election of James Monroe as president
    c. the War of 1812
    d. the tariff issue

40. All of the following were prominent issues of political debate during the first eighty years of American independence *except*:   c
    a. women's rights
    b. education
    c. large federal budget deficits
    d. improvements of canals, roads, and harbors

41. The greatest influx of settlers into America occurred during the   a
    a. 1840s and 1850s.
    b. 1790s.
    c. 1810s and 1820s.
    d. 1740s.

42. Which of the following occurred first?   **b**

    a. Kansas-Nebraska Act
    b. Gabriel Prosser's rebellion
    c. publication of *Uncle Tom's Cabin*
    d. Missouri Compromise

43. Which of the following occurred first?   **c**

    a. Seneca Falls Convention
    b. abolition of black slavery
    c. publication of Mary Wollstonecraft's *Vindication of the Rights of Woman*
    d. Second Great Awakening

44. Which of the following areas was the last to be acquired by the United States?   **d**

    a. northern Maine
    b. Florida
    c. Louisiana
    d. southern New Mexico

45. Which of the following had *not* become a state by 1870?   **a**

    a. Oklahoma
    b. Maine
    c. Oregon
    d. Nevada

46. All of the following were American entrepreneurs *except*:   **b**

    a. Stephen Girard
    b. John Cotton
    c. Jay Gould
    d. Samuel F. B. Morse

47. All of the following involved battles between whites and native Americans *except*:   **c**

    a. the Pequot War
    b. King Philip's War
    c. the Goliad massacre
    d. the Battle of the Thames

48. Which of the following was *not* a native American?   **d**

    a. King Philip
    b. Tecumseh
    c. Joseph Brant
    d. Gabriel Prosser

49. With which of the following people would you have been *least* likely to have a   **a**
    serious discussion about religion?

    a. Samuel Slater
    b. Junìpero Serra
    c. George Whitefield
    d. Joseph Smith

50. All of the following were authors of controversial publications *except*: **b**
    a. Thomas Paine
    b. Lydia Sigourney
    c. Mary Wollstonecraft
    d. Harriet Beecher Stowe

51. Which of the following people was *not* associated with government finance? **d**
    a. Alexander Hamilton
    b. Salmon Chase
    c. Nicholas Biddle
    d. Frederic Church

52. Which of the following is an accurate statement about the rights of women in America before the Civil War? **c**
    a. In the colonial period, women had the same rights as men.
    b. Women in America had fewer rights than women in Europe.
    c. Women formed organizations to protest their lack of political and economic rights.
    d. all of the above

53. What did Winfield Scott, David G. Farragut, and Henry Knox have in common? **a**
    a. They were American officers who were associated with important victories.
    b. They were naval officers who fought for the American cause in three different wars.
    c. They all were army officers who fought in the Civil War.
    d. They were officers who later went on to run for high public office.

54. Which of the following was an American painter? **b**
    a. George Fitzhugh
    b. Asher Durand
    c. James Oglethorpe
    d. John Slidell

55. Which of the following years was *not* a year of general economic collapse in the United States? **c**
    a. 1857
    b. 1837
    c. 1799
    d. 1819

56. Which of the following had the least in common with the other three? **d**
    a. Sojourner Truth
    b. Nat Turner
    c. Denmark Vesey
    d. James Henry Hammond

57. Which author is correctly matched with something that he wrote?   **a**
    a. William Alcott, *The Young Man's Guide*
    b. Adam Smith, *Democracy in America*
    c. James Fenimore Cooper, *The Impending Crisis of the South*
    d. Frederick Douglass, "A Model of Christian Charity"

58. What did the Ku Klux Klan, the Order of the Star Spangled Banner, the *Awful Dis-*   **b**
    closures, and the Naturalization Act of 1798 have in common?
    a. They revealed the strong sectional divisions that existed in American society.
    b. They expressed or reflected the fact that throughout American society there
       was a strong fear of foreigners.
    c. They demonstrated the continuing popularity of organizations opposed to
       unpatriotic behavior.
    d. They were founded or written by foreigners.

59. What did the Homestead Act, the Ordinance of 1785, and the Yazoo cases have in   **c**
    common?
    a. They all were opposed by German-Americans.
    b. They all protected the rights of native Americans.
    c. They all involved the distribution of land.
    d. They all complicated American relations with England.

60. Which of the following is generally considered to be a "southern" writer?   **d**
    a. Henry David Thoreau
    b. Thomas Jefferson
    c. J. E. B. Stuart
    d. William Gilmore Simms

61. Which of the following was *not* included in the first five amendments that were   **a**
    added to the Constitution after the ratification of the Bill of Rights?
    a. women being granted the right to vote
    b. separate ballots for president and vice president
    c. limitations on the federal judiciary
    d. the abolition of slavery

62. All of the following were secretary of state *except*:   **b**
    a. William H. Seward
    b. John Tyler
    c. Martin Van Buren
    d. Thomas Jefferson

63. What did Millard Fillmore, John Tyler, and Andrew Johnson have in common?   c

    a. They all were presidents of the United States who died during their second term in office.
    b. They all were presidents of the United States who were defeated for reelection because of an economic depression.
    c. They all were presidents of the United States who had not been elected to the position.
    d. none of the above

64. Which of the following treaties did *not* result in territorial gains for the United States?   d

    a. Adams-Onís Treaty
    b. Treaty of Guadalupe Hidalgo
    c. Webster-Ashburton Treaty
    d. Jay Treaty

65. Which of the following contributes the *least* to an understanding of antebellum American foreign policy?   a

    a. Barbary Wars
    b. Monroe Doctrine
    c. Manifest Destiny
    d. the *Alabama* Claims

66. Which of the following Supreme Court cases dealt with native Americans?   b

    a. *McCulloch* v. *Maryland*
    b. *Worcester* v. *Georgia*
    c. *Commonwealth* v. *Hunt*
    d. all of the above

67. All of the following were Supreme Court cases during Chief Justice John Marshall's tenure *except*:   c

    a. *Marbury* v. *Madison*
    b. *Dartmouth College* v. *Woodward*
    c. *Dred Scott* v. *Stanford*
    d. *Gibbons* v. *Ogden*

68. Which of the following is in correct chronological order?   d

    a. Constitutional Convention, Jay Treaty, Louisiana Purchase, Northwest Ordinance
    b. Northwest Ordinance, Jay Treaty, Constitutional Convention, Louisiana Purchase
    c. Jay Treaty, Constitutional Convention, Northwest Ordinance, Louisiana Purchase
    d. Northwest Ordinance, Constitutional Convention, Jay Treaty, Louisiana Purchase

69. Which of the following is in correct chronological order?   **a**
    a. Fugitive Slave Law, Missouri Compromise, Gadsden Purchase, Morrill Land Grant Act
    b. Missouri Compromise, Fugitive Slave Law, Gadsden Purchase, Morrill Land Grant Act
    c. Fugitive Slave Law, Morrill Land Grant Act, Missouri Compromise, Gadsden Purchase
    d. Gadsden Purchase, Fugitive Slave Law, Missouri Compromise, Morrill Land Grant Act

70. Which of the following is in correct chronological order?   **b**
    a. Battle of Tippecanoe, Battle of Fallen Timbers, Battle of Antietam, Battle of Long Island
    b. Battle of Long Island, Battle of Fallen Timbers, Battle of Tippecanoe, Battle of Antietam
    c. Battle of Fallen Timbers, Battle of Long Island, Battle of Tippecanoe, Battle of Antietam
    d. Battle of Antietam, Battle of Long Island, Battle of Fallen Timbers, Battle of Tippecanoe

71. Which of the following is in correct chronological order?   **c**
    a. opening of the Erie Canal, invention of the cotton gin, completion of the transcontinental railroad, California gold rush
    b. California gold rush, opening of the Erie Canal, invention of the cotton gin, completion of the transcontinental railroad
    c. invention of the cotton gin, opening of the Erie Canal, California gold rush, completion of the transcontinental railroad
    d. invention of the cotton gin, opening of the Erie Canal, completion of the transcontinental railroad, California gold rush

72. Which of the following states the order in which these political parties were   **d**
    founded?
    a. Democratic, Federalist, Know-Nothing, Whig
    b. Federalist, Know-Nothing, Whig, Democratic
    c. Whig, Federalist, Democratic, Know-Nothing
    d. Federalist, Democratic, Whig, Know-Nothing

73. Which of the following presidents exercised the greatest amount of power while in   **a**
    office?
    a. Abraham Lincoln
    b. Andrew Jackson
    c. Thomas Jefferson
    d. John Adams

74. Which of the following correctly lists the cities in the order that they were   b
    founded?
    a. St. Augustine, New Orleans, Chicago, Boston
    b. St. Augustine, Boston, New Orleans, Chicago
    c. Boston, New Orleans, St. Augustine, Chicago
    d. New Orleans, Boston, Chicago, St. Augustine

ESSAY QUESTIONS

75. How did relations between whites and native Americans change during the centuries
    from the first European settlements until the 1870s? Why? When were relations the
    best, and when were they the worst? How did individual attitudes and official govern-
    ment policies change during those years?

76. Why was slavery introduced into the New World? How did the slave system evolve in
    North America? During the American Revolution, twenty thousand or more American
    slaves ran away from their masters, but no similar flight occurred during the Civil War.
    What had happened between those two wars? Why was there a change?

77. How did the role and status of women in America change from the colonial period
    through the mid–nineteenth century? Why? How did American women differ from
    European women? How were the conditions that women faced shaped by race and
    class? How were women affected by the political changes that took place throughout
    the period? By the mid–nineteenth century, what issues still remained to be resolved
    regarding the "Woman Question"?

78. From the first European settlements in America through the Civil War, the idea of
    "reform"—political, moral, religious, and intellectual—was integral to American devel-
    opment. Yet the goals, motivations, and assumptions of reformers varied greatly over
    the years. Discuss the varieties of reform movements in America and how they affected
    American society.

79. In what ways was the American political system more democratic in 1870 than it had
    been in 1670? Did changes in society itself make America more democratic? Did Amer-
    ican politics and society during those two centuries become more democratic for some
    groups, and less democratic for others? Explain.

80. Historian Carl Degler has written that "capitalism came [to America] in the first ships."
    How did American capitalism evolve from the colonial period through the 1860s? How
    did the major forms of business enterprise and the entrepreneurial spirit change? What
    did not change? How did these changes affect average Americans?

81. It is sometimes suggested that from the colonial period onward American history was
    on a course that had to lead to a civil war. Trace some of the following issues from the
    colonial period forward and discuss how they contributed to the events of 1861: eco-
    nomic development, social differences, sectionalism, slavery and racial issues, legal tra-
    ditions, ways of thinking, ways of viewing the world.

82. Discuss the evolution of the American legal and constitutional system by considering the following: elements of the European legal/constitutional tradition that were brought to America, the colonial legal/constitutional legacy, the Articles of Confederation and the Constitution, and the evolution of the Constitution during the first eighty years of the federal government.

83. What were the basic principles of American foreign policy during the first ninety years of the United States? What were the major accomplishments and major failures in foreign affairs during those years? In what ways did American domestic politics affect American foreign policy, and American foreign relations affect American domestic politics?

84. How did organized religion affect the political, economic, and social development of America up to the Civil War? What religions developed in the United States, and why? Who were the most prominent American religious figures, and what kinds of influence did they have?

85. Who was the most successful American president between 1789 and 1877? Who was the least successful? Define your standard of success. Explain the challenges facing your two choices, and why one met those challenges and the other failed.

86. Throughout American history two forces—nationalism and sectionalism—have pulled in opposite directions. Explore those two sentiments in the two centuries leading to the Civil War. How did they manifest themselves in American politics, culture, economics, and religion?

87. In 1776, Thomas Paine suggested that America "under a government of her own" could be "as happy as she pleases: she hath a blank sheet to write upon." What, in your estimation, are the most important things that America wrote on her slate in the more than two centuries between the first settlements and the end of the Civil War? Why?

CHAPTER 16

The Frontier West

IDENTIFICATIONS

Identify the following. Be as specific as possible, and include names, dates, and relevant facts as appropriate. Be sure to explain the *significance* of the person or term.

1. *rancheros*

2. William F. "Buffalo Bill" Cody

3. "Custer's Last Stand"

4. Interstate Commerce Act

5. Carlisle Indian School

6. the Dawes Severalty Act

7. Helen Hunt Jackson

8. Wovoka

9. Red River War and Wounded Knee

10. Promontory Point

11. the Pacific Railroad Act of 1862

12. *Munn* v. *Illinois*

13. Juan Cortina

14. California

15. barrios

16. *Las Gorras Blancas*

17. Homestead Act

18. Comstock Lode

19. "frontier thesis"

20. Oklahoma "sooners"

MULTIPLE-CHOICE QUESTIONS

Choose the answer that *best* completes the statement or answers the question.

21. Which of the following contributed to the fighting style of the Plains Indians?　**b**
    a. gunpowder introduced by Chinese immigrants in the nineteenth century
    b. horses introduced by the Spanish in the sixteenth century
    c. firearms introduced by Hessian soldiers in the eighteenth century
    d. swords introduced by the Spanish in the sixteenth century

22. All the following were nomadic Plains Indians who hunted buffalo *except*:　**c**
    a. Lakota Sioux　　　　　　　　　　　　　　　　　　　　　　　　**SG**
    b. Cheyenne
    c. Hopi and Zuni
    d. Blackfeet and Crow

23. White settlers migrating to the West gave which of the following to the Plains　**c**
    Indians?
    a. knowledge of fire
    b. quinine
    c. smallpox
    d. opium

24. Lakota Sioux culture included　**d**
    a. the belief that life is a series of circles—the circles of relatives, band, tribe, and nation.
    b. belief in a hierarchy of plant and animal spirits whose help could be invoked through the Sun Dance.
    c. ceremonies in which young men "sacrificed" themselves through self-torture to gain access to spiritual power.
    d. all of the above

25. Why did Plains Indians tribes traditionally follow the buffalo migration?　**c**
    a. primarily for sport, and for young men to practice the skills necessary for warfare
    b. to supply the demand for hides for the buffalo robes popular in eastern carriages and sleighs
    c. to provide for food, shelter, fuel, tools, weapons, and other necessary items
    d. to domesticate the bison for agriculture

26. The Board of Indian Commissioners was   **b**
    a. a council of representatives from all the tribes of the Plains Indians that established Indian self-government on reservations.
    b. an agency established by Congress to convert the Indians on reservations to Christianity and to teach them farming.
    c. a militant Indian organization dedicated to preserving tribal customs.
    d. an Indian social-welfare organization that encouraged Indians to produce traditional crafts for sale.

27. The Treaty of Fort Laramie resulted in   **b**
    a. the surrender of Sitting Bull and his exile to a reservation in Florida.
    b. the end of the Powder River War and the setting aside of the Great Sioux Reserve "in perpetuity."
    c. protection of the Bozeman Trail, which guaranteed that Indians could continue traditional nomadic migration patterns.
    d. the relocation of Chief Joseph and the Nez Percés Indians to land in Canada.

28. General George Armstrong Custer's real purpose in bringing his troops into the   **c**
    Black Hills of South Dakota was
    a. to find a location for a new fort.
    b. to convert the Indians to Christianity, using force if necessary.
    c. to confirm rumors about the existence of gold.
    d. to negotiate a peace treaty with the Sioux at Little Bighorn.

29. When army officer Richard H. Pratt said he wanted to "kill the Indian and save the   **d**
    man," he meant,
    a. Indians had to be killed in order to save white men who were settling the frontier.
    b. killing heathen Indians would save their souls.
    c. he wanted to kill Geronimo for kidnapping one of Pratt's fellow officers.
    d. he wanted to equip Indians with the skills necessary to live in modern American society, which meant Indians had to give up their own culture.

30. What was the Ghost Dance?   **b**
    a. a "shaking" circle dance taught to Indians by Shakers in order to convert them to the Shaker religion
    b. a ritual where Indians danced until they were dizzy and fell into a trance in which they saw visions of the future
    c. a performance by "Princess Wovoka" that became popular in Buffalo Bill's Wild West show
    d. a traditional wedding dance in which Sioux women asked the ghosts of their ancestors to ensure fertility

31. Which Indians adjusted somewhat more successfully to the reservation system, preserving traditional ways while, through complex cultural adaptation, selectively incorporating elements of the new order?   c
    a. the Five Civilized Tribes
    b. the Sioux
    b. the Navaho
    d. the Maya

32. Railroads throughout the West were built by   d
    a. Chinese immigrants.
    b. Irish immigrants.
    c. blacks and Mexican-Americans.
    d. all of the above

33. Which of the following were the largest landholders in the West?   c
    a. the banks
    b. cattle barons
    c. the railroads
    d. gold miners

34. What were the terms of the Homestead Act?   a
    a. It offered 160 acres of land to any settler who would pay a $10 registration fee, live on the land for five years, and cultivate and improve it.
    b. It offered 40 acres and a mule to former slaves who relocated to the frontier after the Civil War.
    c. It granted ex-soldiers from Homestead, Pennsylvania, a parcel of western land as payment for service during the Civil War.
    d. It was devised by Massachusetts Senator Henry Homestead to break up Indian reservations and provide 160 acres of land to Indians for farming.

35. Western agriculture benefited from all of the following advances in technology *except*:   c
    a. the patenting of barbed wire
    b. efficient steel plows
    c. the development of the cotton gin
    d. improved windmills

36. Which of the following statements accurately describes western farmers?   a
    a. They generally specialized in single cash crops such as wheat or corn because the expense of setting up farm operations was so high.
    b. They generally used black sharecroppers to farm portions of their large landholdings.
    c. They were rugged frontier individualists, not dependent on external forces such as the railroads or the international grain market.
    d. They represented the American dream because they needed only a few hundred dollars and a parcel of land from the government to get rich in "agribusiness."

37. Dry farming was   b
    a. farming in frontier areas where the sale of alcohol was prohibited.
    b. plowing deeply and harrowing lightly to raise a covering of dirt that would retain moisture after a rainfall.
    c. specializing in "dry" grains such as corn, oats, and wheat, rather than more perishable produce such as fruit and vegetables.
    d. a method of drying up flood plains to reclaim land for agriculture.

38. The persistence rate for homesteaders (staying on the land a decade or more) was   d
    highest among
    a. former black slaves.
    b. Irish urban laborers.
    c. Chinese immigrants.
    d. German peasant immigrants.

39. Frontier communities were characterized by   a
    a. cooperation among neighbors as a form of insurance in a rugged environment.
    b. communal households as nuclear families gave way to frontier polygamy.
    c. deep suspicion of neighbors or any outsiders who were not kin.
    d. homosexuality since there were no women on the frontier.

40. Which of the following statements best describes the attitude of western state gov- b
    ernments regarding woman suffrage?
    a. They believed that the West was a place where "men were men and women were women," and only men should vote.
    b. They believed that women had made important contributions to settlement and that woman suffrage would attract female settlers.
    c. They preferred to wait and see how the "experiment" of woman suffrage would work out in the more progressive eastern states.
    d. They refused to grant women suffrage because they feared women would vote for prohibition, put an end to gambling and brothels, and in general "clean up government."

41. The Patrons of Husbandry was   d
    a. an organization that provided mail-order brides to bachelor farmers.
    b. a group of feminists who sought equality for husbands and wives.
    c. a fraternal organization of the Dutch descendants of New Netherland "patroons."
    d. an organization of farmers, also called the Grange.

42. In the case of *Wabash* v. *Illinois* the Supreme Court ruled that   c
                                                                                        SG
    a. states could regulate railroads and other businesses serving the public in order to protect public safety.
    b. the federal government could not interfere in business operating wholly or partly in a particular state.
    c. states could not regulate interstate railroad rates.
    d. the Interstate Commerce Act was unconstitutional.

43. The Interstate Commerce Commission was established to   a
    a. investigate and oversee railroad activities.
    b. control fluctuations in the international grain market.
    c. encourage interstate cooperation in commercial ventures.
    d. encourage Americans not to buy imported goods.

44. The Granger Laws   a
    a. were state laws that fixed the maximum rates that railroads could charge.   SG
    b. limited the number of cattle that could be grazed on the open range.
    c. opened new land on Indian reservations to white settlers.
    d. were the first federal laws regulating business enterprises.

45. Relations between Anglos and Mexican-Americans in Texas in the 1840s and 1850s   b
    were characterized by
    a. intermarriage.
    b. harassment of Mexican-Americans by Anglos and retaliation by Mexican
       bandits.
    c. friendship cemented by their mutual hatred of blacks and Indians.
    d. peaceful coexistence because most Mexican-Americans assimilated into Anglo
       society.

46. The cultural adaptation of Spanish-speaking Americans to Anglo society was rela-   b
    tively smooth in
    a. California.
    b. Arizona and New Mexico.
    c. Texas.
    d. none of the above

47. Virginia City, Nevada, experienced all of the following after the discovery of the   c
    Comstock Lode *except*:
    a. an orgy of speculation and building
    b. vigilante justice
    c. a religious revival
    d. a population boom

48. Joseph G. McCoy turned the cattle industry into a bonanza by   d
    a. building a new stockyard in Abilene.
    b. guaranteeing the transport of his steers in railcars, thus earning a kickback
       from the railroads.
    c. surveying and shortening the Chisholm Trail.
    d. all of the above

49. Which of the following statements best describes cowboys?   d
    a. Cowboys were well-paid, earning more than laborers and generally enjoying comfortable working conditions.
    b. Cowboys were almost always white, since there was a deep prejudice against blacks and Mexicans among cattlemen.
    c. Cowboys were usually the owner-operators of cattle ranches.
    d. none of the above

50. Nat Love and Bose Ikard were   b
    a. the real names of Butch Cassidy and the Sundance Kid.
    b. black cowboys.
    c. the discoverers of the Comstock Lode.
    d. coauthors of popular Western dime novels about "Deadwood Dick."

51. The "range wars" pitted which two groups against each other?   a
    a. cattlemen and farmers
    b. cowboys and Indians
    c. Mexican bandits and Anglo farmers
    d. renegade soldiers and Indians

52. Texas fever was   c
    a. a land boom in the 1850s that poured settlers into Texas.
    b. a smallpox epidemic that settlers from Texas spread when they migrated farther west.
    c. a disease that killed thousands of cattle.
    d. none of the above

53. The wheat boom in the Dakota Territory produced the nation's first "agribusinesses," which depended on all of the following *except*:   d
    a. large investments of capital
    b. heavy investments in labor
    c. heavy investments in equipment
    d. government subsidies

54. The Five Civilized Tribes were   a
    a. punished for siding with the Confederacy during the Civil War by the relocation to their reservations of thousands of Indians from other tribes.
    b. rewarded for siding with the Union during the Civil War by being granted exclusive use of the Indian Territory.
    c. Christian Indians who could read and write and had adopted the ways of white men.
    d. the only Indians granted the right to vote along with black freedmen.

55. The days of the open range and great cattle drives came to an end after 1866 for all   **c**
    the following reasons *except*:   **SG**
    a. overgrazing and crowding of the range
    b. severe winters and dry summers in 1885 and 1886
    c. decline in the demand for beef as more people turned to cheaper food
    d. expansion of the railroads throughout the West

56. The Oklahoma Land Rush of 1889 occurred when   **a**
    a. thousands of settlers rushed into the Oklahoma Territory on April 22, 1889,
       to stake out homesteads.
    b. gold was discovered in the Oklahoma Territory.
    c. oil was discovered in the Oklahoma Territory.
    d. Congress forced the Santa Fe Railroad to sell land it had been hoarding.

57. The mythic frontiersman appeared as a hero in   **d**
    a. the novels of James Fenimore Cooper.
    b. the novels of Henry James.
    c. the dime novels of the 1860s and 1870s.
    d. both a and c

58. "Buffalo Bill" Cody's Wild West show   **d**
    a. offered demonstrations of steer roping and rodeo contests.
    b. featured Sitting Bull staring malevolently at the crowd.
    c. presented mock battles of army scouts and Indians as morality dramas of
       good versus evil.
    d. all of the above

59. Which of these individuals—a president, a painter, and a writer—were deeply   **c**
    influenced by the frontier myth, enjoyed the physical challenges of the West, and
    rejected the constraints of the genteel urban world of their youth?
    a. Franklin Roosevelt, Georgia O'Keeffe, Henry James
    b. Grover Cleveland, Jackson Pollock, Helen Hunt Jackson
    c. Theodore Roosevelt, Frederick Remington, Owen Wister
    d. Franklin Roosevelt, Frederic Church, Hamlin Garland

60. *The Virginian* was   **d**
    a. a work of social realism that showed the hard physical labor of the cattle
       range.
    b. an exposé of the brutalities of Indian warfare and the forced removal of the
       Indians to reservations.
    c. a farm novel about the risks and perils of commercial agriculture.
    d. none of the above

61. Who was Frederick Jackson Turner?   b
    a. a painter of American western landscapes
    b. a historian who put forth the thesis that the frontier was the key to the American character
    c. author of *Ramona*, a tale of doomed love set on a California Spanish-Mexican ranch
    d. author of *Roughing It*, a mining novel

62. Hidatsa culture was characterized by   c
    a. a matriarchy.
    b. the ownership of private property.
    c. emphasis on reciprocal obligations between tribal members.
    d. marriage within the same clan or kinship group.

63. By 1900 Hidatsa culture had   b
    a. changed very little since Lewis and Clark visited in 1804.
    b. preserved elements of communal society, but had changed substantially in less than fifty years.
    c. died out entirely because of smallpox.
    d. died out entirely because of the complete assimilation of the Hidatsa into white society.

64. What did mining, cattle ranching, and wheat farming have in common?   c
    a. Most people who tried their hand at them made money.
    b. Slow economic growth made them safe investments.
    c. Boom and bust economic cycles affected them.
    d. The work itself was not hard.

65. What novelist's works delivered the popular message that anyone with ambition,   d
    self-discipline, hard work, and a little luck could get ahead economically?   SG
    a. Helen Hunt Jackson
    b. Owen Wister
    c. Hamlin Garland
    d. Horatio Alger

ESSAY QUESTIONS

66. For the most part, white Americans found Indian culture to be very alien. In what ways did Indian culture (practices and beliefs) differ from that of whites? How did white Americans attempt to change the ways of the Indians?

67. What methods did the United States government use to remove Indians from western land so that non-Indians could use it? In what ways did the various Indian tribes react to these methods?

68. What was the role of the railroad in westward expansion and economic development? Did settlers have a positive or negative view of the railroad? Why?

69. Landownership is part of the "American dream." Describe the acts of Congress that played a part in redistributing western land. Were those acts successful in distributing the land equally among the common people? Why or why not?

70. Americans have a reputation for "exploitation." Do you agree with this characterization? Discuss whether whites exploited the West in terms of buffalo, mineral ore, land, and human labor power. Give facts to support your position.

71. American history has often been the history of white, Anglo-Saxon males. To draw a more complete picture of the frontier experience, discuss the role of the following groups in settling the West: women, blacks, Chinese immigrants, and Mexican-Americans.

72. The Grange was organized to address farmers' economic problems and to provide "an opportunity for social, intellectual, and moral improvement." Describe the conditions that gave rise to this type of organization. What did the Grange do to solve those problems, and was it successful?

73. Describe the "boom-bust" economic cycles of mining, cattle ranching, and farming. What economic and environmental factors contributed to this pattern? How did these cycles affect settlers in the West?

74. Describe the "mythic frontiersman" and give examples of how this character has been portrayed in American culture. Did myths about the frontier reflect reality or an idealized version of frontier life? Why have Americans had such a fondness for the frontier myth?

75. Historian Frederick Jackson Turner's "frontier thesis" saw the frontier as the key to understanding American history. Elaborate on Turner's belief that the American character was largely determined by the existence of a frontier. Do you agree or disagree with Turner? Explain why.

MAP QUESTIONS

Choose the letter on Map A of the western United States that correctly identifies each of the following:

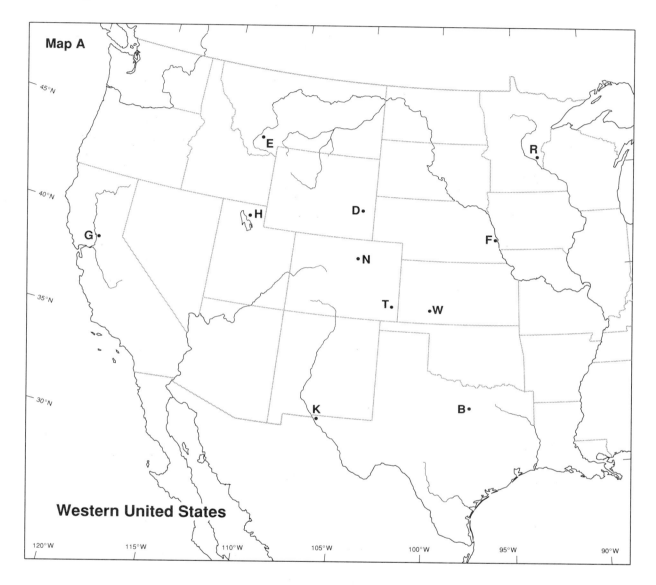

Map A

Western United States

76. St. Paul, Minnesota   R

77. Fort Worth, Texas   B

78. Sand Creek, Colorado   T

79. Fort Laramie, Wyoming   D

80. Virginia City, Montana   E

81. Omaha, Nebraska   F

82. Sacramento, California   G

83. Promontory Point, Utah   H

Choose the letter on Map B of the western United States that correctly identifies each of the following:

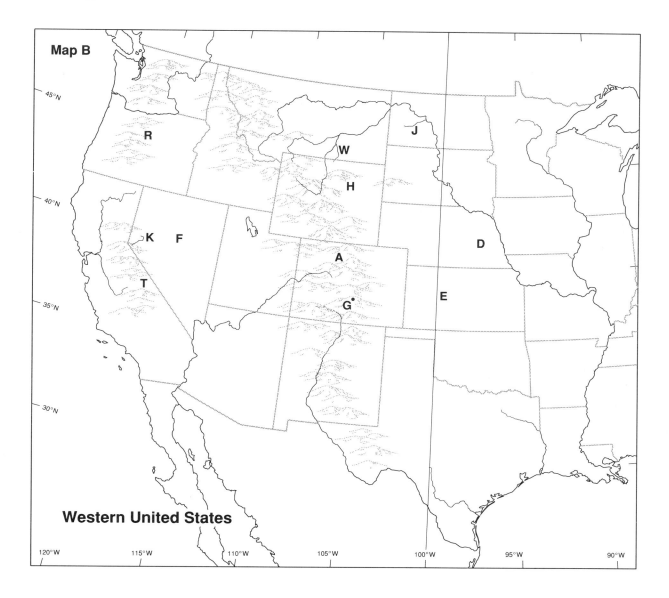

Map B

45°N

40°N

35°N

30°N

R

J

W

H

K F

A

T

G

E

D

Western United States

120°W   115°W   110°W   105°W   100°W   95°W   90°W

84. Rocky Mountains   A

85. Sierra Nevadas   T

86. Cascade Mountains   R

87. Great Plains   D

88. 100th meridian

E

89. Great Basin

F

90. Pike's Peak

G

91. Bozeman Trail

H

92. Little Bighorn River, Montana

W

93. Knife River, North Dakota

J

94. Carson River, Nevada

K

Choose the letter on Map C of the western United States that correctly identifies each of the following:

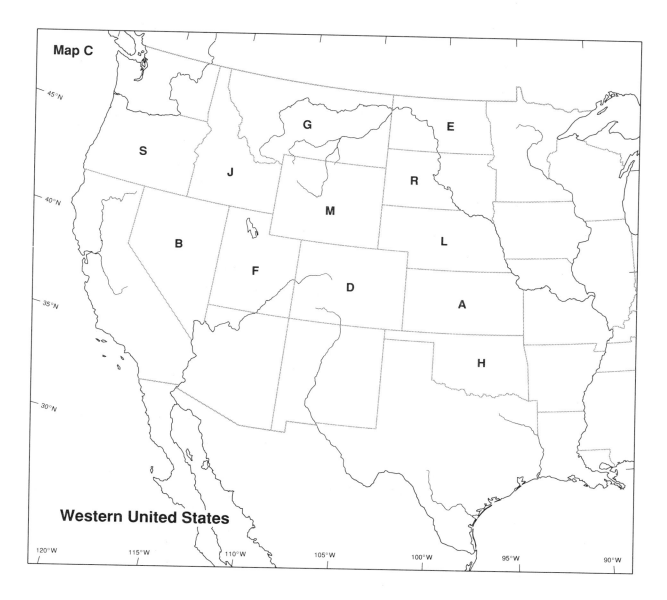

95. Kansas   A

96. Nevada   B

97. Nebraska   L

98. Colorado   D

99. North Dakota   **E**

100. Utah   **F**

101. Montana   **G**

102. Oklahoma   **H**

103. Wyoming   **M**

104. Idaho   **J**

CHAPTER 17

The Rise of Industrial America

IDENTIFICATIONS

Identify the following. Be as specific as possible, and include names, dates, and relevant facts as appropriate. Be sure to explain the *significance* of the person or term.

1. Andrew Carnegie

2. vertical and horizontal integration

3. Standard Oil Trust

4. Sherman Antitrust Act

5. *United States* v. *E. C. Knight Company*

6. National Labor Union

7. Knights of Labor

8. American Federation of Labor

9. Terence V. Powderly

10. the Chinese Exclusion Act

11. Samuel Gompers

12. "yellow dog contracts"

13. Pinkertons

14. Haymarket Bombing

15. Eugene V. Debs

16. Henry George's *Progress and Poverty*

17. Edward Bellamy's *Looking Backward*

18. Karl Marx's *Das Kapital*

19. Henry Clay Frick

20. Isaac Singer

MULTIPLE-CHOICE QUESTIONS

Choose the answer that *best* completes the statement or answers the question.

21. The World's Columbian Exposition in 1892 was   **b**

    a. a summit conference on North and South American governments held in Colombia to promote industrial development in the Americas.
    b. the Chicago World's Fair.
    c. a meeting held in the District of Columbia to expose industrial working conditions.
    d. the first international labor relations conference held at Columbia University in New York City.

22. The Chicago World's Fair included all of the following *except*:   **d**

    a. the Electricity Building
    b. the Manufactures and Liberal Arts Building
    c. Machinery Hall
    d. Aviation Hall

23. The following statements are true about the period from 1860 to 1900 *except*:   **a**

    a. U.S. textile and iron production tapered off.
    b. Boom-bust business cycles produced two major depressions.
    c. Manufacturing output soared.
    d. The number of persons engaged in manufacturing quadrupled.

24. Which of the following was characteristic of modern industrial America after the   **d**
Civil War?

    a. the rapid spread of technological innovation and the factory system
    b. a drop in price levels and a rise in interest rates
    c. the impulse to drive rivals out of business and consolidate monopolistic power
    d. all of the above

25. The use of technology in industry in the second half of the nineteenth century   **c**

    a. required a better-educated work force.
    b. allowed traditional craftsmen and artisans to maintain their dominance over production.
    c. made it possible for manufacturers to hire cheap unskilled or semiskilled labor.
    d. made it possible for manufacturers to eliminate human labor power altogether.

26. What was one of the ways that railroad companies pioneered in large-scale corporate enterprise?   a

    a. the issuance of stock to meet their huge capital needs
    b. the merger of ownership and management
    c. the unification of production facilities
    d. none of the above

27. In 1900, U.S. railroads   b

    a. were so profitable that the federal government borrowed vast sums of money from them.
    b. had a combined debt that was five times that of the federal government.
    c. had finally broken even financially after decades of start-up costs.
    d. were largely financed by a handful of elite, wealthy families.

28. At the end of the Civil War, what communications system did the railroads use to coordinate their complex flow of railcars?   c

    a. the newly invented telephone
    b. the Pony Express
    c. the telegraph
    d. There was no communications system to coordinate rail travel.

29. How was the country divided into four time zones in 1883?   b

    a. by the federal government to assist the railroads in coordinating their timetables
    b. by the railroads as one of a number of measures to standardize the industry
    c. by an overwhelmingly popular referendum vote
    d. by fundamentalists who believed "God's time" was based on the rising and setting of the sun

30. Andrew Carnegie borrowed many of the successful management methods he used in the steel industry from his earlier experiences as   d

    a. a bookkeeper in the textile industry in his native Scotland.
    b. a secretary for the Singer Sewing Machine Company.
    c. a foreman in the meatpacking industry in Chicago.
    d. an employee of the Pennsylvania Railroad.

31. What did Andrew Carnegie consider "the eighth wonder of the world"?   c

    a. Carnegie Hall
    b. the American railroad system
    c. the manufacturing process of the steel business
    d. the United States Constitution

32. The United States Steel Company was   c

    a. Andrew Carnegie's steel company.
    b. the steel company operated by the United States government when it nationalized the steel trust.
    c. the first business capitalized at more than $1 billion.
    d. the first company to issue stock to meet its huge capital needs.

33. What was one of the secrets of John D. Rockefeller's success?   **a**

    a. He paid attention to the minutest details.
    b. He pioneered a division of labor in which he concentrated on financial matters and delegated the technical operations of the industry to his managers.
    c. He concentrated on the "big picture," and didn't get bogged down in details.
    d. He didn't waste a lot of money on advertising.

34. The Sherman Antitrust Act   **d**

    a. fined violators up to $5,000 with a year in jail.
    b. was interpreted by the Supreme Court in ways sympathetic to big business.
    c. failed to define clearly either "trust" or "restraint of trade."
    d. all of the above

35. The Supreme Court in the *United States* v. *Knight Company*   **a**
    SG

    a. diminished the effectiveness of the Sherman Antitrust Act by ruling that manufacturing was not interstate commerce.
    b. declared the Granger Laws unconstitutional because states could not regulate interstate commerce.
    c. ruled that all trusts and monopolies in interstate commerce were illegal and could be broken up by the federal government.
    d. held that employers could force employees to sign and abide by "yellow dog contracts."

36. Which of the following was invented by Thomas Edison?   **d**

    a. a stock-quotation printer and the mimeograph machine
    b. the phonograph, the microphone, and the motion-picture camera
    c. an electricity-generation system and the storage battery
    d. all of the above

37. All of the following were factors in the South's late economic development *except*:   **c**

    a. illiteracy
    b. scarcity of towns and cities in the South
    c. lack of natural harbors and waterways
    d. lack of capital

38. The Singer Sewing Machine Company used all of the following to sell sewing machines *except*:   **a**

    a. time-sharing plans
    b. installment buying
    c. a vigorous advertising program
    d. retail stores

39. How did the invention of the sewing machine affect women?   **d**

    a. Women were hired to demonstrate the sewing machine's usefulness to potential buyers.
    b. Women were relieved of the tedium of sewing the family apparel by hand.
    c. Women sewed long hours for low wages in sweatshops.
    d. all of the above

40. The rapid industrial development of the United States between 1860 and 1900   **b**
    a. increased the demand for and the importance of skilled artisans.   SG
    b. produced an economy dominated by enormous corporations.
    c. increased the opportunities for small and medium-sized companies to succeed.
    d. reduced the use of women and child laborers in mines and mills.

41. By the 1880s, most southern farmers   **b**
    a. were the wealthiest, most stable members of southern society, farming vast plantations with large crews of black field hands.
    b. specialized in growing cash crops like cotton and tobacco, and were dependent on outside producers for food, shoes, and agricultural implements.
    c. had left the land to become industrial workers because western competition drove southern farms out of business.
    d. were self-sufficient since they reverted to subsistence farming.

42. The New South Creed was   **a**
    a. a belief held by industrialists that the South's natural resources and cheap labor made it a natural site for industrial development.
    b. a belief held by white supremacists that "the South will rise again" through the subjugation of the black race.
    c. a belief held by fundamentalist Southern Baptists that the "Second Coming" of Christ was close at hand.
    d. a belief held by aristocratic southern families that the South would flourish again only if it returned to the plantation system.

43. How did southern cotton mills differ from northern cotton mills in the 1880s?   **b**
    a. Southern cotton mills hired mostly single women.
    b. Southern cotton mills were located in the countryside rather than cities.
    c. Southern mill workers were paid better than northern mill workers because paternalistic southern mill owners treated workers more like family.
    d. Southern cotton mills used traditional handicraft methods rather than machinery to produce cloth.

44. By 1920, where was the center of the nation's textile manufacturing?   **c**
    a. New England
    b. New York City's "garment district"
    c. the South
    d. outside the United States because manufacturers were moving their plants overseas

45. How did industrialization affect skilled craftsmen?   **a**
    a. Subdividing the manufacture of a product into smaller jobs meant that an individual no longer manufactured an entire product.
    b. Skilled craftsmen were needed to operate machinery.
    c. The tension of assembly-line work caused formerly sober, discipline craftsmen to drink on the job.
    d. Skilled craftsmen were transformed into "aristocrats" in the world of labor.

46. What was the "contract system" of hiring labor?   **b**

    a. Workers insisted on union contracts.

    b. Large companies negotiated with subcontractors who hired and supervised the unskilled, seasonal help.

    c. Master craftsmen hired their own helpers and paid them out of their own pockets.

    d. none of the above

47. In the late nineteenth century, child labor   **a**

    a. was common in the coal mines and cotton mills.

    b. was uncommon because children were not strong enough to handle the large machines and fast pace of factory production.

    c. was uncommon because children had to stay in school until age sixteen.

    d. was uncommon because for the first time childhood was seen as a distinct stage of life reserved for innocence, play, education, and maternal love.

48. Which immigrants were most likely to be found in skilled trades in the 1880s?   **b**

    a. Irish

    b. German

    c. French-Canadian

    d. Chinese

49. Women joined the work force in growing numbers in the late nineteenth century because   **b**

    a. of the influence of the feminist movement on farm girls and immigrant daughters who worked primarily to be independent of their families.

    b. changes in agriculture brought young farm women into the industrial labor force, and immigrant daughters worked to supplement meager family incomes.

    c. industrialists thought women would have a civilizing influence on the brutal factory conditions.

    d. trade unions won a series of court cases opening employment opportunities for women.

50. Which of the following statements about upward mobility in the late nineteenth century is the most accurate?   **d**

    a. Andrew Carnegie's rise from poverty to colossal wealth was typical of the opportunities open to immigrants in America.

    b. Few industrial leaders came from the privileged classes because they were too soft to make it in the world of competitive capitalism.

    c. Skilled workers had few opportunities to rise to the top in small companies.

    d. Those immigrants who got ahead in the late nineteenth century were more likely to go from rags to respectability than from rags to riches.

51. How evenly was wealth distributed in America in 1890?   **a**
    a. 10 percent of American families owned 73 percent of the nation's wealth.
    b. 50 percent of American families—a large middle class—owned 73 percent of the nation's wealth.
    c. Wealth was so evenly distributed that America was essentially a classless society.
    d. none of the above

52. All of the following impeded the growth of unions *except*:   **d**
    a. divisions between skilled craftsmen and common laborers
    b. ethnic and religious diversity of the working class
    c. hostility toward unions from the public, employers, and government
    d. lack of interest on the part of workers because their real wages were rising and conditions were improving

53. In 1866, the newly organized National Labor Union embraced a wide range of   **b**
    reformist and political goals *except*:
    a. ending convict labor.
    b. relaxing restrictions on immigration.
    c. endorsing the cause of working women.
    d. establishing a federal department of labor.

54. The Knights of Labor advocated a great association of all workers *except*:   **c**
    a. Catholics and Jews
    b. women
    c. bankers, doctors, lawyers, stockbrokers, professional gamblers, and liquor dealers
    d. immigrants

55. Terence V. Powderly, head of the Knights of Labor, advocated   **d**
    a. a gradual end to the wage system and the reorganization of society on cooperative principles.
    b. temperance.
    c. the admission of blacks into local Knights of Labor assemblies.
    d. all of the above

56. In the West, the immigrants who bore the brunt of labor hostility in the 1870s and   **b**
    1880s were
    a. Jewish immigrants.
    b. Chinese immigrants.
    c. Irish Catholic immigrants.
    d. Russian immigrants.

57. Samuel Gompers, head of the American Federation of Labor, advocated   a

    a. "trade unionism, pure and simple," concentrating on practical issues like wages and hours.
    b. "one big union," welcoming both skilled and unskilled workers.
    c. broad social reforms by getting prolabor politicians elected.
    d. that skilled craftsmen give up their autonomy in order to create solidarity with unskilled workers in the union.

58. "Yellow dog" contracts were   b

    a. contracts in which employers agreed not to hire Chinese immigrants.
    b. contracts in which workers promised not to strike or join a union.
    c. contracts that guaranteed that only union members would be hired.
    d. none of the above

59. Labor relations at the end of the nineteenth century were   c

    a. relatively peaceful because welfare paternalism prevailed and employers treated employees like family.
    b. relatively peaceful because employers had successfully eliminated labor unrest.
    c. characterized by violence and thousands of strikes.
    d. occasionally turbulent, but most grievances were dealt with effectively through collective bargaining.

60. The Haymarket Square bombing in 1886 resulted in   d

    a. increased sympathy for workers and unions.
    b. the election of several German-born anarchists to the Illinois state legislature.
    c. the arrest of the police who fired on the crowd.
    d. intensified animosity toward labor unions.

61. The steel mills of Homestead, Pennsylvania,   b

    a. were the pride of Andrew Carnegie, and the safest, cleanest mills in the steel industry.
    b. were hot and noisy, and serious accidents were common.
    c. had instituted a forty-hour week to reduce the rate of industrial accidents.
    d. employed thousands of workers, of whom more than half were black migrants from the South.

62. In the Pullman strike   a

SG

    a. the federal government used an injunction and troops against workers, and jailed the union leaders.
    b. the state of Illinois tried eight anarchists for a bombing, found them guilty, and executed four of them.
    c. workers walked out to protest conditions at Carnegie's steel mills, but eventually returned to work without gaining any improvements.
    d. the Knights of Labor led railroad workers in a demand for the eight-hour day and finally got it from the railroads.

63. Adam Smith, author of *The Wealth of Nations*, argued that   **a**
    a. self-interest acted as an "invisible hand" in the marketplace, automatically regulating the supply of and demand for services.
    b. mechanization would become the "invisible hand" and automation would eliminate human labor.
    c. wealth should be distributed evenly throughout society: each according to his need, each according to his ability.
    d. a single tax would solve the nation's uneven distribution of wealth.

64. Who argued that poverty was not the result of unchangeable natural laws and   **b**
    could be eliminated by government intervention and social planning?   **SG**
    a. William Graham Sumner
    b. Lester Frank Ward
    c. Andrew Carnegie
    d. John D. Rockefeller

65. The Socialist Labor party was   **c**
    a. an anarchist organization that rejected Marxism and preached the destruction of capitalism, the violent overthrow of the state, and the immediate introduction of a stateless utopia.
    b. an alliance of reform-minded socialites and labor activists.
    c. a Marxist-oriented political party which attracted only 1,500 members in 1890.
    d. the Knights of Labor.

ESSAY QUESTIONS

---

66. Just as certain features of the Chicago World's Fair caused ambivalence—perhaps anxiety, alienation, and amazement—for visitors from farms and small towns, many Americans were ambivalent about the changes taking place in the nation as it was transformed by industrialization in the late nineteenth century. Explain that response.

67. Using examples from the railroad, steel, oil, and sewing machine industries, describe changes in the second half of the nineteenth century that resulted in the vast expansion of the *scale* of industry. Include financing, management, manufacturing operations, working conditions, the labor force, the role of the businessman, and marketing.

68. How effective was the Sherman Antitrust Act as a weapon against "Big Business"? Was "Big Business" the only kind of "combination" the act was used against in the late nineteenth century?

69. In 1892, the commissioner of patents proudly declared: "America has become known the world around as the home of invention." How did invention become a "big business" during this period? Pick three late-nineteenth-century inventions, and discuss how they eased the drudgery of everyday life and reshaped social interactions. Were the effects of these inventions entirely positive?

70. Discuss the factors that drew more and more women into the work force during the second half of the nineteenth century. What kinds of women were likely to work outside their homes? What kind of work was available to them?

71. Why did the South lag behind the North in industrial development? What was the New South Creed, and how did the South start to catch up in manufacturing? How did shifts in the southern economy affect blacks and poor rural whites?

72. Describe the traditional "working-class culture" of skilled craftsmen in the first half of the nineteenth century. How did industrialization affect the working conditions and status of these craftsmen? What did they do in response to industrialization?

73. Immigrants often saw America as a land of opportunity. What was the reality of the opportunity for most immigrants? Did an immigrant's ethnic background—German, Irish, Chinese, Slavic, French-Canadian—have an effect on his or her place in America, particularly in the work force?

74. Compare and contrast the strategies, membership, leadership, and philosophies of the National Labor Union, the Knights of Labor, and the American Federation of Labor. How successful was each organization in attaining its goals?

75. Compare and contrast in terms of class structure, wealth, and industrial society the social philosophies of Social Darwinists Andrew Carnegie and William Graham Sumner; reformers Lester Frank Ward, Henry George, and Edward Bellamy; and Marxist socialists.

MAP QUESTIONS

Choose the letter on the accompanying map of the eastern United States that correctly identifies each of the following:

Eastern United States

76. Pittsburgh, Pennsylvania   **R**

77. Birmingham, Alabama   **E**

78. Chattanooga, Tennessee   S

79. Homestead, Pennsylvania   D

80. Mesabi Range, Minnesota   B

81. Titusville, Pennsylvania   F

82. Cincinnati, Ohio   G

83. Chicago, Illinois   H

84. Pullman, Illinois   A

CHAPTER 18

The Transformation of Urban America

IDENTIFICATIONS

Identify the following. Be as specific as possible, and include names, dates, and relevant facts as appropriate. Be sure to explain the *significance* of the person or term.

1. Jacob Riis

2. Castle Garden, Ellis Island

3. dumbbell tenements

4. "Big Jim" Pendergast

5. William Marcy Tweed and Tammany Hall

6. Thomas Nast

7. New York Children's Aid Society

8. Young Men's and Young Women's Christian Associations

9. Anthony Comstock and the New York Society for the Suppression of Vice

10. Walter Rauschenbusch's *Christianity and the Social Crisis*

11. Jane Addams and Hull House

12. Frederick Law Olmsted

13. Louis Sullivan

14. Richard Morris Hunt

15. Salvation Army

16. Charity Organization Society

17. Social Gospel movement

18. city-beautiful movement

19. Institutional Church League

20. new immigrants and old immigrants

MULTIPLE-CHOICE QUESTIONS

Choose the answer that *best* completes the statement or answers the question.

21. The Milwaukee smallpox riots of 1894 pitted which of the following groups against each other?   **b** **PT**
    a. Catholics against Jews
    b. middle-class political appointees and sanitary engineers against immigrants
    c. immigration and naturalization officials against immigrants
    d. Polish against blacks

22. What was the cause of the Milwaukee smallpox conflict in 1894?   **a** **PT**
    a. City public-health regulations were not sensitive to ethnic cultural traditions and did not have the approval of ethnic politicians.
    b. Hospital officials refused to admit Polish patients.
    c. The Catholic church refused to give last rites to the Polish dying of smallpox.
    d. all of the above

23. Starting in the 1830s, how were urban residential patterns affected by the expansion of transportation?   **c**
    a. Wealthy residents moved from the suburbs to the center of cities to be near the financial district.
    b. The rich and poor lived in close proximity.
    c. The wealthy moved to the city's edge, while the poor gravitated inward.
    d. Urban centers became "walking cities" since everyone lived within walking distance from their jobs.

24. Which statement was not a drawback of the horse-drawn streetcars?   **d**
    a. Overworked and abused horses often died.
    b. The hitching and unhitching of horses took a great deal of time.
    c. Horse droppings fouled city streets.
    d. The horsecars could only carry a dozen passengers at a time.

25. The American streetcar system encouraged urban sprawl by   **b**
    a. charging according to the distance traveled.
    b. charging a flat fee.
    c. financing house mortgages in the suburbs.
    d. none of the above

26. How did streetcar lines affect the downtowns of cities?   c
    a. They created "ghost towns" in the middle of cities because urban dwellers moved to the suburbs.
    b. Merchants like John Wanamaker, Rowland H. Macy, and Marshall Field moved their big department stores to the suburbs.
    c. With cross-town routes limited, commuters had to pass through downtown, which revitalized downtown shopping.
    d. Factories sprang up downtown because raw materials could be brought directly to the factories on streetcars.

27. Residential mobility was a characteristic of which of the following groups?   d
    a. immigrants
    b. farm people
    c. the old elite
    d. all of the above

28. How was Omaha, Nebraska's mobility pattern typical of many American cities between 1880 and 1900?   a
    a. Fewer than one-third of all Omaha residents lived in the same place for more than five years.
    b. Omaha was a stable community where most families had lived for three generations or more.
    c. Omaha gradually lost much of its population as its manufacturing base moved to outlying rural areas.
    d. Omaha gradually gained population as manufacturing moved to the city.

29. Young farm women led the exodus from rural areas to cities mainly because   b
    a. they were seeking husbands.
    b. farm work was performed increasingly by males.
    c. they were fleeing their strict upbringings for the freedom of the cities.
    d. they were turning their backs on a way of life that demanded their labor for subsistence tasks.

30. Who were the "new immigrants" who poured into the United States between 1890 and 1920?   d
    a. Scandinavians and Germans
    b. Irish
    c. English, Scottish, and Welsh
    d. immigrants from southern and eastern Europe, and Armenians

31. Which technological advance made immigration to the United States after the Civil War faster and ultimately cheaper?   b
    a. improvements in sailing ships
    b. improvements in steam-powered vessels
    c. the introduction of the first planes
    d. all of the above

32. In 1890, approximately what portion of the population of greater New York had   d
   been born abroad or were children of foreign parents?
   a. one out of five
   b. almost one-third
   c. approximately one-half
   d. four out of five

33. Among the reasons why people emigrated to the United States were   d
   a. overpopulation in their homeland.
   b. crop failure and famine in their homeland.
   c. industrial depression in their homeland.
   d. all of the above

34. Upon reaching America, immigrants immediately faced   a
   a. a physical examination.
   b. a literacy test.
   c. a naturalization test.
   d. all of the above

35. Whether newly arrived immigrants stayed in the city in which they landed or   c
   moved on largely depended on
   a. their education.
   b. their occupation.
   c. how much money they had.
   d. if their passports were approved for travel within the United States.

36. Which statement best represents urban residential patterns among ethnic groups?   b
   a. Immigrants preferred to mix in with the general population in order to assim-
      ilate more quickly into American culture.
   b. Immigrants preferred to live near others not merely of their own nationality,
      but from their own village or region in the old country.
   c. Religion was the primary factor in ethnic residential patterns because immi-
      grants congregated around their churches.
   d. Common language was the primary factor in ethnic residential patterns,
      regardless of national origin.

37. In the mid nineteenth century, urban police were   d
   a. part of the state militia.
   b. unofficial vigilante groups of citizens.
   c. nonexistent because the homogeneous cities had virtually no crime.
   d. often responsible for such functions as street cleaning and running lodging
      houses for the homeless, in addition to preventing crime.

38. The Blood Tubs and the Bowery Boys were   c
   a. settlement-house boys' clubs.
   b. urban football clubs.
   c. immigrant street gangs.
   d. vaudeville acts.

39. Which statement is not true about the police at the end of the nineteenth century?   d
    a. They often profited from vice instead of fighting it.
    b. They were often sympathetic to the social customs of the immigrants they policed.
    c. They became the targets of reformers who wanted to raise the professional standards of the police force by removing it from the political patronage system.
    d. They successfully conformed to the stricter moral standards of reformers.

40. "Machine politics" was   b
    a. urban politics influenced by the new industrial elite who were known as bosses.
    b. urban politics controlled by the boss of an unofficial political organization designed to keep a particular party or faction in office.
    c. a social theory in which all interest groups in society meshed together like the parts of a machine.
    d. urban politics influenced by the ideas of reformers.

41. Political bosses typically performed all of the following functions *except*:   b
    a. delivered votes at election time
    b. ran settlement houses
    c. served as informal welfare agents for the needy and troubled in the neighborhood
    d. dispensed patronage jobs, contracts, and other political favors

42. Thomas Nast's famous cartoon "Let us prey" was directed against   d
    a. industrialists.
    b. fundamentalist preachers.
    c. Senator Clarence Lexow's investigation of the New York City police force.
    d. Boss Tweed.

43. "Goo-goos"   b
    a. was an ethnic slur for Chinese immigrants.
    b. were good-government reformers.
    c. was the name of a New York City street gang.
    d. were goons hired by political bosses to intimidate opponents.

44. Middle-class reformers differed from political bosses in their approach to the urban poor   d
    a. by creating organizations to systematically help the poor.
    b. by distancing themselves from the values and customs of the urban poor.
    c. by attempting to Americanize immigrant slum dwellers.
    d. all of the above

45. The Young Men's Christian Association and the Young Women's Christian Association were formed largely to   a
    a. assist rural young men and women who migrated to the city.
    b. help youngsters migrate west.
    c. convert Jewish immigrants.
    d. convert Indians.

46. The Salvation Army   b
    a. was a branch of the military formed to clean up the slums.
    b. was organized along pseudomilitary lines, and attracted the urban poor through street meetings and soup kitchens to inculcate middle-class values.
    c. was a social-welfare organization based on new ideas of gently persuading the urban poor to adopt middle-class values.
    d. was organized by urban immigrants to police their own ghettos.

47. Anthony Comstock was   d
    a. a Chicago gangster.
    b. a political boss.
    c. a birth-control advocate.
    d. a moral-purity crusader.

48. William S. Rainsford's Institutional Church League argued that   c
    a. bad habits such as drinking, laziness, and lack of cleanliness kept immigrants poor, and that adopting middle-class values would improve the immigrants' standard of living.
    b. social workers should concentrate on reforming poor children who learned bad habits from their parents.
    c. the urban poor were not personally responsible for their poverty, and that the wealthy also were morally responsible for eradicating poverty by prosecuting slumlords and sweatshop owners.
    d. the criminal element in urban society should be institutionalized in order to be reformed.

49. The Social Gospel movement was founded within   b
    a. Catholicism.
    b. Protestantism.
    c. Judaism.
    d. socialism.

50. The settlement-house movement distinguished itself from other urban social-welfare organizations by   c

    a. helping poor immigrants settle on western homesteads to relieve urban over-crowding.
    b. helping the urban poor purchase their own homes because of the belief that owning private property leads to the adoption of middle-class values.
    c. insisting that charity workers live in slum neighborhoods to better understand the living conditions of the poor.
    d. not being concerned about the urban poor's propensity for drinking and gambling.

51. Which of the following was associated with settlement houses?   b

    a. Josephine Shaw Lowell
    b. Jane Addams
    c. Carry Nation
    d. Sister Carrie

52. Neo-classical urban planners such as Richard Morris Hunt   d

    a. placed classical statues and formal gates in city parks.
    b. advocated uniform building heights and formal, regular designs for the urban landscape.
    c. proposed awe-inspiring urban architecture to encourage good citizenship and stability in the urban immigrant population.
    d. all of the above

53. In 1871, Chicago was forced to reconstruct much of its downtown as a result of   c
    a(n)

    a. flood.
    b. tornado.
    c. fire.
    d. earthquake.

54. The first skyscraper was built in   b

    a. Boston.
    b. Chicago.
    c. Philadelphia.
    d. New York City.

55. The skyscraper depended on all of the following technological innovations *except*:   c

    a. fireproofing
    b. the elevator
    c. the flying buttress
    d. the internal metal frame

56. The city-beautiful movement focused on   d

    a. upgrading the quality of immigrant housing.
    b. improving sanitary conditions in the slums.
    c. creating a pastoral atmosphere in urban settings.
    d. erecting monumental public buildings.

57. The most dangerous aspect of urban life in the late nineteenth century was   d
    a. opium addiction.
    b. the increase of murders and robberies.
    c. air pollution.
    d. inadequate water and sewage systems.

58. Which of the following expresses the trend in urban organization in the late nine-   c
    teenth century?
    a. decentralization
    b. local control
    c. annexation and consolidation
    d. all of the above

59. The largest urban consolidation in the late nineteenth century was   d
    a. Chicago.
    b. San Francisco.
    c. Boston.
    d. New York City.

60. The concept of the service city was   a
    a. that a city of diverse inhabitants should efficiently meet their collective
       needs—water supply, sewage, garbage collection, fire protection.
    b. an ideal advocated by Jane Addams, who urged college-educated women to
       devote themselves to serving the urban poor.
    c. that cities would shift from a manufacturing base to a service economy.
    d. that bosses should serve the needs of ward residents through patronage.

61. An electric streetcar system was first developed in   a
    a. Richmond, Virginia.   SG
    b. Chicago, Illinois.
    c. Denver, Colorado.
    d. New York, New York.

62. Which of the following immigrant groups was made up mostly of poor peasants   c
    who settled heavily in northeastern cities and had a high rate of remigration?   SG
    a. Germans
    b. eastern European Jews
    c. Italians
    d. Armenians

63. Which of the following would be most likely to challenge the statement that moral   b
    deficiencies of the immigrant poor caused their poverty?   SG
    a. Josephine Shaw Lowell and the Charity Organization Society
    b. William S. Rainsford and the Social Gospel ministers
    c. Josiah Strong in his book *Our Country*
    d. Robert M. Hartley and the Association for Improving the Conditions of the
       Poor

64. Jane Addams and her coworkers at Hull House did all of the following *except*:   **b**   **SG**
    a. establish a day nursery for the children of working mothers
    b. pressure Congress to restrict the flow of poor immigrants to the United States
    c. pressure legislators to enforce sanitation regulations and pass laws protecting the urban poor
    d. run classes, a laundry, an employment bureau, and recreation programs

65. The Lexow investigation found   **a**   **SG**
    a. that in exchange for payoffs the police permitted gamblers, prostitutes, and saloonkeepers to operate unmolested in poor immigrant neighborhoods.
    b. that landlords permitted their dumbbell tenement buildings to become unsanitary, overcrowded firetraps.
    c. that blacks, Italians, Chinese, and other minorities were kept out of middle-class neighborhoods by restrictive real-estate covenants.
    d. that the inadequate sewage system of New York contributed to recurrent outbreaks of typhoid and cholera.

ESSAY QUESTIONS

66. How did the growth in the size and diversity of late-nineteenth-century cities cause alarm over the loss of traditional values regarding community life and social stability? How did middle-class reformers respond to changes in urban life?

67. Compare the approaches of the following social-welfare organizations to urban problems: the New York Children's Aid Society, the Young Men's Christian Association, the Salvation Army, the New York Charity Organization Society, the Institutional Church League, and Hull House. How did Protestantism influence their reform philosophies? What were their goals and methods? How successful were these groups?

68. Describe how machine politics functioned in urban America in the late nineteenth century. What services did political bosses provide? Why did reformers object to machine politics?

69. Discuss the impact of transportation improvements in the nineteenth century on   **SG** American cities. How did transportation changes affect who came to cities, where people lived in cities and suburbs, and where they worked and shopped?

70. Describe America's immigration patterns in the late nineteenth century. Why did immigrants leave their homeland, and what did they find when they came to America? How did the customs and values of immigrants clash with those of native-born Americans?

71. How did the phenomenal growth of American cities affect sanitation (water, sewage) and public safety (crime, fire)? How did different cities meet these growing needs? What was the concept of the "service city"?

72. What was the city-beautiful movement? How did urban planners hope the aesthetic design of a city would affect residents? Whose value did these designs reflect?

73. Compare urban growth in New York City, Chicago, and Boston. Describe how parks, land reclamation, and new kinds of architecture shaped the urban landscape.

74. Describe rural-urban migration patterns in the late nineteenth century. Who was most likely to migrate from rural areas to towns and cities, and why? What kinds of adjustments did rural Americans have to make when they moved to cities?

75. How did the Milwaukee smallpox epidemic in 1894 reflect tensions between immigrants and middle-class reformers?

MAP QUESTIONS

Choose the letter on the accompanying map of the United States that correctly identifies each of the following:

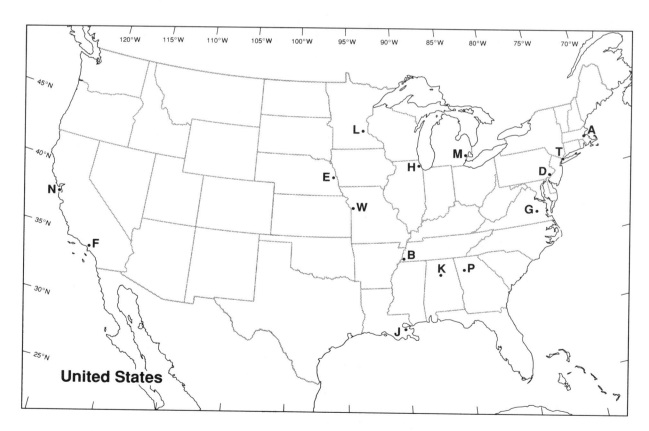

76. Omaha, Nebraska   **E**

77. Memphis, Tennessee   **B**

78. New Orleans, Louisiana   **J**

79. Philadelphia, Pennsylvania   **D**

80. Chicago, Illinois   **H**

81. New York, New York   **T**

82. Boston, Massachusetts   **A**

83. Birmingham, Alabama   **K**

84. Minneapolis, Minnesota   **L**

85. Kansas City, Missouri   **W**

86. San Francisco, California   **N**

87. Richmond, Virginia   **G**

88. Detroit, Michigan   **M**

89. Atlanta, Georgia   **P**

90. Los Angeles, California   **F**

CHAPTER 19

Daily Life, Popular Culture, and the Arts, 1860–1900

IDENTIFICATIONS

Identify the following. Be as specific as possible, and include names, dates, and relevant facts as appropriate. Be sure to explain the *significance* of the person or term.

1. John Harvey Kellogg and Charles W. Post

2. Aaron Montgomery Ward and Richard Warren Sears

3. F. W. Woolworth

4. blue Monday

5. the cooperative family work ethic

6. Victorian morality and worldview

7. Catherine Beecher's *The American Woman's Home*

8. Rowland H. Macy, John Wanamaker, and Marshall Field

9. Palmer House, Waldorf Astoria, and Palace

10. rise of the research university

11. John L. Sullivan

12. vaudeville

13. Coney Island

14. Scott Joplin and ragtime

15. the "new woman"

16. genteel culture

17. Samuel Langhorne Clemens's *Adventures of Huckleberry Finn*

18. Theodore Dreiser's *Sister Carrie*

19. literary realism and literary naturalism

20. Chautauqua   PT

21. modernism

22. Frank Lloyd Wright's prairie houses

23. Frances Willard and the Woman's Christian Temperance Union

24. the bicycling vogue of the 1880s and 1890s

25. Gibson girls

26. Mary Wilkins Freeman

27. Kate Chopin

28. William Torrey Harris and Joseph Mayer Rice

29. local-option referenda

MULTIPLE-CHOICE QUESTIONS

Choose the answer that *best* completes the statement or answers the question.

30. What change took place in American clothing during the last third of the nine-   a
    teenth century?
    a. Clothing became a more important badge of social class because mechaniza-
       tion increased the availability of clothing for the elite and middle classes.
    b. As the number of immigrants to the United States increased, an increasing
       proportion of clothing was made by individual seamstresses working in their
       homes.
    c. Clothing increasingly became democratized because mechanization required
       less elaborate designs.
    d. Clothing became more ornate because immigrants from eastern Europe were
       willing to work for low wages in the garment industry.

31. Why were new products by such promoters as John Harvey Kellogg, Charles W.   b
    Post, or Lydia Pinkham very successful in the late nineteenth century?

    a. Increasing numbers of American women were enjoying bicycle riding.
    b. Middle- and upper-class Americans had become increasingly health-con-
       scious, and a broad range of American society had come to believe that mate-
       rial and physical improvements were within everyone's reach.
    c. New low-cost, mass-market magazines like *Ladies' Home Journal* and *Cos-
       mopolitan* encouraged Americans to purchase products that would benefit
       American agriculture.
    d. There was a greater market for convenience foods, because women were
       expanding the acceptable sphere of their activities outside the home.

32. Which of the following people had the *most* influence on the reorientation of   c
    rural consumer standards during the late nineteenth century?

    a. Lydia Pinkham
    b. Charles Eliot Norton
    c. Aaron Ward
    d. Frank Woolworth

33. All of the following were prominent developments in American sales and market-   d
    ing during the late nineteenth century *except*:

    a. the creation of nationwide "chains" that stressed low prices and consumer
       savings
    b. increased advertising that bombarded consumers with new choices about
       what to buy
    c. nationwide marketing of products through catalogs
    d. growing interest in "truth in advertising" legislation

34. In the decades after the Civil War, social rank came to be determined by several   a
    new factors, including

    a. lifestyle and self-identification.
    b. occupation and income.
    c. location and political party.
    d. gender and intellectual interests.

35. What change took place during the late nineteenth century in the relationship   b
    between artisans and unskilled workers?

    a. Artisans came to believe that unskilled workers were not worthy of acquiring
       skills until they had learned English.
    b. Because of increased mechanization, skilled artisans began to identify with
       the middle class and look down on unskilled workers in their own industry.
    c. Thanks to the growing strength of the trade-union movement, artisans and
       unskilled workers found new unity in their struggles with the capitalist class.
    d. A rift developed between artisans and unskilled workers because the number
       of artisans was growing rapidly while the number of unskilled workers was
       shrinking steadily.

36. By the late 1890s, the wealthiest 12 percent of the United States owned approxi-   c
    mately what portion of the nation's aggregate wealth?

    a. 1.5%
    b. 44%
    c. 86%
    d. 12.5%

37. What was the family structure of most Americans during the last third of the nine-   d
    teenth century?

    a. a household that frequently contained borders and servants
    b. a household that did not include grandparents and other relatives
    c. a nuclear family
    d. all of the above

38. Which of the following increased during the last third of the nineteenth century?   b

    a. the size of the average family
    b. average life expectancy
    c. the birthrate
    d. all of the above

39. In the late nineteenth century, who was most likely to practice birth control?   a

    a. the manager of a paint factory
    b. a Kansas wheat farmer
    c. an unskilled worker in a Chicago slaughterhouse
    d. an immigrant living in New York City

40. What was the dominant institution in the daily life of southern blacks during the   c
    late nineteenth century?

    a. the nuclear family
    b. the fraternal organization
    c. the extended kinship network
    d. the amusement park or dance hall

41. During the late nineteenth century, how could a working-class family afford to   d
    own a house and get ahead economically?

    a. It could take out a long-term mortgage that might eventually be paid off a
       generation or more later.
    b. There was no chance of purchasing a house, and because of declining wages
       most working-class families sank further into poverty.
    c. The husband and wife first had to agree to limit the size of the family to only
       one child, because there would be no way they could support more than that.
    d. As many family members as possible would have to work and pool their
       wages.

42. The view of human nature associated with Victorianism was founded on which of   **a**
the following assumptions?
   a. that people could improve themselves and society could improve itself
      because human nature was basically good
   b. that humans were naturally inclined to evil and therefore had to be restrained
      from dragging society down into the depths of self-indulgence
   c. that spontaneity and self-expression were matters of individual choice and
      should not be restricted by government or society
   d. none of the above

43. What was the importance of "culture" for American Victorians?   **b**
   a. It helped to separate the lower classes from the respectable middle classes.
   b. It was an agency of social uplift that could help those Americans aspiring to
      middle-class status.
   c. It was a code word for decadence, they believed, because art museums were
      repositories of immoral works.
   d. It was a derogatory term generally used to describe the lower classes' cheap
      copies of famous paintings.

44. During the 1880s and 1890s, which new obligation was added to the traditional   **c**
middle-class woman's role as director of the household?
   a. to cultivate her special maternal gifts, especially her sensitivity toward chil-
      dren and her aptitude for religion
   b. to seek outlets for her creative energies outside the home
   c. to nurture her family's cultural improvement by fostering an artistic environ-
      ment of ornamentation, knickknacks, and well-arranged furniture
   d. to foster a home environment which would encourage her husband to share
      both his breadwinning duties and her homemaking duties

45. The aim and effect of the department store was to   **d**
   a. overcome middle- and upper-class reluctance to spend.
   b. transform shopping from a humdrum activity into an adventure.
   c. function as a kind of social club and home away from home for comfortably
      fixed women.
   d. all of the above

46. In his 1904 travel book *The American Scene*, what did writer Henry James describe   **a**
as "a synonym for civilization"?
   a. the first-class hotel
   b. the modern department store
   c. the Metropolitan Museum of Art in New York
   d. the Victorian concept of "culture"

47. What purpose did college football have, according to its defenders in the late nine- **b**
    teenth century?
    a. It epitomized American democratic ideals, because all Americans played or
       watched the game.
    b. It was a character-building sport that could function as a surrogate frontier
       experience in an increasingly urbanized society.
    c. It was a safe sport that the nation's future business and professional leaders
       could undertake without fear of injury.
    d. all of the above

48. What was the major change that took place during the late nineteenth century in **c**
    the teaching of medicine, architecture, engineering, and law?
    a. College faculties were purged of anyone who was not a native-born American.
    b. Colleges refused to train these professionals because the American public had
       demonstrated strong prejudice against them.
    c. Standards were raised and professionalized.
    d. State boards of education agreed that training for such professions would
       best be accomplished at European universities.

49. What was the new approach to higher education that institutions such as Cornell, **d**
    the University of Wisconsin, Johns Hopkins, and Harvard began to provide in the
    late nineteenth century?
    a. to train the sons of the elite in classical languages, theology, logic, and
       mathematics
    b. to concentrate on only a few subjects in which the university could excel
    c. to reward faculty members for devoting their full energies to excellence in
       teaching rather than useless research
    d. to create an environment where any person could find instruction in any
       study

50. Why did leisure-time activities become increasingly important to the working class **a**
    during the late nineteenth century?
    a. Factory labor was growing more routine and impersonal, and social interac-
       tions at the workplace were increasingly inhibited.
    b. Working-class Americans viewed leisure activity as a method of rising to
       middle-class status.
    c. American employers were increasingly emphasizing leisure and relaxation as
       a method of keeping their work force happy and healthy.
    d. Leisure-time activities brought Americans of all ethnicities together and there-
       fore contributed to a process of Americanization that most workers desired.

51. During the late nineteenth century, the working-class saloon was all of the follow- **b**
    ing *except*:
    a. a center for immigrant politics
    b. a meeting place for husbands and wives
    c. a place to escape the socially isolating routines of the factory
    d. a location for ethnic groups to reinforce their identities

52. In the late nineteenth century, bare-knuckles prizefighting was thought of as   d
    a. an arena where lower-class men could assert their physical prowess.
    b. an antidote for a tendency toward effeteness among males of the privileged classes.
    c. a method of reaffirming racial or ethnic identity.
    d. all of the above

53. "His colors are the Stars and Stripes, / He also wears the green, / And he's the   c
    grandest slugger that / The ring has ever seen." These lines refer to
    a. Abner Doubleday.
    b. John Philip Sousa.
    c. John L. Sullivan.
    d. Jake Kilrain.

54. The form of theatrical entertainment that drew the largest audiences in late-   a
    nineteenth-century America was
    a. vaudeville.
    b. opera.
    c. Shakespearean comedy.
    d. burlesque.

55. A typical vaudeville performance might include each of the following *except*:   b
    a. a trained animal routine
    b. a medley of popular arias from grand opera
    c. flying-trapeze artists
    d. comic skits ridiculing the trials of urban life

56. For a late-nineteenth-century unmarried working-class woman, amusement parks   c
    exerted a powerful lure because
    a. the parks offered opportunities to supplement meager wages through evening or weekend employment.
    b. the parks provided opportunities for the entire family to have a wholesome outing.
    c. the parks were places to meet friends, get away from parental supervision, and try out the latest dance steps.
    d. the parks had employment bureaus where factory owners recruited for high-paying jobs.

57. Why did ragtime quickly become a national craze during the 1890s, especially   d
    among the working class?
    a. The music displayed a fresh originality.
    b. It was considered to have "wild" and complex rhythms.
    c. It originated in brothels and was associated with blacks.
    d. all of the above

58. Charles Eliot Norton, Richard Watson Gilder, E. L. Godkin, and others like them   **a**
    were interested in accomplishing all of the following *except*:
    a. exploring new forms of fiction and broadening literature's appeal to the general public
    b. setting up new guidelines for serious literature
    c. censoring sexual allusions, vulgar slang, disrespectful treatments of Christianity, and unhappy endings in literature
    d. improving American taste in interior furnishings, textiles, ceramics, wallpaper, and books

59. Which of the following magazines was viewed in the late nineteenth century as an   **b**
    important forum for serious writing?
    a. *McClure's*
    b. *North American Review*
    c. *Cosmopolitan*
    d. *Ladies' Home Journal*

60. Which of the following stories might be described as an example of naturalism?   **c**
    a. a story about New England village life that emphasized the distinctive dialect of the people and the colorful details of local life
    b. a novel in which a young farm boy goes to the big city to make his fortune, finds that Christianity is his true love, and returns home to live a quiet, comfortable, and happy life with his childhood sweetheart.
    c. a bleak and fatalistic story about an innocent girl's exploitation and ultimate suicide in the harsh environment of an urban slum
    d. a sensationalist exposé of the political corruption and misdeeds of a giant holding company

61. Which of the following is the story of an innocent and attractive girl from Wisconsin who is seduced by a traveling salesman, moves in with the married proprietor of a fancy saloon, and eventually pursues a career in the theater?   **d**
    a. *Huckleberry Finn*
    b. *The Country of the Pointed Firs*
    c. *Maggie: A Girl of the Streets*
    d. *Sister Carrie*

62. One of the goals of the Chautauqua program was to   **a**
                                                          PT
    a. provide a pleasurable way of learning subjects that would lead to spiritual and intellectual uplift and self-improvement.
    b. offer the benefits of a country club to working-class families that otherwise would not be able to get away from the city.
    c. offer a condensed university curriculum during a summer's stay in a bucolic resort.
    d. devise practical approaches to solving everyday problems.

63. The Victorian belief in self-improvement and moral uplift could be seen in action at

    a. Coney Island.
    b. Chautauqua.
    c. the Waldorf Astoria.
    d. Wellesley and Smith colleges.

b
PT

64. The work of which of the following individuals was *not* an example of "modernism" in architecture or painting during the late nineteenth century?

    a. architect Frank Lloyd Wright
    b. painter Thomas Eakins
    c. architect Richard Morris Hunt
    d. painter Albert Pinkham Ryder

c

65. The work of Frances Willard of the Woman's Christian Temperance Union shows that many women in the late nineteenth century could

    a. rebel against the fundamental assumptions of middle-class family structure and the woman's role within the family itself.
    b. undercut, through their militant reform activities, the very club movement that they professed to favor.
    c. use a fad such as bicycling without corsets as the symbol of liberation from patriarchy.
    d. challenge the cult of domesticity and expand woman's sphere while at the same time remaining committed to woman's nurturing and supportive role within the family.

d

66. All of the following were independent women's colleges that were affiliated with older men's colleges *except*:

    a. Wellesley
    b. Radcliffe
    c. Pembroke
    d. Barnard

a

67. Which of the following is *not* an indicator of women's changing relationship to men during the last decades of the nineteenth century?

    a. the rise of bicycling as a popular activity among young women
    b. the growing popularity of catalog and department stores
    c. the substantial rise in the divorce rate in these years
    d. the popularity of Charles Dana Gibson's magazine illustrations

b

68. Which of the following suggests that public education in the late-nineteenth-century United States had become entangled in ethnic and class differences?

    a. the proliferation of private and parochial schools
    b. the controversy over compulsory education
    c. the debates over classroom decorum
    d. all of the above

d

69. The purpose of "local-option" referenda sponsored by middle-class urban reform-   c
    ers was to
    a. encourage working-class leaders to support impeccably groomed urban
       parks.
    b. allow local Anti-Saloon League chapters to decide whether or not to admit
       women as members.
    c. close saloons in specific cities.
    d. allow all citizens to have the option of deciding what type of school—public,
       private, or parochial—their children would attend.

70. The overall impact of industrialization on American life in the late nineteenth cen-   c
    tury was   SG
    a. to reduce the gulf between the standards of living of the rich and the poor.
    b. to make class distinctions less apparent.
    c. to improve the level of living for many families.
    d. to drive fine quality goods off the market in favor of mass-produced, shoddy
       products.

71. Which of the following correctly presents income distribution in late-nineteenth-   b
    century America?   SG
    a. The middle class was the largest class, controlling better than 50 percent of
       national wealth.
    b. The working class composed more than 40 percent of the nation but con-
       trolled only 1.5 percent of its wealth.
    c. The upper-class elite controlled about 20 percent of the country's wealth.
    d. The wealth was almost evenly divided among classes, with upper, middle, and
       working classes each controlling roughly one-third of national income.

72. Which of the following statements about American families between 1860 and   c
    1900 is correct?   SG
    a. Working-class families generally had fewer children than upper- and middle-
       class families.
    b. Blacks and immigrants were more likely to live in nuclear families; the upper
       and middle classes formed extended kinship networks.
    c. Immigrant working-class families expected children to go to work by age ten
       or twelve, and all members of the family contributed to its support.
    d. Birth control was unknown, and all families continued to have seven to eight
       children on average.

73. A member of the working class in the late nineteenth century would have been   d
    most likely to read   SG
    a. *The Nation.*
    b. *The Century.*
    c. *Atlantic Monthly.*
    d. *The National Police Gazette.*

74. Who coined the term "conspicuous consumption" to describe the excessive mate-   c
    rialism and flaunting of wealth of America's captains of industry?   SG
    a. Mark Twain
    b. Annie MacLean
    c. Thorstein Veblen
    d. W. E. B. Du Bois

ESSAY QUESTIONS

75. Discuss the effects of industrialization and the growth of big corporations on the   SG
    American standard of living, class structure, and class distinctions from 1860 to
    1900.

76. From the 1860s to 1900, the lives of most Americans underwent fundamental
    transformations. Explain these transformations by examining changes in the fam-
    ily unit, in consumer behavior, in leisure-time activities, and in the basic unity—or
    lack of unity—of the American class structure.

77. Explain some of the developments that transformed American consumer patterns
    during the late nineteenth century. Discuss, for example, the introduction of new
    products, changes in product marketing (advertising and stores), evolving atti-
    tudes of consumers toward shopping and products, and the impact of these pat-
    terns on the American class structure.

78. Discuss the transformation of family life in the late nineteenth century: changes in
    family size and structure, the changing expectations for family comfort and conve-
    nience, and the changing roles of individual family members.

79. Describe how the American class structure was shifting during the late nineteenth
    century. How were the "determinants" of class changing? What evidence can you
    find of a growing split between the working class and the middle class of the
    United States during these years? Discuss, especially, the divisions that existed in
    American society over cultural issues and morality.

80. Compare the responsibilities of women in southern black families, poor white
    midwestern farm families, urban working-class families, and middle-class families.
    Explain the "cult of domesticity." How did middle-class expectations about
    women's role within the home change during the last half of the nineteenth
    century?

81. Compare the late-nineteenth-century working-class and middle-class family in
    terms of changing approaches to "getting ahead"; economic responsibilities of
    family members; and attitudes toward leisure, amusement, culture, and education.

82. How did the Victorian worldview shape standards of middle-class morality in the   PT
United States? How did it help to justify the middle-class style of life? What effect
did it have on American women and the American working class? In what sense
was the Chautauqua movement the epitome of middle-class beliefs about progress
and reform? Why did a reaction set in against those attitudes and assumptions?

83. Why did genteel cultural standards come under attack toward the end of the nineteenth century? Who led the attack? Explain how "modernism" symbolized one
of the challenges to the genteel tradition. Why did the genteel mores of the middle class, rather than urban working-class culture, prove more vulnerable?

84. What was meant by the term "new woman"? Explain how the concept of the "new
woman" came about. How, at first, were leaders of women's groups able to
expand the sphere in which women could legitimately function—but at the same
time uphold the traditional view of womanhood and woman's role in society.

CHAPTER 20

Politics and Expansion in an Industrializing Age

IDENTIFICATIONS

Identify the following. Be as specific as possible, and include names, dates, and relevant facts as appropriate. Be sure to explain the *significance* of the person or term.

1. Greenback party

2. Bland-Allison Act

3. Sherman Silver Purchase Act

4. James G. Blaine

5. the Half-Breeds and the Stalwarts

6. Pendleton Act

7. Billion Dollar Congress

8. the farmers' alliance movement

9. subtreasury system

10. Populist party

11. convict-lease system

12. *Civil Rights Cases*

13. *Plessy* v. *Ferguson*

14. Coxey's Army

15. Panic of 1893 and Depression of 1893–1897

16. free silver and bimetalism

17. William Jennings Bryan

18. Mark Hanna and the "front-porch campaign"

19. Alfred T. Mahan's *The Influence of Sea Power Upon History*

20. Liliuokalani and Sanford B. Dole

21. Butcher Weyler

22. William Randolph Hearst, Joseph Pulitzer, and yellow journalism

23. de Lôme letter

24. the *Maine*

25. Teller and Platt amendments

26. Emilio Aguinaldo

27. Anti-Imperialist League

28. "Open Door" notes

29. Hay-Herrán and Hay-Bunau-Varilla agreements

MULTIPLE-CHOICE QUESTIONS

Choose the answer that *best* completes the statement or answers the question.

30. What two issues dominated national politics in the 1870s and 1880s?   a
    a. the money supply and civil-service reform
    b. civil-service reform and working conditions in factories
    c. the money supply and urban slums
    d. civil-service reform and imperialism

31. During the late nineteenth century, the centers of Democratic political strength   b
    included all of the following *except*:
    a. the South
    b. the upper Midwest
    c. major northern industrial cities
    d. southern sections of border states

32. During the late nineteenth century, which of the following groups was *not* likely   c
    to vote Republican?
    a. native-born middle-class and business and professional men
    b. corporate tycoons
    c. leaders of trade unions
    d. northern Civil War veterans

33. Which of the following factors was *most* likely to determine one's party affiliation   d
during the late nineteenth century?

    a. economic standing

    b. geographic location

    c. age

    d. family, ethnic, or religious ties

34. Which of the following accurately describes voter participation during the late   a
nineteenth century?

    a. It was generally very high—usually from 80 percent up to 95 percent.

    b. It was generally low because the major political parties were not discussing
real issues.

    c. It varied from election to election—sometimes very high, sometimes very low.

    d. It was very high on the local level but very low on the national level.

35. Why did the federal government during the late nineteenth century tend to ignore   d
the social consequences of industrialization?

    a. Presidents were weak and Congress held the political initiative.

    b. Within the Congress, there was little party discipline and little concern for
national issues.

    c. Americans did not expect the federal government to intervene in economic or
social affairs.

    d. all of the above

36. On the grassroots level in the late nineteenth century, what sorts of issues would   b
be *most* likely to animate political debate?

    a. the import duties that were charged on hundreds of commodities

    b. issues such as prohibition and tax support to parochial schools that pitted
ethnic and social groups against each other

    c. national legislation to improve working conditions and control the railroads

    d. the need to modernize the American navy so that it could compete with
navies of the great powers

37. Which of the following groups is properly paired with its position on limiting or   c
expanding the money supply?

    a. urban workers: limit—because it would increase their buying power by mak-
ing each dollar worth more

    b. bankers: limit—because it would raise interest rates and push prices down

    c. southern and western farmers: expand—because they wanted to make it eas-
ier to pay off their debts

    d. business leaders: expand—because there would be more money to borrow
for business expansion

38. Which of the following is *not* associated with the question of the money supply in the late nineteenth century?   **a**

    a. *Plessy* v. *Ferguson*
    b. Sherman Silver Purchase Act
    c. Crime of '73
    d. Bland-Allison Act

39. What did the civil-service reformers of the late 1870s and early 1880s want?   **b**

    a. a government bureaucracy that would help free immigrants from poverty
    b. a civil service staffed by gentlemen who needed nothing and wanted nothing from government except the satisfaction of using their talents
    c. a federal law that would appoint Roscoe Conkling director of government personnel
    d. laws that would help to sustain the dignity of the federal civil service

40. The Pendleton Act provided for   **a**

    SG

    a. civil-service reform.
    b. using silver as well as gold to back paper currency.
    c. separate but equal facilities for blacks and whites.
    d. higher protective tariff rates.

41. During the course of the 1884 presidential campaign,   **d**

    a. Mugwumps bolted from the Republican party.
    b. Cleveland admitted he had fathered an illegitimate child.
    c. a clergyman denounced Democrats as the party of "rum, Romanism, and rebellion."
    d. all of the above

42. Grover Cleveland, the only Democrat elected president between 1856 and 1912, believed that government should   **a**

    a. refrain from paternalistic meddling in the economy.
    b. actively intervene in the economy to guide the nation's industrial development.
    c. work to develop a humanitarian form of industrialism.
    d. regulate the trusts and provide drought relief to western farmers.

43. Which of the following groups is correctly paired with its position on the tariff?   **b**

    a. businessmen involved in foreign trade: they wanted protection against foreign competition
    b. farmers of the West and South: they opposed tariffs for raising the price of equipment and impeding the sale of American farm products abroad
    c. shoe manufacturers: they opposed tariffs for being the "mother of trusts"
    d. producers of coal, hides, timber, wool: they wanted lower tariffs to encourage foreign trade

44. Why did Grover Cleveland propose a reduction of the tariff rates?   c
    a. He thought that the government had no right to meddle in the economy.
    b. He believed that lower tariffs would encourage the growth of industry in the United States.
    c. The tariff was feeding a large and growing federal budget surplus.
    d. The tariff worked to the disadvantage of small farmers.

45. President Cleveland believed that pensions for veterans should be   d
    a. distributed by the Grand Army of the Republic, which was better qualified than the federal government to know who deserved them.
    b. awarded to all disabled veterans.
    c. eliminated entirely as an unpleasant reminder of an unpleasant Republican war.
    d. thought of as an honor roll and reserved for those who deserved them.

46. Which of the following is associated with the administration of Benjamin Harrison?   a
    a. a record-high tariff
    b. the decision to cease government purchases of silver
    c. government attacks on entrenched economic interests
    d. the decline of political activism in the agrarian South and West

47. The farmers' alliance movement   b
    a. was restricted to the agrarian South, because agriculture was prosperous elsewhere.
    b. initially advocated farmers' cooperatives and eventually turned to politics.
    c. was never able to build a large membership.
    d. limited itself to a social and educational role and attempted to remain as noncontroversial as possible to gain maximum support in Congress.

48. Under the subtreasury system,   c
    a. the federal government was to establish a series of branch banks to hold federal deposits and help to control the money supply.
    b. late-nineteenth-century American capitalists attempted to corner all the silver that was held outside the federal treasury.
    c. farmers could store crops in government warehouses and then borrow against those crops until prices rose.
    d. the federal government would provide special agricultural loans from a fund created out of grain excise taxes.

49. All of the following were goals of the Populist party *except*:   a
    a. having government take over and run the railroads   SG
    b. increasing the money supply
    c. raising the protective tariff
    d. having the people elect U.S. senators instead of state legislatures choosing them

50. During post-Reconstruction southern states disfranchised blacks through all of the   a
following techniques *except*:
    a. outright legal prohibitions
    b. literacy tests
    c. poll taxes
    d. property requirements

51. During the late nineteenth century, what was the relationship between the south-   d
ern agrarian protest movement and southern attitudes toward blacks?
    a. Some Populists wanted to build an interracial movement and tried to defend
       the rights of blacks.
    b. Most southern populists were antiblack.
    c. The white elite tried to inflame agrarian racism and stimulate urban black
       sentiment against agrarian radicalism.
    d. all of the above

52. In late-nineteenth-century cases dealing with the rights of blacks, the Supreme   b
Court decided that
    a. the Fourteenth Amendment protected citizens from private acts of discrimi-
       nation but not from governmental acts.
    b. racial segregation was constitutional as long as each race had equal facilities.
    c. poll taxes and literacy tests were illegal.
    d. the civil-rights clauses of the Fifteenth Amendment were unconstitutional.

53. The "separate but equal" doctrine meant that   c
    a. although the executive and legislative branches had separate powers and
       responsibilities, the two branches were constitutionally equal in importance.
    b. southern schools were segregated, but they had similar buildings, equivalent
       equipment, and equally qualified and equally paid teachers.
    c. as long as facilities were equivalent, they did not have to be integrated.
    d. the northern and southern approaches to race relations were completely dif-
       ferent, but as far as blacks were concerned they amounted to the same thing.

54. How were blacks treated in the North during the late nineteenth century?   a
    a. Public opinion sanctioned widespread de facto discrimination.
    b. The influence of northern labor unions kept northern society racially inte-
       grated and equal.
    c. Most Democratic politicians in northern cities used their political machines
       to make white supremacy the official policy.
    d. The abolitionist legacy was still strong in the North and so most northerners
       continued to strive for an egalitarian society.

55. In the 1892 election, the Populist party   b
    a. became the first "third party" in American history to win the presidency.
    b. received over one million votes across the nation.
    c. won by a large margin in New England and the traditionally Republican farm
       regions of the Midwest.
    d. swept every state of the former Confederacy.

56. As a result of the 1892 election   c

   a. voters indicated their desire to return to the activist policies of Grover Cleveland.
   b. Benjamin Harrison was defeated by a razor-thin margin.
   c. prospects for interracial agrarian reform in the South died.
   d. Benjamin Harrison was given a mandate to continue his policies of peace and prosperity.

57. Economically, the 1880s and early 1890s were years of   d

   a. rapid industrial growth.
   b. speculative mania.
   c. agricultural stagnation.
   d. all of the above

58. Confidence in the gold standard had weakened in the early 1890s for all of the fol-   a
    lowing reasons *except*:

   a. a decline in the conversion of Treasury certificates into gold
   b. the steady flow of gold out of the country
   c. the inflationary policies of the Democrats
   d. a decline in revenue brought about by the high tariff

59. Which statement is a correct description of economic conditions during the sec-   a
    ond Grover Cleveland administration?

   a. Farm prices plummeted and unemployment reached 25 percent.
   b. Record industrial expansion taxed the nation's supply of credit.
   c. The economy collapsed as the nation went off the gold standard.
   d. Government intervention in the financial market helped to keep the economy healthy.

60. Coxey's Army wanted   b

   a. another increase in veterans' benefits.
   b. a $500 million public-works program funded with paper money.
   c. a chance to go to Cuba to join the Rough Riders.
   d. a gold standard to stabilize the economy.

61. What did Grover Cleveland think was the way to deal with the depression of   c
    1893–1897?

   a. sell $62 million in gold to Wall Street bankers J. P. Morgan and August Belmont
   b. enact the Sherman Silver Purchase bill
   c. defend the gold standard and bolster government gold reserves
   d. purchase 3.5 million ounces of silver

62. The Wilson-Gorman Tariff   d

   a. lowered duties.
   b. made many concessions to protectionists.
   c. included a tax on income.
   d. all of the above

63. What lesson could political leaders of the period learn from the 1894 midterm   a
    elections?

    a. The economic upheavals the country was suffering were also causing political
       upheavals.
    b. The people were uniting behind their president to combat the nation's eco-
       nomic woes.
    c. In times of economic distress, third parties tend to lose strength.
    d. all of the above

64. What was the major issue in the 1896 presidential election?   b

    a. agrarian unrest
    b. free silver
    c. imperialism
    d. personal corruption

65. In the 1896 election, William McKinley's strength came from all of the following   c
    areas *except*:

    a. the Northeast
    b. the Midwest
    c. sparsely settled Great Plains and Rocky Mountain states
    d. cities

66. In the 1880s and 1890s, many Americans argued that the United States should take   d
    a more expansionist role in the world because

    a. to be a great nation, the United States had to have an empire.
    b. American economic health depended on finding overseas markets for Ameri-
       can products.
    c. Americans had a mission to bring Christianity and civilization to the world's
       weaker races.
    d. all of the above

67. Who was *not* an American expansionist in the late nineteenth century?   a

    a. Andrew Carnegie
    b. John Hay
    c. Alfred T. Mahan
    d. Henry Cabot Lodge

68. America's international relations in the 1880s and 1890s can be seen in events in   b
    Samoa, where

    a. American pineapple growers overthrew the native queen and requested
       American annexation.
    b. the United States established a joint protectorate with Germany and Great
       Britain.
    c. a hurricane destroyed the American fleet and convinced the State Department
       that far-flung entanglements were not worth the cost.
    d. economic stability and Spanish rule were threatened by a rebellion.

69. American ties to Hawaii in the late nineteenth century were strengthened through all the following *except*:

    a. American missionary activity

    b. American sugar planters

    c. American relations with the Hawaiian throne

    d. American naval activity

    c

70. The "Yellow Press," the de Lôme letter, the *Maine*, and Butcher Weyler are all associated with American involvement in

    a. Chile.

    b. Venezuela.

    c. Panama.

    d. Cuba.

    d

71. The Teller Amendment asserted that

    a. the United States had no desire for control of Cuba.

    b. the United States had the right to arbitrate the Venezuelan boundary dispute.

    c. the United States had the right to intervene in Cuban affairs to ensure Cuban stability.

    d. the United States had as much right as any European nation to trade with China.

    a

72. Which of the following was *not* a colony ceded to the United States by Spain as a result of the Spanish-American War?

    a. the Philippines

    b. Cuba

    c. Guam

    d. Puerto Rico

    b

73. What was John Hay referring to when he spoke of a "splendid little war"?

    a. that blacks had served with distinction in the Spanish-American War

    b. that American troops fighting in Cuba had proven themselves to be well trained and well equipped

    c. that the short and successful war with Spain had awakened a new consciousness of national strength

    d. that a small and antiquated American navy had taken advantage of American spirit to whip the larger and more modern Spanish fleet

    c

74. How did the United States deal with Cuba in the years after the Spanish-American War?

    a. by keeping American troops in Cuba for a number of years

    b. by improving public health, education, and sanitation on the island

    c. by asserting the right to intervene in Cuba when it was necessary

    d. all of the above

    d

75. In the Philippines after the Spanish-American War,   **a**
   a. Filipino resistance fighters fought a protracted and bloody guerrilla war against United States rule.
   b. American agricultural producers, hoping to establish a tariff against Filipino products, engineered quick independence for the former Spanish colony.
   c. Filipino patriots petitioned the United States Congress for annexation and statehood.
   d. the United States imposed military rule and announced that self-government could not be granted until the Philippines had achieved economic self-sufficiency.

76. The United States response to events in China during the last years of the nineteenth century was to   **b**
   a. send an American gunboat to force the Manchu dynasty to capitulate.
   b. request equal trading privileges and announce the desire to preserve China's territorial integrity.
   c. demand that an arbitration commission be established.
   d. send covert aid to the Harmonious Righteous Fists in an effort to overthrow the anti-Western Manchu empress.

77. During the late nineteenth century, while imperialistic European powers were acquiring overseas colonies, the United States   **c**
   a. plunged headlong into an orgy of empire building that rivaled that of Great Britain.
   b. turned its back on the world and focused on the rapid economic growth within its own borders.
   c. tended to follow a quest for a more informal economic empire in which Washington could play a subordinate and supporting role to private enterprise.
   d. tried repeatedly but without success to acquire valuable colonies.

78. How did the United States acquire the Panama Canal?   **d**
   a. through a treaty signed with Colombia
   b. by a military invasion of Panama
   c. purchase of the completed canal from the French company
   d. none of the above

79. American imperialists argued that United States participation in the race for colonies would do all of the following *except*:   **a**
      SG
   a. cause lower taxes in the United States
   b. provide bases for the United States navy
   c. provide the United States with new markets
   d. bring civilization to backward peoples

80. The free-silver position of the Democrats and Populists in 1896 failed to win much support from urban labor because   **d** **SG**
  a. it would destroy labor unions.
  b. factory workers were relatively prosperous in the 1890s.
  c. workers liked Grover Cleveland and "laissez faire."
  d. workers feared it would result in higher food prices.

81. Which nineteenth-century political figure championed civil-service reform, joined the Mugwump revolt against James C. Blaine, and criticized American imperialism?   **c** **SG**
  a. Alfred T. Mahan
  b. Benjamin Harrison
  c. Carl Schurz
  d. John Hay

ESSAY QUESTIONS

82. What is the meaning of the statement "late nineteenth-century politics was an exuberant affair"? Explain by discussing the factors that shaped American politics in this period and that distinguished late-nineteenth-century politics from politics of a century later. Show how politics functioned. Who voted for whom, and what determined those voting patterns? How did economic conditions eventually lead to a basic political realignment?

83. Consider the presidential campaigns of the period 1876–1900. Which had the most significant and enduring impact? Discuss the issues, candidates, outcomes, and impacts. Which presidential campaign was the most colorful or most interesting? Who were the personalities, what were the issues, and why do you find the campaign colorful? Compare the two campaigns that you have chosen, and explain what they reveal together about late-nineteenth-century presidential politics.

84. What were the major social problems facing the United States in the late nineteenth century? Explain to what extent the federal government attempted to address those problems.

85. The late-nineteenth-century American money supply can appear to be a very tangled web indeed. Try to untangle it. What was the purpose of expanding or contracting the supply? What difference did it make whether the federal government issued paper money, gold, or silver? Who supported each position, and why? Explain how the "money question" was both an economic *and* a political problem.

86. What difficulties did the American farmer confront in the late nineteenth century? How did farmers react to those difficulties? What organizations did they form and what were their goals and demands? How did the government respond?

87. Discuss what happened to blacks in the post-Reconstruction South. What impact did these developments have on national politics? How did the federal government react to these developments?

88. During the late nineteenth century, the American economy was experiencing new pressures and strains, yet no branch of the federal government—executive, legislative, or judicial—was prepared to deal with those strains. What were the economic conditions experienced during this period by farmers, urban workers, and business leaders? What strains was the economy experiencing? How did the government react, and why? What were the consequences for farmers, urban workers, business leaders, and the economy as a whole?

89. The author of your text says that the depression of the 1890s "was memorable . . . not only for the suffering that it brought but also for the lessons that it taught." Explain the causes and describe the impact of the depression. What lessons did it teach? How did it alter political and social thought as the twentieth century approached?

90. Why did expansionist sentiment grow in the United States from the 1880s onward? Who were the proponents of American expansion, and what were their reasons? Discuss economic, emotional, political, and strategic factors. Give examples of how this expansionist sentiment manifested itself in Latin America and Asia.

91. What were the causes of the Spanish-American War? What were the main events of the war? What were the consequences? Who opposed American involvement in the war? Why?

MAP QUESTIONS

Choose the letter on the accompanying map of world that identifies each of the following:

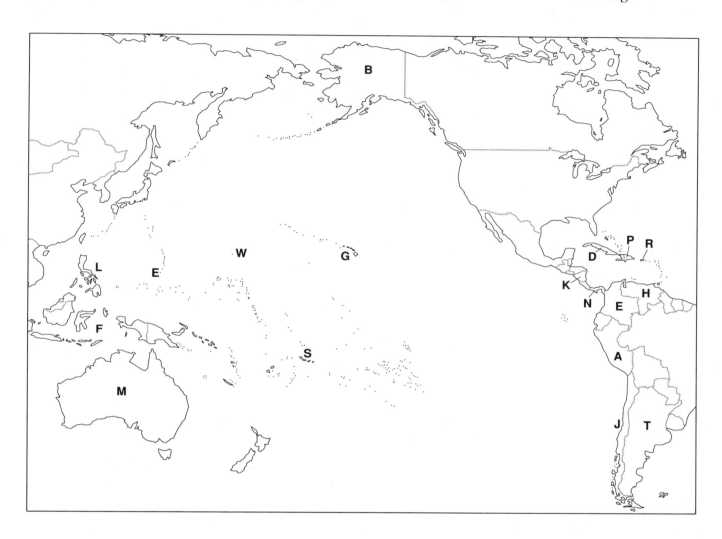

92. Venezuela   **H**

93. Chile   **J**

94. Panama   **N**

95. Cuba   **D**

96. Puerto Rico   **R**

97. Samoa   **S**

98. Guam   **E**

99. Philippine Islands   **L**

100. Hawaii   **G**

101. Alaska   **B**

CHAPTER 21

The Progressive Era

IDENTIFICATIONS

Identify the following. Be as specific as possible, and include names, dates, and relevant facts as appropriate. Be sure to explain the *significance* of the person or term.

1. Triangle Shirtwaist fire

2. Jim Crow laws

3. ragtime, the blues, and jazz

4. Florence Kelley   **PT**

5. Frederick W. Taylor's *Principles of Scientific Management*

6. *Danbury Hatters* case

7. International Ladies' Garment Workers' Union

8. Big Bill Haywood and the Industrial Workers of the World

9. Eugene V. Debs and the Socialist Party of America

10. Thorstein Veblen's *The Theory of the Leisure Class*

11. Herbert Croly's *The Promise of American Life, New Republic*

12. John Dewey

13. Oliver Wendell Holmes, Jr.

14. Frank Norris's *The Octopus* and Upton Sinclair's *The Jungle*

15. muckrakers

16. Robert La Follette

17. "white slave" hysteria and the Mann Act

18. Anti-Saloon League and the Woman's Christian Temperance Union

19. Booker T. Washington's "Atlanta Compromise" speech

20. W. E. B. Du Bois

21. National Association for the Advancement of Colored People

22. the Woman's party

23. Charlotte Perkins Gilman

24. *Northern Securities* case

25. Theodore Roosevelt's "square deal"

26. Ballinger-Pinchot affair

27. Bull Moose party

28. New Nationalism and New Freedom

29. Federal Reserve Act

30. the "Brandeis brief"

MULTIPLE-CHOICE QUESTIONS

Choose the answer that *best* completes the statement or answers the question.

31. Immigration to the United States from southern and eastern Europe *peaked* in   a
approximately which of the following periods?
    a. 1900–1910
    b. 1870–1880
    c. 1910–1920
    d. 1890–1900

32. How would you compare progressivism with earlier reform movements?   b
    a. Since progressivism sprang from the American reform tradition, its assumptions and goals were identical to those of earlier movements.
    b. Unlike earlier reformers, progressives thought of government as a major ally.
    c. Progressive reformers were much more individualistic than earlier reformers had been.
    d. Earlier movements had been limited to political reform, while the progressives concentrated on social and economic reform.

33. During the first two decades of the twentieth century, what was the greatest   c
source of urban population growth?
    a. exodus from rural and small-town America
    b. increasing birthrate within the cities themselves
    c. immigration
    d. medical advances that ended the major urban diseases

34. Which of the following correctly ranks the sources of foreign immigration to the   d
    United States during the first two decades of the twentieth century?
    a. China, southern and eastern Europe, Japan
    b. southern and eastern Europe, China, Japan
    c. Japan, China, southern and eastern Europe
    d. southern and eastern Europe, Japan, China

35. During the early twentieth century, American cities went through a period of rapid   d
    growth, during which
    a. many of them had great difficulty providing the basic necessities of safe
       water, sewage facilities, garbage collection, and fire protection.
    b. they were hampered by considerable municipal corruption.
    c. health conditions in immigrant wards were so bad that their death rates were
       sometimes twice the national average.
    d. all of the above

36. What happened to the white-collar middle class in the United States from 1900 to   a
    1920?
    a. It more than doubled in size and grew at over twice the rate for the work
       force as a whole during the same period.
    b. Its size remained about the same, but its influence declined dramatically in
       proportion to the rest of the population.
    c. It disappeared because the changing nature of the American economy
       required mainly blue-collar workers.
    d. Although it was growing dramatically, it wasn't growing as fast as the work
       force as a whole.

37. Why did the number of professional organizations, and the membership in them,   b
    increase markedly during the first two decades of the twentieth century?
    a. The middle class viewed such organizations as the best way to impress the
       old aristocratic families.
    b. Such organizations provided a sense of professional identity for the white-
       collar middle class.
    c. Such organizations helped to provide the middle class with an entrée into
       local political organizations.
    d. Until the twentieth century, professional organizations were looked upon as
       badges of shame or poverty.

38. In the early twentieth century, middle-class women began to think of employment   c
    outside the home as
    a. a badge of shame.
    b. a way of keeping the divorce rate down.
    c. a rewarding and satisfying activity.
    d. something that was usually boring, frustrating, and isolating.

39. Jim Crow laws were   a
    a. a method of imposing strict segregation on, for example, streetcars, trains, schools, parks, public buildings, and cemeteries.
    b. declared in the *Danbury Hatters* case to be unconstitutional.
    c. laws instituted by many northern municipalities in the early twentieth century in an effort to ensure honest and effective government.
    d. none of the above

40. What do jazz, ragtime, and the blues have in common?   b
    a. They originated in black areas of Chicago in the late nineteenth century.
    b. They originated as black musical idioms.
    c. They were musical forms outlawed by the Jim Crow laws.
    d. They were brought to the United States by immigrants from eastern Europe.

41. In 1910, approximately what percentage of the nation's children between the ages   c
    of ten and fifteen worked outside the home?
    a. 1%
    b. 95%
    c. 15%
    d. 50%

42. During the years from 1880 to 1930, what happened to the number of children   d
    aged ten to fifteen in the work force?
    a. It increased steadily.
    b. It declined steadily.
    c. It remained the same.
    d. It increased but then began to decline.

43. By 1900, what was the general attitude of most employers toward work-related   a
    accidents and illnesses?
    a. Few employers accepted any responsibility for the frequent accidents and illnesses, and even fewer provided vacations and retirement benefits.
    b. Most had been convinced by progressive reformers that each employer had to take care of his or her own employees and help them prepare for a healthy retirement.
    c. Few were prepared to deal with the problem themselves, but most had become convinced that the federal government should institute a workers' compensation program.
    d. Most believed that programs to help workers during times of illness would result in a nation of sissies.

44. In a typical American factory town like Alton, Illinois, in the 1890s, what reaction   d
    would be likely from the town's leaders to the news that a local factory was   PT
    employing eight-year-old children?

    a. "The town's economic health depends on maintaining things the way they
       are."
    b. "Such child laborers are too tough to educate anyway, so employment is the
       best thing for them."
    c. "It's good to get them to work in factories, because then the city won't have
       to provide them with public aid."
    d. all of the above

45. "Taylorism" meant   b

    a. adopting progressive reforms in an effort to make business more humane.
    b. trying to increase efficiency by standardizing job routines and rewarding the
       fastest workers.
    c. combining several competing corporations into one larger holding company.
    d. providing workers with better wages and working conditions in an effort to
       prevent government regulation or outside unionization.

46. What was unusual about the International Ladies' Garment Workers' Union?   a

    a. It organized laborers at the lower end of the scale.
    b. It concentrated on skilled crafts.
    c. It advocated the end of the wage system.
    d. It made widespread use of violence.

47. The American Federation of Labor's main source of strength was in   b

    a. factories and mills.
    b. skilled trades.
    c. farm workers.
    d. urban white-collar workers.

48. The Wobblies   c

    a. advised blacks to concentrate on economic advancement through vocational
       education and, for the time being, accept the South's Jim Crow laws.
    b. were a conservative, craft-based union.
    c. preached revolution, the class struggle, and the abolition of the wage system.
    d. was the nickname that municipal bosses gave to progressive "good-govern-
       ment" reformers.

49. At the high tide of socialist strength in the United States,   d

    a. the Socialist Party of America nearly captured the presidency, in 1920.
    b. socialists won only a few minor municipal elections.
    c. both major national political parties adopted the full socialist program as a
       way of halting Socialist party growth.
    d. the Socialist party elected a congressman and many municipal officers; it
       received over 900,000 votes for president; and it had a membership of over
       100,000.

50. Which of the following statements about progressivism is accurate?   **d**
    a. It was a political response to industrialism and its social by-products.
    b. It differed from populism in that progressivism was more urban and enlisted more journalists, academics, and social theorists.
    c. Progressives wanted to reform the evils spawned by capitalism, but they wanted to preserve the capitalist system itself.
    d. all of the above

51. In what respect were the populist and progressive movements similar?   **d**
    SG
    a. They were primarily urban-based movements.
    b. They wanted to bring about inflation by backing the currency with gold and silver.
    c. They fought against segregation and other forms of racial discrimination.
    d. They advocated government intervention in economic matters to handle problems arising from industrialization.

52. Which of the following would *not* have been a goal of a progressive reformer?   **a**
    a. abolition of private ownership of the means of production
    b. legislation to protect workers and regulate business
    c. reforming the structure of government on the municipal level
    d. immigration restriction and other coercive social-control strategies

53. What did the writings of Richard Ely, Thorstein Veblen, Charles and Mary Beard, William James, and Herbert Croly have in common?   **c**
    a. They formed the intellectual and ideological foundations of Social Darwinism.
    b. They were the most prominent examples of the intellectual assault on progressivism that began around 1920.
    c. They implicitly supported the need for far-reaching reforms of American society.
    d. They were misread by progressives to mean that socialism was the nation's only hope of social reform.

54. Which of the following was written by Thorstein Veblen?   **b**
    a. *Woman's Work in Municipalities*
    b. *The Theory of the Leisure Class*
    c. *The New History*
    d. *Democracy and Social Ethics*

55. In *The Promise of American Life*, Herbert Croly argued that   a

    a. the United States needed an activist government that would serve all citizens; and concepts such as democracy, nationalism, and individualism had to be redefined.
    b. engineers, because of the stern discipline of their profession, were better fitted to lead society than the business class.
    c. the theory of evolution through "survival of the fittest" supported an ideology of unrestrained economic competition.
    d. the central dynamic of American history was not the actions of Washington policy makers but the social and political experience of generations of western pioneers.

56. According to John Dewey, schools should   c

    a. teach self-reliance, hard work, and honesty.
    b. serve as the handmaidens of industry by teaching subjects that were most needed by the business world.
    c. become the instruments of reform by embracing the new ethic of social interdependence.
    d. guard against experimentalism and preserve the role of the teacher as the unquestioned authority.

57. What legal philosophy was Oliver Wendell Holmes, Jr., propounding when he   d
    said, "The life of the law has not been logic; it has been experience"?

    a. In a world that was basically irrational, only legal principles were completely logical.
    b. American law was becoming based too much on the whims of judges, and it had to return to its foundations in ancient court cases.
    c. The English laws that had been laid down in the time of Henry IV were the epitome of logic and rightfully the basis of American jurisprudence.
    d. Law has to evolve as society changes and cannot rely exclusively on sacred legal principles and ancient precedents.

58. The term "muckrakers" referred to   b

    a. procurers involved in the white slave trade.   SG
    b. journalists and writers who exposed political corruption and corporate wrongdoing.
    c. opponents of Woodrow Wilson.
    d. women who spread mud on the grounds of the White House to protest being denied the vote.

59. The following were muckraking journalists *except*:   c

    a. Lincoln Steffens
    b. Ida Tarbell
    c. Gifford Pinchot
    d. Maria Van Vorst

60. All of the following were reform mayors *except*: **b**
    a. Hazen Pingree
    b. Abe Reuf
    c. Tom Johnson
    d. Samuel M. "Golden Rule" Jones

61. Municipal reformers wanted to do all of the following *except*: **c**
    a. "throw the rascals out"
    b. replace the private monopolies on water, gas, electricity, and public transportation with publicly owned companies
    c. weaken the ties of party loyalty and reduce voter interest, thereby reducing the rates of voter participation and ensuring that only the best qualified, best informed, least prejudiced voters would vote
    d. bring efficiency and expertise to municipal government with professional managers and administrators

62. Among the political changes that reformers wished to bring to state government during the early years of the twentieth century was **a**
    a. giving voters the power to enact laws directly.
    b. simplifying the procedure for voting by giving voters preprinted ballots bearing the name of a specific candidate.
    c. ensuring the most qualified senators by shifting their election to the state legislatures.
    d. having candidates for public office be selected by the party leadership rather than through the more cumbersome and time-consuming process of having all party members vote.

63. Which of the following was a typical urban reform instituted during the first two decades of the twentieth century? **d**
    a. public-health programs
    b. legislation against overhead electrical wires
    c. majestic new public buildings and recreational resources
    d. all of the above

64. What was the goal of urban planners and architects like Daniel Hudson Burnham? **d**
    a. to rebuild the typical American city with stronger materials so that a catastrophe like the 1906 San Francisco earthquake and fire would never be repeated
    b. to reroute the flow of railroad and vehicular traffic at grade level directly through the heart of the city, so that all urban dwellers would see and appreciate such symbols of economic progress
    c. to eliminate slums by building low-income housing on previously unused lakefront property
    d. to rebuild the urban landscape with grand boulevards, imposing squares, monumental buildings, and extensive recreational facilities, and thereby restore the public's pride in metropolitan America

65. The "Wisconsin Idea" referred to

    a. the new city-manager and commission forms of municipal government.

    b. the attempts of Midwest progressives to limit immigration, stop prostitution, and prohibit the sale of liquor.

    c. the municipal ownership of public utilities advocated by Mayor Tom Johnson.

    d. the program of economic and political reforms by state government pioneered by Governor Robert La Follette.

d
SG

66. To a middle-class American living around 1910, which of the following statements would reveal the most about the morality of the movies?

    a. Movies were typically shown in immigrant-district nickelodeons.

    b. One of the first movies to tell a real story was called *The Great Train Robbery*.

    c. Theda Bara was actually Theodosia Goodman, the daughter of a Cincinnati tailor.

    d. Films were made for commercial profit.

a

67. The Mann Act of 1910

    a. established the Pure Food and Drug Administration.

    b. made it a federal crime to transport a woman across a state line for immoral purposes.

    c. limited unions' right to set up boycotts in support of strikes.

    d. none of the above

b

68. What was the fundamental difference between the temperance movement in the Progressive Era and the temperance crusades of earlier eras?

    a. Progressive reformers had greater faith in human nature and therefore believed that temperance could be achieved if individual drunkards abandoned their alcoholic ways.

    b. Temperance in the Progressive Era was a purely secular movement because Protestant minsters refused to have anything to do with typical progressive leaders.

    c. The progressive movement focused on legal abolition of alcohol rather than the persuasion of individual drunkards to "take the pledge."

    d. Progressive Era temperance work stayed on a state and local level and avoided the national political arena.

c

69. Why did many progressives advocate restricting immigration to the United States?

    a. They believed that the typical recent immigrant was a hairy, low-browed, big-faced person of obviously low mentality.

    b. They believed that urban planners had to be given time to clear the slums and redesign the boulevards so that immigrants would see America at its best.

    c. They believed that it was cruel to allow immigrants to come to America if they were going to have to work in unhealthy factories.

    d. They feared that immigrants would support labor unions and thereby reduce the influence of individual progressive organizations.

a

70. Which of the following is *not* representative of progressive attitudes toward blacks?   **b**
    a. the argument that granting women the vote would strengthen white supremacy by doubling the white vote
    b. Mary White Ovington's study of blacks in New York City, *Half a Man*
    c. Woodrow Wilson's admiration for the D. W. Griffith epic, *The Birth of a Nation*
    d. the typical reaction progressives had to the lynching, disfranchising, and discrimination that blacks faced

71. Booker T. Washington believed that the best way for blacks to improve their status in the United States was to   **c**
    a. struggle militantly against all forms of racial discrimination in order to gain educational opportunity.
    b. form a nationwide council to work for federal laws against lynching.
    c. accommodate themselves to segregation and disfranchisement while at the same time working hard and proving their economic value to society.
    d. leave the United States and return to their African origins.

72. W. E. B. Du Bois is best known for his book   **a**
    a. *The Souls of Black Folk.*
    b. *The Passing of the Great Race.*
    c. *Up from Slavery.*
    d. *How the Other Half Lives.*

73. Who was a white leader of the movement for black rights during the early decades of the twentieth century?   **b**
    a. Ida Wells-Barnett
    b. Oswald Garrison Villard
    c. Woodrow Wilson
    d. Charles B. Davenport

74. All of the following were leaders of the woman-suffrage movement *except*:   **c**
    a. Carrie Chapman Catt
    b. Susan B. Anthony
    c. Josephine Dodge
    d. Alice Paul

75. Which of the following statements most accurately compares the strategies of Carrie Chapman Catt and Alice Paul?   **b**
    a. Paul opposed woman suffrage, arguing that women already had vast behind-the-scenes influence; Catt led the struggle for woman suffrage.
    b. They both favored woman suffrage, but Paul advocated direct pressure on the federal government for a constitutional amendment, while Catt's strategy included lobbying legislators on a state-by-state basis.
    c. They both favored woman suffrage, and they both agreed on a militant two-pronged strategy that included simultaneous lobbying of both state and federal legislators.
    d. none of the above

76. Which of the following women is *not* properly paired with her reform activity?   **d**
    a. Florence Kelley: federal child-labor laws
    b. Margaret Sanger: birth control
    c. Charlotte Perkins Gilman: equality in the workplace, consolidation of domestic tasks, and state-run day-care centers
    d. Emma Goldman: work-related diseases and health hazards

77. In the coal strike of 1902, Theodore Roosevelt   **c**
                                                      SG
    a. followed Cleveland's precedent of deploying federal troops.
    b. refused to intervene.
    c. insisted that labor and management submit the dispute to arbitration.
    d. sided with the employers against the union.

78. "Corporations and combinations have become indispensable in the business world . . . it is folly to try to prohibit them, but it is also folly to leave them without thoroughgoing control." This quotation summarizes the position on the big-business question of which politician?   **c**
                                                                                   SG
    a. Woodrow Wilson
    b. William McKinley
    c. Theodore Roosevelt
    d. Robert La Follette

79. The Elkins and Hepburn acts   **a**
    a. strengthened the Interstate Commerce Act of 1887 by raising penalties and increasing the regulatory powers of the Interstate Commerce Commission.
    b. reversed the breakup of the Standard Oil Company.
    c. instituted strict regulation of the meatpacking industry.
    d. established the Federal Reserve System.

80. What helped to bring about the passage in 1906 of the Pure Food and Drug Act and the Meat Inspection Act?   **d**
    a. the revelation that Colden's Liquid Beef Tonic contained 26.5 percent alcohol
    b. the disgusting descriptions in *The Jungle*
    c. proregulation pressure from the larger food-processing, meatpacking, and medicinal companies
    d. all of the above

81. Who said, "I aimed at the nation's heart, but hit it in the stomach"?   d
    a. Theodore Roosevelt about the four-way election of 1912
    b. Alice Paul, about the practical impact of her campaign for woman suffrage
    c. John D. Rockefeller, about his sponsorship of medical research on venereal disease
    d. Upton Sinclair, about the revolting descriptions in his novel *The Jungle*

82. What might be considered Theodore Roosevelt's most enduring domestic legacy?   a
    a. increased public interest in environmental conservation
    b. halting the growth of large and monopolistic corporations
    c. improving racial attitudes in Washington, D.C.
    d. cementing the relationship between capital and labor

83. Which of the following was *not* one of the causes for the growing split in the   b
    Republican party during the administration of William Howard Taft?
    a. Taft's abandonment of the fight for tariff reduction
    b. Taft's refusal to pursue further antitrust cases
    c. Taft's support of Uncle Joe Cannon
    d. the firing of Gifford Pinchot

84. Which of the candidates in the 1912 presidential election advocated the most far-   d
    reaching changes for American society?
    a. Theodore Roosevelt
    b. Woodrow Wilson
    c. William Howard Taft
    d. Eugene Debs

85. The Federal Reserve Act, signed into law by Woodrow Wilson, provided for   a
    a. a decentralized system that was under both public and private control.
    b. a decentralized system that was completely in private hands but was regulated by the government.
    c. a largely centralized system that was completely under government control.
    d. a centralized system under private control with no branches.

86. All of the following were reform measures enacted in the Wilson administration   b
    except the
    a. Federal Trade Commission Act.
    b. National Reclamation Act.
    c. Federal Reserve Act.
    d. Clayton Antitrust Act.

87. The significance of Louis Brandeis's appointment to the Supreme Court lay in the   c fact that
    a. President Wilson was willing to stand by him despite the fierce battle over his nomination.
    b. bigotry was discovered for the first time to exist in the high reaches of the federal government.
    c. Brandeis's innovative approach to the law implicitly advocated making the legal system more responsive to new social realities.
    d. President Wilson demonstrated himself to be without prejudice because he was willing to nominate a Jew to the Court.

ESSAY QUESTIONS

---

88. Compare the conditions of black Americans in the North and the South during the Progressive Era. Compare the approaches of Booker T. Washington and W. E. B. Du Bois in dealing with those conditions. What forms of black culture evolved during these years? What organizations did blacks form? What were the attitudes of progressives toward the plight of blacks? Were the problems of blacks handled differently at the federal, state, and local levels?

89. According to progressives, what factory conditions needed reform? Why did   PT diverse groups—political bosses, some business leaders, and immigrant groups— support reform? Why did many business leaders argue that reform was unnecessary? Give examples of specific reforms.

90. What were the different strands of the American labor movement during the early decades of the twentieth century? How did the goals of various unions differ? What were the most important successes and the most important failures of the labor movement during this period, and why?

91. What kinds of Americans made up the ranks of the progressive movement? What were their intellectual and ideological origins? What were their political and social goals? What sorts of organizations did they form? Evaluate their "scientific" approach to solving social problems. How did they spread the progressive reform message to the American people?

92. What were the economic, social, environmental, and political goals of the progressive municipal reformers? To what extent were they successful?

93. "Progressive social thought included a number of disturbing ingredients—an assurance of moral and intellectual superiority, an exaggerated confidence in the social applications of science, an uncritical acceptance of the use of state power to coerce individual behavior—that all too readily could turn repressive and destructive." Explain and evaluate this statement.

94. What were the principal reform activities that women engaged in during the Progressive Era? Why did the woman suffrage movement, especially, receive a boost during this period? Who were the leaders of the suffrage movement, and how did their goals and techniques differ? How did these reform activities begin to change the cultural assumptions about woman's proper sphere?

95. Explain why you agree or disagree with the following statement about progressive SG reform: "The Roosevelt Era . . . had been a period of beginnings, of a scattering of pioneer legislation . . . . The Wilson Era, building on this foundation, was a period of sweeping achievement." Back what you say with as much specific evidence as possible.

96. Compare Theodore Roosevelt and Woodrow Wilson as representatives of two strains of national progressivism. Compare their personalities, their political techniques, and their political, economic, and social goals and philosophies. Which of the two men was more conservative, which more progressive?

97. Discuss the legacy of progressivism in terms of the new view of government that the movement legitimized for large numbers of Americans. In what sense was progressivism part of an American ideological tradition, but with a new twist?

CHAPTER 22

World War I

IDENTIFICATIONS

Identify the following. Be as specific as possible, and include names, dates, and relevant facts as appropriate. Be sure to explain the *significance* of the person or term.

1. Roosevelt Corollary to the Monroe Doctrine

2. gentlemen's agreement

3. Great White Fleet

4. dollar diplomacy

5. Pancho Villa and Black Jack Pershing

6. *Lusitania* notes

7. National Security League and the preparedness movement

8. *Arabic* and *Sussex* pledges

9. Charles Evans Hughes

10. Zimmermann Telegram

11. Selective Service Act of 1917

12. Bernard Baruch and the War Industries Board

13. Herbert Hoover and the Food Administration

14. Liberty Loans

15. George Creel, Committee on Public Information

16. Jeannette Rankin

17. Randolph Bourne

18. Espionage Act of 1917

19. *Schenck* v. *United States*

20. East St. Louis and Chicago race riots

21. Nineteenth Amendment

22. Eighteenth Amendment

23. Fourteen Points

24. Meuse-Argonne campaign

25. Versailles treaty

26. League of Nations

27. Henry Cabot Lodge

28. A. Mitchell Palmer and the Red Scare

MULTIPLE-CHOICE QUESTIONS

Choose the answer that *best* completes the statement or answers the question.

29. The Roosevelt Corollary   a
    SG

    a. claimed that the United States had the right to act as a policeman in Latin America to keep order and prevent chronic wrongdoing.

    b. was issued to justify the role the United States played in ending the Russo-Japanese War.

    c. reversed that part of the Monroe Doctrine that stated the United States would not intervene in European affairs.

    d. warned the European powers and Japan not to exclude American business interests from China.

30. A practical demonstration of the principles that Theodore Roosevelt announced to   b
Congress in December 1904 can be seen in events in the Dominican Republic, where the United States

    a. supported a revolution to oust the repressive dictator and institute a liberal democracy.

    b. operated the customs service and took over the management of the foreign debt.

    c. invited two rival powers to a peace conference at Portsmouth, New Hampshire.

    d. sent in twenty-five hundred marines to protect American investments.

31. Theodore Roosevelt's reaction to the Russo-Japanese War included all of the following *except*:   c

    a. he was pleased to see Russian expansionism checked
    b. he was concerned that a Russian defeat would disrupt the balance of power
       in the Far East
    c. he wished to strengthen the balance of power by encouraging Japanese
       expansion in the Far East
    d. he wanted the two sides to negotiate a settlement

32. The "gentlemen's agreement" was   d

    a. an understanding between Theodore Roosevelt and J. P. Morgan on regula-
       tion of the trusts.
    b. an agreement between the leaders of the United States, Great Britain, and
       Germany on the territorial integrity of China.
    c. an agreement between Woodrow Wilson and William Jennings Bryan over the
       formulation of foreign policy.
    d. an arrangement in which Japan agreed to end emigration of Japanese labor-
       ers to the United States.

33. President Taft's "dollar diplomacy" can be seen in American actions in   a

    a. Nicaragua.
    b. Mexico.
    c. Japan.
    d. Germany.

34. Which of the following statements about Woodrow Wilson's Latin American policy   b
    is *not* correct?

    a. He pledged never again to seek one additional foot of territory by conquest.
    b. He sent marines to Nicaragua to punish the Sandinistas for an attack on an
       American-owned plantation.
    c. He sent marines to Santo Domingo to restore stability and protect American
       investments.
    d. He used American troops to force a Mexican leader to abdicate.

35. Which of the following best describes Woodrow Wilson's policy toward Mexico?   c

    a. cautious concern about upsetting the balance of power south of the border
    b. idealistic plans for encouraging political and social democracy
    c. moralistic pronouncements backed by military force
    d. a refusal to have anything to do with Mexico until the Mexican people
       learned to elect good leaders

36. What was the initial reaction of most Americans to the outbreak of World War I in   a
    Europe?

    a. They wanted to ensure that the United States could stay out of the conflict.
    b. They wanted the United States to declare war against Germany.
    c. They didn't care because the United States had no ties to Europe.
    d. They gleefully saw the war as a golden opportunity for American business to
       make money.

37. What was President Wilson's first official response when war broke out in Europe in 1914?   **c**
    a. He announced a blockade of Europe on behalf of the Allied Powers.
    b. He announced an embargo of all American products, so that the United States would not repeat the mistakes of the War of 1812.
    c. He announced a declaration of neutrality and called on the nation to be neutral in thought as well as action.
    d. He announced a preparedness campaign in order to promote armaments and military training.

38. After the American declaration of neutrality in 1914,   **d**
    a. Britain mined the North Sea and announced that it was to be considered a war zone.
    b. Germany used torpedo-equipped submarines to interfere with American shipping.
    c. The British interfered with American shipping bound for Germany.
    d. all of the above

39. In the *Lusitania* notes,   **a**
    a. the United States demanded that Germany cease unrestricted submarine warfare.
    b. Germany cautioned Americans against traveling on British or French vessels.
    c. the United States announced its intention to go to war to defend its rights as a neutral country.
    d. Germany announced its intention of resuming unrestricted submarine warfare.

40. All of the following opposed American participation in World War I *except*:   **b**
                                                                                          SG
    a. Jane Addams
    b. John Dewey
    c. Eugene Debs
    d. Randolph Bourne

41. The members of the preparedness movement advocated   **c**
    a. preventing Americans from traveling on foreign ships.
    b. an international denunciation of war as immoral.
    c. rearmament and universal military training.
    d. neutral mediation of the war to end it by Christmas.

42. Secretary of State William J. Bryan resigned because   **b**
                                                                   SG
    a. he felt Wilson should have asked for a declaration of war after Germany sank the *Lusitania*.
    b. he believed Wilson's *Lusitania* notes and insistence that Germany stop unrestricted submarine warfare would embroil us in the war.
    c. he wanted Wilson to protest more strongly against British violation of American neutrality.
    d. he wanted to challenge Wilson for the presidential nomination in 1916.

43. Why did the United States begin to lend money to the European powers after
    August 1915?   d

    a. The Wilson administration believed that it had to make more than just a sym-
       bolic show of support for the Central Powers.
    b. Respected legal authorities in the United States had decided that neutrality
       regulations did not apply to financial loans.
    c. Theodore Roosevelt had convinced Woodrow Wilson that the United States
       had to do everything in its power short of war to ensure Allied victory.
    d. The Wilson administration feared the economic, financial, and social conse-
       quences of American industry failing to secure European business.

44. Which of the following nations had the most effective propaganda campaign dur-
    ing World War I?   a

    a. Great Britain
    b. Germany
    c. France
    d. none of the above

45. The main issue in the 1916 presidential elections was   b

    a. progressive reform.
    b. the war in Europe.
    c. Philippine independence.
    d. the personal ethics of Charles Evans Hughes.

46. The Germans resumed unrestricted submarine warfare because they believed it
    would   c

    a. keep the United States out of the war.
    b. make Great Britain declare war on the United States.
    c. help them achieve victory before American troops reached the front.
    d. force the United States to officially declare war.

47. Germany alienated sentiment in the United States in all of the following ways
    except: d

    a. financing espionage in American war plants
    b. sinking American merchant ships
    c. promising Mexico the return of Texas, Arizona, and New Mexico
    d. making secret contributions to the campaign of Charles Evans Hughes

48. The United States was drawn into World War I because of   d

    a. economic investments in the Allied cause.
    b. American cultural links to England.
    c. German attacks on American shipping.
    d. all of the above

49. When the United States entered World War I, the American army was   **a**
    - a. woefully unprepared, with little combat experience and an aging officer corps.
    - b. at its peak of fighting form after a year-long preparedness campaign.
    - c. staffed mainly with green draftees.
    - d. staffed with recruits and draftees drawn only from young men with the highest IQs.

50. The War Industries Board   **d**
    - a. allocated raw materials.
    - b. established production priorities.
    - c. coordinated competing businesses.
    - d. all of the above

51. In order to manage the nation's agriculture during World War I, Herbert Hoover   **c**
    - a. instituted strict government controls over what was grown and what consumers were able to purchase.
    - b. withheld meat, wheat, and sugar from the Allies as a form of political pressure.
    - c. employed a combination of propaganda and voluntary efforts to assure adequate food supplies.
    - d. acted as a private watchdog to prevent the government from interfering with private agricultural initiative.

52. The Woman's Land Army was   **a**
    - a. a corps of volunteer farmers organized to replaced drafted males.
    - b. a female contingent of the American Expeditionary Force.
    - c. a group of women who ran the railroads under the U.S. Railroad Administration.
    - d. the nickname for the American nursing corps at the front.

53. Which of the following statements best indicates the policy that the United States government followed toward business during World War I?   **b**
    - a. The government busted more trusts during the war years than in the preceding dozen years.
    - b. The government nationalized the railroads and created 5,000 government agencies to supervise home-front activities.
    - c. The government believed that the war for democracy would be won by showing the world that private industry could do the job without regulation.
    - d. The government imposed many new regulations on business and industry but supervised them with a minimum of bureaucracy.

54. Which of the following statements about the experiences of blacks during World   **b**
War I is correct?   **SG**

    a. Black soldiers found the French even more racist than American whites were.
    b. Black soldiers served in segregated regiments and divisions.
    c. Blacks found it impossible to get jobs in northern industry.
    d. Blacks followed the advice of Booker T. Washington to "put down their buckets where they were," and for that reason few moved north.

55. What message did the Wilson administration drum into American citizens during   **a**
World War I?

    a. If you weren't in the armed forces, you'd better be buying war bonds, and if you weren't buying war bonds, you were pro-German.
    b. The war for democracy could best be won in an atmosphere of complete free speech and thought.
    c. The war had to be financed only through voluntary purchases of bonds, not through involuntary taxes, since some Americans opposed the war.
    d. all of the above

56. The Creel Committee on Public Information   **b**

    a. was established by Woodrow Wilson to ensure that the American people had access to the full truth about the war.
    b. used propaganda to warn against spreading pessimistic stories about the war.
    c. was a propaganda agency secretly sponsored by the German foreign ministry.
    d. attempted to turn public opinion against immigrants by painting them as agents of foreign revolution.

57. Generally, what attitude did most American intellectuals, cultural leaders, and   **c**
reformers have about United States participation in World War I?

    a. They were opposed because they believed that the war was a dirty and cruel business.
    b. Because they had supported President Wilson in his domestic crusades, they now felt obliged to support him in his international crusade.
    c. They saw the war as a struggle to defend culture and believed that increased government activism during wartime would lead to increased reform at home.
    d. They tended to oppose the war because they believed that German culture was superior and the German social-welfare system more humane.

58. During World War I, many German-Americans   **d**

    a. fled the United States and returned to Germany to defend their relatives.
    b. enlisted in the United States Navy in order to prove their patriotism.
    c. engaged in subversive activities and terrorism on behalf of the Imperial German government.
    d. were harassed and abused, and accused by the American government of being anti-American.

59. Which of the following statements best captures Woodrow Wilson's attitude   a
    toward American pacifists during World War I?

    a. He had contempt for their stupidity.
    b. He believed that they were, at heart, German spies.
    c. He admired their idealism and logic.
    d. He hoped that their voices of dissent would keep American resolve pure and
       strong.

60. What do Randolph Bourne, Jeannette Rankin, and Eugene V. Debs have in   b
    common?

    a. They were all pro-German.
    b. They were all opposed to World War I.
    c. They all worked for the Creel Committee.
    d. They were all convicted of advocating socialism.

61. In the case of *Schenck* v. *United States* the Supreme Court   b
                                                                       SG
    a. held that the U.S. Railroad Administration had acted unconstitutionally in tak-
       ing over privately owned rail lines.
    b. upheld convictions under the Espionage Act on the ground that the gov-
       ernment could curtail free speech when exercise of it presented a "clear and
       present danger" to the country.
    c. ruled that segregated facilities for whites and blacks were acceptable as long
       as the accommodations were equal.
    d. held that the federal government did *not* have the right to propagandize
       American citizens as George Creel's Committee on Public Information was
       doing.

62. Which statement most accurately reflects the situation facing organized labor dur-   c
    ing World War I?

    a. Wartime pressures brought about a record number of strikes.
    b. In an effort to ensure ideological conformity and to prevent dissent, the
       National War Labor Board generally pursued anti-labor policies.
    c. Union membership nearly doubled during the war.
    d. Because of the booming wartime economy and a shortage of male workers,
       most workers were required to work twelve-hour days.

63. Which of the following is true about the American economy during World War I?   d

    a. Factory production increased by one-third.
    b. Prices rose by 60 percent.
    c. Cigarette consumption increased 350 percent.
    d. all of the above

64. Which of the following would you *not* have been likely to find in a typical Ameri-   a
    can industrial center like Bridgeport, Connecticut, in 1916?   PT

    a. peaceful labor-management relations
    b. rapid factory expansion
    c. a boom mentality among the people
    d. hostility to recent immigrants

65. Why did black Americans migrate to northern cities during World War I?   c
    a. The federal government had used the wartime emergency as an opportunity to end southern sharecropping.
    b. Southern blacks knew that race relations in the North were idyllic compared with those in the South.
    c. They were seeking the economic opportunities afforded by northern industrial expansion.
    d. They knew of the northern race riots and decided to move north to help their brothers.

66. World War I affected American women in all the following ways *except*:   c
    a. thousands of women were able to serve in the military at home and in France
    b. a million women worked in industry during the years 1917–1918
    c. hundreds of thousands of women entered the work force for the first time and developed new careers for the future
    d. a constitutional amendment was ratified giving women the right to vote

67. Why did temperance advocates receive a boost from World War I?   d
    a. They pointed out that the biggest breweries—like Pabst, Schlitz, and Anheuser-Busch—had German names.
    b. They said it was unpatriotic to use grain to manufacture whiskey and gin at a time when food had to be conserved.
    c. They said that beer was a German plot to undermine America's moral fiber and fighting qualities.
    d. all of the above

68. The Fourteen Points were   a
    a. Woodrow Wilson's statement of American war aims.
    b. Herbert Hoover's guidelines for conserving food.
    c. the Russian Bolsheviks' conditions for not revealing the secret treaties made prior to 1914.
    d. the Creel Committee's guidelines for censorship.

69. Which of the following was *not* one of the reasons that Woodrow Wilson's efforts   d
    at the Versailles Peace Conference were hampered even before he left the United States?
    a. Wilson decided to go to the conference personally.
    b. The Democrats lost control of Congress in the November elections.
    c. Wilson failed to appoint any prominent Republicans to the peace commission.
    d. The Germans had already rejected the Fourteen Points as a basis of negotiations.

70. The Versailles treaty   c
    a. was the embodiment of Woodrow Wilson's vision of a liberal peace.
    b. was agreed upon after brief and harmonious negotiations.
    c. was harshly punitive in that it stripped Germany of territory and saddled that country with immense reparations.
    d. showed the desire of the western powers to integrate the new Russian government into the international system.

71. After the armistice, some members of the American Expeditionary Force went to   d
    Russia to
    a. join the Bolsheviks in establishing a new world order.
    b. train Russian soldiers so that they could contain Germany.
    c. demonstrate the warm relations that existed between the United States and Russia.
    d. assist Russian forces attempting to overthrow Lenin.

72. In the debate over the ratification of the Versailles treaty, what was the position of   b
    the group led by Henry Cabot Lodge?
    a. no treaty under any circumstances
    b. a treaty with significant modifications
    c. a treaty with minor changes
    d. a treaty exactly as Wilson presented it

73. In the two years after the conclusion of World War I, which of the following   a
    occurred in the United States?
    a. wide-scale harassment of suspected radicals, violence against blacks, and a rash of strikes
    b. a resurgence of the liberal reform spirit of the prewar years
    c. a renewed commitment to the Wilsonian vision of a liberal democratic world
    d. the political vindication of Woodrow Wilson at the polls

74. The presidential election of 1920 demonstrated that   c
    a. the American people still loved Woodrow Wilson.
    b. the spirit of reform was still alive.
    c. the nation was spiritually drained and wanted normalcy.
    d. the people were tired of Wilson but wanted the League.

ESSAY QUESTIONS

75. The text characterizes Theodore Roosevelt's foreign policy as a "balance-of-power chess game," William Howard Taft's as a "concentration on business opportunities," and Woodrow Wilson's as a policy of "moralism." Discuss those evaluations by discussing the Roosevelt, Taft, and Wilson policies regarding Japan, China, Latin America, and the Caribbean.

76. In 1914 Woodrow Wilson proclaimed American neutrality and asked the American   SG
people to be neutral in thought as well as action. In April 1917 Wilson asked
Congress to declare war on Germany. What brought about this turnaround in
American policy toward World War I?

77. What were the experiences of American soldiers during World War I? How did
army life and training change the outlook of hundreds of thousands of Americans?
Why were these new experiences important?

78. Explain how the United States government exercised unprecedented control over
the American economy during World War I. Give examples. Why were these con-
trols accepted? What precedent did they establish?

79. World War I had a dramatic impact on life at home. Discuss the impact—both   PT
positive and negative—that it had on blacks, women, workers, and farmers. Use
Bridgeport, Connecticut, as an example of the way that the war disrupted American life.

80. Why were propaganda, thought control, and repression used with such success in
the United States during World War I? Was ideological conformity necessary? Was
repression necessary? What would have happened if opponents of the war had
been allowed to present their views without restrictions? What does your text
mean when it speaks of the "dark underside of the war spirit"?

81. Once the United States had entered World War I, what were its goals? How did
Wilson's Fourteen Points set forth broad-ranging and idealistic goals for a new
world? Did Wilson—and the United States—achieve those goals? Why or why
not?

82. To what extent was Woodrow Wilson successful in shaping the Versailles treaty?
What could he have done to produce a different treaty? Should Wilson have been
more realistic about what he could accomplish at Versailles?

83. Why did Woodrow Wilson view the League of Nations as the cornerstone of his
new liberal world order? What actions did he take to get the League approved?
Why was it rejected? Who was to blame? What was the role of Henry Cabot
Lodge? What were Lodge's reservations? What would the changes have done to
the League if they had been approved?

84. How did the war further the goals of progressivism and yet also undermine its best
side? How do you account for the race riots and Red Scare that occurred at the
end of the war?

MAP QUESTIONS

Choose the letter on the accompanying map of the world that correctly identifies each of the following:

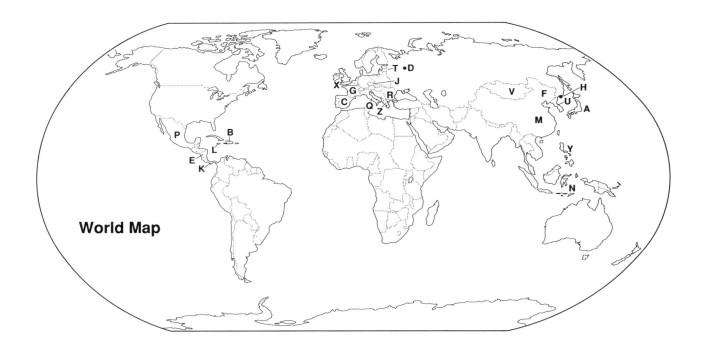

World Map

85. Dominican Republic and Haiti   **B**

86. Alsace and Lorraine   **X**

87. Nicaragua   **E**

88. Mexico   **P**

89. Manchuria   **F**

90. China   **M**

91. Korea   **U**

92. Japan   **A**

93. the Balkans   **R**

94. Italy   **Q**

95. Vladivostok, Russia   **H**

96. Czechoslovakia   **J**

97. Estonia, Latvia, Lithuania   **T**

CHAPTER 23

The 1920s

IDENTIFICATIONS

Identify the following. Be as specific as possible, and include names, dates, and relevant facts as appropriate. Be sure to explain the *significance* of the person or term.

1. "American Plan"

2. McNary-Haugen bill

3. "Teapot Dome"

4. the Washington Naval Arms Conference

5. Kellogg-Briand Pact

6. Sheppard-Towner Act

7. Charles A. Lindbergh

8. F. Scott Fitzgerald

9. Sinclair Lewis

10. Harlem Renaissance

11. *Birth of a Nation*

12. Marcus Garvey

13. fundamentalism

14. the Scopes Trial

15. Billy Sunday

16. Al Capone

17. Alice Paul

18. Ty Cobb, the Georgia Peach

19. Nicola Sacco and Bartolomeo Vanzetti

20. Aimee Semple McPherson

MULTIPLE-CHOICE QUESTIONS

Choose the answer that *best* completes the statement or answers the question.

21. Commerce in the 1920s was increasingly characterized by   **b**
    a. the thriving of "mom and pop" businesses and other independent entrepreneurs.
    b. a chain-store invasion in which "mom and pop" businesses had to compete with consolidated corporations.
    c. the establishment of cooperatives owned and operated by workers and consumers.
    d. the increase of women-owned businesses as American women took more control over consumerism.

22. By the mid-1920s, the use of electricity was   **b**
    a. still insignificant as many people resisted "new-fangled" appliances.
    b. becoming common as 60 percent of new homes were wired for electricity.
    c. nearly universal in the United States.
    d. mostly used in factory production.

23. In the 1920s the automobile   **d**
    a. was still just a plaything of the rich.
    b. lost much of its potential market as people turned to the new forms of mass transit available.
    c. was produced mostly for the overseas market since Americans could not afford the high-priced American models.
    d. saw a big increase in popularity, with vehicle registrations jumping from 8 million in 1920 to 27 million in 1929.

24. In the 1920s American investments in foreign production   **a**
    a. increased as American corporations invested abroad to supply overseas markets efficiently and acquire raw materials.
    b. decreased as investment opportunities in United States production grew.
    c. were outlawed in order to keep the American dollar at home.
    d. decreased, particularly in Latin America, because foreign governments began to nationalize their industries.

25. All the following contributed to the general prosperity of the 1920s *except*:   b

    a. the development of new consumer goods industries, especially home electrical appliances   SG

    b. federal minimum-wage laws that saw to it that workers were well paid, and thus had additional purchasing power

    c. the growth of the automobile industry

    d. a marked increase in productivity brought about by new technology and industrial techniques such as the moving assembly line.

26. The search for greater integration in the corporate order in the 1920s was expressed by all the following *except*:   a

    SG

    a. hiring more blacks in management positions

    b. the formation of trade associations

    c. a more bureaucratic management structure

    d. the consolidation of public utilities

27. Henry Ford "led the way" in industry by   c

    a. pioneering a style of management which delegated corporate decisions to professionals in specialized divisions.

    b. instituting worker-management teams to share decision making about production.

    c. paying his workers high wages to encourage consumerism.

    d. paying his workers low wages to increase the profit margin.

28. Which statement best describes the post–World War I American attitude toward businessmen?   a

    a. Post-war America venerated the magnates of business.

    b. Americans considered corporate leaders to be "robber barons."

    c. There was a growing hostility to the growth of the "military-industrial complex."

    d. Post-war America held businessmen in contempt as war profiteers.

29. Bruce Barton's *The Man Nobody Knows* was about   b

    a. Henry Ford, who was considered a secretive man.

    b. Jesus Christ, as a managerial genius who organized the twelve apostles.

    c. "the Common Man," who advertisers would have to study in order to understand his needs and fantasies.

    d. Warren Harding, who was a political unknown when he ran for president.

30. Women in the work force in the 1920s   c

    a. swelled the union movement.

    b. found increased job opportunities on assembly lines.

    c. faced systematic wage discrimination.

    d. increased proportionally so that almost half of women were working outside the home.

31. Which of the following statements about industrial workers in the 1920s is   a
    correct?   SG
    a. The wages of unskilled labor increased very little during the decade.
    b. More workers than ever before in American history belonged to unions by
       1929.
    c. Regional wage differences between North and South largely disappeared dur-
       ing the decade.
    d. In the 1920s, for the first time, the majority of industrial workers were
       female.

32. The union movement weakened in the 1920s because   d
    a. overall wage rates rose steadily in the 1920s.
    b. the older craft-based pattern of union organization was ill-suited to the new
       mass-production industries.
    c. management was hostile to labor organizing.
    d. all of the above

33. "Welfare capitalism" refers to   a
    a. corporations providing employee benefits in the hope of preventing the
       establishment of unions.
    b. the high rate of unemployment in the 1920s, when many people had to go on
       welfare.
    c. the trade-union philosophy that the welfare of the workers should be the first
       concern of capitalism.
    d. none of the above

34. Which sector of the economy did not prosper in the 1920s?   b
    a. manufacturing
    b. agriculture
    c. the "service" sector
    d. financial services

35. All the following are associated with the Harding administration *except*:   d
                                                                                    SG
    a. the Teapot Dome scandal
    b. the Washington Naval Arms Conference
    c. probusiness policies such as raising tariff rates
    d. passage of the McNary-Haugen Act to raise farm prices

36. In the 1920s the Supreme Court overturned several progressive reform measures   c
    including
    a. the Smoot-Hawley Tariff.
    b. a price-support plan to help the American farmer by purchasing farm sur-
       pluses.
    c. a law imposing a punitive tax on the products of child labor.
    d. "The American Plan."

37. Which of the following does *not* demonstrate Coolidge's "hands-off" philosophy   b
    of government?
    a. his reaction of aid to Mississippi River flood victims
    b. his support of high protective tariffs
    c. his veto of the McNary-Haugen farm bill
    d. none of the above

38. The Washington Naval Arms Conference was   a
    a. a significant early arms-control effort.
    b. where the Kellogg-Briand Pact was signed.
    c. typical of the isolationist foreign policy of the 1920s.
    d. responsible for the escalation of the arms race among the United States,
       Great Britain, and Japan.

39. In the election of 1924,   c
    a. Catholicism and prohibition were the two big issues.   SG
    b. the Democratic presidential nominee, John W. Davis, won by a narrow mar-
       gin over the Republican, Calvin Coolidge.
    c. labor, farm, and reform groups revived the Progressive party and ran Robert
       La Follette for president.
    d. the Democratic party nominated William Jennings Bryan for president for the
       fourth time.

40. An Equal Rights Amendment advocated by Alice Paul and the National Woman's   d
    party
    a. unified the feminist movement in the 1920s, which had become splintered
       after women won the vote.
    b. attracted the support of young women, who looked up to the feminists for
       their civic idealism.
    c. was supported by an alliance of professional women and labor activists.
    d. was opposed by most feminists.

41. The Sheppard-Towner Act   d
    a. appropriated funds for rural prenatal and baby-care centers staffed by public-
       health nurses.
    b. was supported by President Harding.
    c. was denounced by the American Medical Association.
    d. all of the above

42. The decade of the 1920s was the first one in which   c
    a. farmers drove down agricultural prices by producing a surplus.   SG
    b. the majority of Americans worked in factories rather than on farms.
    c. the majority of Americans lived in cities.
    d. the majority of Americans owned televisions.

43. Housework in the 1920s   **b**
    a. was made easier for middle-class housewives because they were able to hire immigrant women and farm girls for household help.
    b. was reduced in terms of hours and sheer physical effort thanks to electrification, store-bought clothing, and purchased food.
    c. was "socialized" through cooperative apartments, commercial laundries, and other collective forms of housework.
    d. increased because industrialization and crowded urban conditions made homes dirtier.

44. The automobile affected American life by   **d**
    a. giving young people freedom from parental oversight.
    b. breaking down the isolation of rural life.
    c. letting the prosperous move out to the suburbs, leaving the urban poor behind in the inner cities.
    d. all of the above

45. In the 1920s, mass culture, such as magazines, books, radio, and movies,   **a**
    a. became increasingly standardized as the same amusements were available in all parts of the country.
    b. still retained regional favor in the South, New England, the Southwest, and other areas with strong cultural traditions.
    c. was available only to the middle class, who could afford it.
    d. was strongly influenced by the radical, bohemian art world.

46. The glorification of celebrities in the 1920s was expressed in all the following ways *except*:   **c**
    a. celebrity endorsements of products in advertising
    b. the idolization of sports celebrities
    c. the popularity of "Amos and Andy"
    d. the hero worship of Charles A. Lindbergh

47. The "sexual revolution" of the 1920s   **b**
    a. led to a significant increase in premarital sex.
    b. resulted in the new custom of casual dating.
    c. eradicated the "double standard" of sexual behavior for men and women.
    d. led to a significant increase in the divorce rate.

48. The stereotype of the Jazz Age "flapper"   **a**
    a. epitomized the rebelliousness of the youth culture of the 1920s.
    b. found its greatest realization in the Harlem Renaissance.
    c. was the "spiritual sister" of the suffragist since both suffragists and flappers supported feminist political action.
    d. originated with a drawing by cartoonist Thomas Nast.

49. Which three writers expressed hostility to the moralistic pieties of the old order   d
    and the business pieties of the new?
    a. Bruce Barton, Theodore Dreiser, and Ernest Hemingway
    b. H. L. Mencken, Willa Cather, and Horatio Alger
    c. William Jennings Bryan, H. L. Mencken, and Sinclair Lewis
    d. F. Scott Fitzgerald, Sinclair Lewis, and H. L. Mencken

50. The musical style which epitomized the 1920s was   c
    a. swing.
    b. ragtime.
    c. jazz.
    d. the blues.

51. All the following scientific achievements occurred in the 1920s *except*:   c
    a. discovery of a cure for polio
    b. the first successful launch of a liquid-fuel rocket
    c. discovery of how to create Vitamin D in milk
    d. the first long-range television transmission

52. The Harlem Renaissance of the 1920s   d
    a. witnessed the flowering of black culture, particularly among writers.
    b. depended heavily on white patronage.
    c. had little contact with the black masses.
    d. all of the above

53. The United States immigration policy in 1924   b
    a. restricted immigration from French Canada and Latin America.
    b. was formulated to reduce the influx of immigrants from southern and eastern
       Europe.
    c. limited Asian immigrants through the use of quotas.
    d. opened up all former restrictions on immigration to attract workers for the
       expanding economy.

54. All the following statements are true about the Ku Klux Klan in the 1920s *except*:   c
    a. The Klan was made up of ordinary Americans.
    b. The Klan targeted blacks, Catholics, or Jews, depending on the region.
    c. The Klan dropped the elaborate rituals, titles, and costumes of the Recon-
       struction era in order to attract a mass membership.
    d. Estimates of Klan membership in the 1920s range from 2 to 5 million.

55. Marcus Garvey, founder of the Universal Negro Improvement Association,   a
    advocated
    a. that blacks return to Africa.
    b. that blacks return to the rural South because northern migration had led only
       to the ghetto.
    c. the integration of blacks into white society.
    d. voter registration by blacks to exercise political power.

56. In the early 1920s religious fundamentalists focused especially on which of the fol-   c
    lowing issues?

    a. eradicating slum conditions in cities
    b. the sexual revolution
    c. the theory of evolution
    d. restricting the immigration of Catholics and Jews

57. Evangelist Aimee Semple McPherson   b

    a. confronted the American Civil Liberties Union in a conflict over the theory of
       evolution.
    b. anticipated the television evangelists of a later day in her theatrical sermons.
    c. promoted the Social Gospel, which emphasized social service.
    d. was the author of *This Side of Paradise*.

58. The Sacco-Vanzetti case exposed the divisions in American society between   d

    a. socialists and anarchists.
    b. fundamentalism and civil libertarians.
    c. immigrants and blacks.
    d. conservatives and liberals.

59. Prohibition was opposed by all the following *except*:   b

    a. Al Smith
    b. Billy Sunday
    c. immigrants
    d. college students

60. All the following were reasons why Prohibition failed *except*:   c

    a. Organized crime supplied the country with ample liquor.
    b. It proved impossible to enforce rules of behavior with which a significant
       portion of the population disagreed.
    c. The Republican party under Herbert Hoover gave prohibition only half-
       hearted support.
    d. The Prohibition Bureau was underbudgeted.

61. A prominent issue in the 1928 presidential campaign was the fear that, if elected,   a
    Al Smith would

    a. be dictated to by the Vatican.
    b. enforce prohibition.
    c. have a "kitchen cabinet" made up of women advisers.
    d. all of the above

62. Although Herbert Hoover won the 1928 election by a landslide, which of the fol-   a
    lowing voting patterns suggested "trouble to come" for the Republican party?

    a. Smith carried the nation's twelve largest cities and did well in the midwestern
       farm belt.
    b. the Socialist candidate received an unprecedented number of votes.
    c. Smith swept the "Solid South."
    d. all of the above

63. Herbert Hoover was referred to as   **b**
    a. the Great Commoner.
    b. the Great Engineer.
    c. the Lone Eagle.
    d. the Imperial Wizard.

64. The social philosophy of Herbert Hoover, as expounded in his book *American*   **c**
    Individualism,
    a. exclusively favored big business.
    b. saw unfettered competition as the life force of capitalism.
    c. advocated a cooperative, socially responsible economic order shaped by the voluntary action of capitalist leaders.
    d. advocated direct government intervention in the economy.

65. The first "talkie" was   **b**
    a. D. W. Griffith's *Birth of a Nation*.
    b. Sam Warner's *The Jazz Singer*.
    c. Cecil B. DeMille's *King of Kings*.
    d. Walt Disney's *Steamboat Willy*.

ESSAY QUESTIONS

66. Discuss how advertising and consumerism shaped life in the 1920s. Did advertising and consumerism deliver on the promises they made to Americans? How did women, blacks, and immigrants fit into the picture of American life painted by advertisers?

67. What was the predominant attitude in the 1920s toward business? How did Henry Ford epitomize the business spirit of the era? Discuss the more critical attitudes of intellectuals who did not share these business values.

68. What accounts for the economic growth and prosperity of the 1920s? Who bene-   **SG**
    fited most from that prosperity? Who did not share in it and why?

69. How did the administrations of Warren Harding and Calvin Coolidge mirror the dominant cultural mood of the 1920s? Compare their policies with Progressive Era policies. Compare Herbert Hoover's brand of Republicanism with that of Harding and Coolidge.

70. Were women emancipated in the 1920s? Discuss labor force participation, housework, politics, and cultural changes. Did woman suffrage transform politics as many feminists had hoped? Were the feminist concerns of the 1920s shared by all women—professionals, working-class women, flappers?

71. Discuss the standardization of mass culture in the 1920s, giving examples from magazines, radio, movies, music, and sports. How did the new interest in leisure reflect people's feelings about their jobs? What did the new idolization of celebrities signify about American society?

72. How widespread and important was the "revolution in manners and morals" of the 1920s? Focus particularly on the "sexual revolution," youth culture, the automobile, attitudes toward prohibition, and the attraction jazz and black culture held for some segments of white society.

73. Compare the Harlem Renaissance with the Garvey movement as expressions of black culture in the 1920s. Which movement had the larger mass following and why? What did the resurgence of the Ku Klux Klan suggest about the status of blacks in America?

74. How was the conservative tenor of the 1920s expressed in the resurgence of the Ku Klux Klan, the Scopes Trial and the resurgence of fundamentalism, the Sacco-Vanzetti case, and prohibition. How did liberals react to the conservative mood of the time?

75. Discuss how Al Smith and Herbert Hoover personified the social and cultural schisms of the 1920s. What were the important issues of the 1928 election, and what parts of the electorate supported Smith and what parts supported Hoover?

CHAPTER 24

Crash, Depression, and New Deal

IDENTIFICATIONS

Identify the following. Be as specific as possible, and include names, dates, and relevant facts as appropriate. Be sure to explain the *significance* of the person or term.

1. Black Thursday, Black Tuesday

2. Federal Reserve System

3. Milo Reno, Farmers' Holiday Association

4. the Hundred Days

5. the Civilian Conservation Corps

6. National Recovery Administration

7. Harry Hopkins

8. Tennessee Valley Authority

9. the Federal Securities Act

10. *Schechter* v. *United States*

11. the Social Security Act

12. "Okies"

13. Huey Long

14. Father Coughlin

15. Works Progress Administration

16. Public Works Administration

17. National Labor Relations Act (Wagner Act)

18. Mary McLeod Bethune

19. "Roosevelt Recession"

20. Bankhead-Jones Farm Tenancy Act

21. Hatch Act

22. Brain Trust

23. fireside chat

MULTIPLE-CHOICE QUESTIONS

Choose the answer that *best* completes the statement or answers the question.

24. Which statement is true about the stock market prior to the October 1929 "crash"?   c
    a. Only the very wealthy could afford to play the stock market.
    b. The Federal Reserve Board made no moves to control stock-market speculation.
    c. Nine million Americans speculated in the market with borrowed money.
    d. Stock prices began their downward spiral in 1928.

25. Which of the following suggests that the prosperity of the 1920s was structurally   d
    unstable?
    a. Increased productivity did not generate a corresponding increase in workers' salaries.
    b. Numerous manufacturing industries were overproducing.
    c. Farm prices had been declining throughout the 1920s.
    d. all of the above

26. The "monetarist" theory as to the cause of the stock-market crash blames mainly   a
    a. the Federal Reserve System.
    b. Herbert Hoover.
    c. the capitalist system.
    d. trade unions.

27. The global economy   c
    a. was unaffected by the economic crisis in the United States.
    b. was stimulated by the depression in the United States because European firms were able to take advantage of markets otherwise dominated by American business.
    c. also experienced a crisis when European economies collapsed in 1931.
    d. none of the above

28. The following were all results of the depression *except*:   a

    a. Exports increased as manufacturers tried to dump their excess production on foreign markets.
    b. The gross national product dropped nearly in half.
    c. The banking system was near collapse.
    d. Unemployment soared.

29. In rural counties, such as those surrounding Mason City, Iowa, the Farm Holiday   b
    movement

    a. advocated the eight-hour day for farm workers.
    b. urged farmers to keep products off the market and prevent farm foreclosures.
    c. urged farmers to abandon their failing farms and migrate to urban areas to seek employment.
    d. placed poor urban children with farm families for summer vacations.

30. Herbert Hoover took all the following steps to revive the economy after the stock-   c
    market crash *except*:

    a. urging municipal and state governments to create jobs through public-works projects
    b. setting up the Emergency Committee for Employment to coordinate the efforts of voluntary relief agencies
    c. passing the National Industrial Recovery Act, which embodied ideas of industrial self-regulation and business-government cooperation
    d. encouraging bankers to set up the National Credit Corporation, a private lending agency from which smaller banks could borrow funds to make business loans

31. In 1930 the American public expressed its reaction to Hoover's depression strate-   b
    gies by

    a. calling for his impeachment.
    b. voting for Democrats in the November congressional elections.
    c. voicing their overwhelming approval in a referendum vote.
    d. electing Franklin Delano Roosevelt president.

32. What do the Reconstruction Finance Corporation, the Glass-Steagall Act, and the   c
    National Credit Corporation have in common?

    a. Hoover vigorously opposed all three.
    b. They were all social-welfare programs for dispensing various forms of welfare to the needy.
    c. They all made loans to banks or businesses with the intent of revitalizing the economy.
    d. They were all private, voluntary approaches to revitalizing the economy.

33. Which of the following best characterizes Herbert Hoover's handling of the depression?   **b**
    SG
    a. He followed the advice of Secretary of the Treasury Mellon to do nothing and wait for economic recovery to occur naturally.
    b. His efforts were limited by his fears of unbalancing the federal budget and concentrating too much power and responsibility in the government in Washington.
    c. He refused to have the federal government help failing business corporations.
    d. He initiated vast new programs to employ the jobless, control farm surpluses, and regulate banking and the stock exchange.

34. After the onset of the depression, Herbert Hoover communicated with the American people   **c**
    a. through weekly radio chats.
    b. during an extensive train trip, personally assuring as many Americans as possible that prosperity was just around the corner.
    c. through impersonal press releases.
    d. through newsreels.

35. The ''bonus marchers'' in 1932   **a**
    a. were World War I veterans who marched on Washington to lobby for immediate cash payments of their veterans' bonuses.
    b. were farmers who threatened to dump milk and other agricultural products if they did not receive a government bonus for not producing farm surpluses.
    c. were trade unionists who marched on Washington when industrialists refused to pay the bonuses stipulated in union contracts.
    d. were young people who marched in the Civilian Conservation Corps.

36. Which of the following is true about Roosevelt's 1932 campaign for the presidency?   **b**
    a. Roosevelt was the front-running candidate among the Democrats and won the nomination on the first ballot.
    b. Roosevelt attacked Hoover for reckless spending and insisted that the federal government play a larger economic role *only* as a last resort.
    c. Roosevelt chose fellow New Yorker Al Smith as his running mate.
    d. Roosevelt presented a clear and specific program to the American people on how he would fight the depression.

37. Which of the following did Franklin Roosevelt use during the early years of his administration to fight the depression?   **d**
    a. industrial recovery through business-government cooperation and pump-priming federal spending
    b. agricultural recovery through subsidized crop reduction
    c. short-term emergency relief for the jobless, provided directly by the federal government if necessary
    d. all of the above

38. Eleanor Roosevelt believed her primary role as First Lady was to
    a. serve as an observer for her husband and promote social reform.
    b. be a gracious hostess for the many dignitaries who visited the White House.
    c. personally draft legislation and forge foreign policy.
    d. promote an appreciation of the arts.

a

39. The first woman cabinet member was
    a. Florence Kelley.
    b. Alice Paul.
    c. Eleanor Roosevelt.
    d. none of the above

d

40. Roosevelt's immediate response to the banking crisis included all the following *except*:
    a. proposing the Emergency Banking Act
    b. declaring a "bank holiday," which closed banks for four days
    c. nationalizing the banks
    d. assuring Americans over the radio that they could again entrust their money to banks

c

41. The Civilian Conservation Corps
    a. put half a million young men and women to work in camps across the country.
    b. was a conservative political youth club.
    c. employed jobless young men in rural projects such as reforestation, park maintenance, and erosion control.
    d. was the precursor to the National Guard.

c

42. Which New Deal initiative paid farmers subsidies to take acreage out of production?
    a. the Agricultural Adjustment Act of 1933
    b. the Farm Credit Act
    c. the Farm Holiday movement
    d. the McNary-Haugen bill

a

43. Which of the following was *not* true of the National Industrial Recovery Act?
    a. It embodied ideas of industrial self-regulation and business-government cooperation and drew on the idea of trade associations which had been promoted by Herbert Hoover.
    b. It was declared unconstitutional.
    c. Under it, major industries drafted codes of "fair competition," setting production limits, prescribing wages and working conditions, and forbidding price cutting.
    d. It limited workers' collective bargaining rights.

d

44. A growing antibusiness attitude during the first Hundred Days of the New Deal   b
    could be detected in which of the following programs?

    a. the Reconstruction Finance Corporation
    b. the Federal Securities Act
    c. the National Industrial Recovery Act
    d. all of the above

45. Which of the following agencies was created during Hoover's administration to   d
    help failing business corporations and continued to be active through the New   SG
    Deal years?

    a. Federal Emergency Relief Administration
    b. Tennessee Valley Authority
    c. Federal Deposit Insurance Corporation
    d. Reconstruction Finance Corporation

46. Which federal programs created during the first Hundred Days were later declared   a
    unconstitutional by the Supreme Court?   SG

    a. NRA and AAA
    b. FDIC and HOLC
    c. FERA and CCC
    d. TVA and PWA

47. What was Roosevelt's view of the economic theories of John Maynard Keynes?   d

    a. Roosevelt embraced them wholeheartedly, because Keynes supported balanc-
       ing the budget to cure the nation's economic woes.
    b. Roosevelt vehemently rejected Keynesianism because of its suggestion that
       governments should induce economic recovery through deficit spending.
    c. Roosevelt was lukewarm to Keynes, who had been Herbert Hoover's chief
       economic adviser.
    d. Although the New Deal in effect followed Keynes's suggestions, Roosevelt
       reluctantly tolerated deficit spending as the price of other New Deal goals.

48. The Southern Tenant Farmers' Union was   c

    a. organized by Milo Reno to keep farm products off the market in order to
       raise farm prices.
    b. an all-white farmers' organization, led by the Ku Klux Klan.
    c. an interracial farmers' organization, led by the Socialist party.
    d. an organization to promote cooperation and goodwill between tenant farm-
       ers and landowners.

49. Aside from the economic conditions of the 1930s, farmers on the Great Plains also   b
    suffered from

    a. a cholera epidemic.
    b. drought.
    c. floods.
    d. Indian raids.

50. The power struggle between Harold Ickes and Harry Hopkins over federal public relief policies   a

    a. contrasted Ickes's cautious attitude toward dispensing relief with Hopkins's view that people had to have money quickly, even through "make-work" projects.
    b. centered on whether giving aid to women and children would lead to a breakdown of the family.
    c. pitted Ickes, as a proponent of socialism, against Hopkins, as the defender of capitalism.
    d. became irrelevant when the Supreme Court ruled public relief was the responsibility of the states.

51. The Townsend Plan put forth by Dr. Francis E. Townsend   d

    a. instituted Medicare for the elderly.
    b. instituted social security for the elderly.
    c. eliminated property taxes for the elderly.
    d. none of the above

52. All the following opposed the New Deal *except*:   b

    a. the United States Chamber of Commerce
    b. the Living Newspaper
    c. the American Liberty League
    d. the National Union of Social Justice

53. Two reforms passed during Roosevelt's second term were   a
                                                              SG
    a. Fair Labor Standards Act and National Housing Act.
    b. NRA and AAA.
    c. Social Security Act and Wagner Act.
    d. SEC and WPA.

54. The National Labor Relations Act of 1935 did all the following *except*:   a

    a. outlaw closed shops
    b. guarantee collective bargaining
    c. outlaw blacklisting labor "agitators"
    d. outlaw spying on unions

55. Which New Deal legislation established the principle of federal responsibility for   c
    social welfare and created the basic framework for the welfare system?

    a. the Wagner Act
    b. the Revenue Act of 1935
    c. the Social Security Act
    d. the Federal Securities Act

56. When Franklin Roosevelt said, "There's one issue in this campaign," regarding the election of 1936, he was referring to   d
    a. employment.
    b. taxes.
    c. foreign policy.
    d. himself.

57. All the following are true about the election of 1936 *except*:   c
    a. The Republicans recognized the popularity of New Deal policies and simply asserted that they could administer them better.
    b. Roosevelt beat Alf Landon in the most crushing victory since 1820.
    c. Third-party candidates—Socialist, Communist, and a coalition candidate for Coughlinites, Townsendites, and "Share Our Wealth" advocates—siphoned off an alarming number of Democratic votes.
    d. The Democrats increased their already top-heavy majorities in the Senate and the House of Representatives.

58. By 1936 Roosevelt added which of the following voters to the traditional Democratic base of support?   d
    a. farmers
    b. northern blacks
    c. women
    d. all of the above

59. Overall, the New Deal's record for improving conditions for blacks was   d
    a. poor: Roosevelt proposed no civil-rights legislation and did not throw his support behind anti-lynching legislation.
    b. excellent: New Deal relief programs benefited many unemployed blacks, and Roosevelt appointed hundreds of blacks to policy-making positions in his administration.
    c. often symbolic: Mrs. Roosevelt, for example, attended a meeting of the inter-racial Southern Conference on Human Welfare, and she resigned from the Daughters of the American Revolution when it refused to let black contralto Marian Anderson sing in Constitution Hall.
    d. mixed: because all the preceding statements are accurate.

60. Molly Dewson, head of the Democratic party's women's division, advocated all the following during the New Deal *except*:   b
    a. wooing women voters by emphasizing family issues in campaign materials
    b. pushing a specific feminist agenda and women's rights legislation
    c. appointing more women to federal policy-level positions
    d. requiring that the Democratic platform committee be composed equally of women and men

61. After the 1936 election, Roosevelt attempted to undermine the power of   c
    a. the military.
    b. Congress.
    c. the Supreme Court.
    d. Wall Street.

62. Roosevelt's "court-packing" plan   c
    a. met with approval from Congress, including New Deal supporters and many
       conservatives who felt it was time for a change.
    b. would have violated the constitutional requirement for nine Supreme Court
       justices.
    c. proved unnecessary because Roosevelt was able to replace four members of
       the Supreme Court who died or retired.
    d. turned out to be one of Roosevelt's greatest triumphs.

63. Which program sent photographers such as Dorothea Lange around the country   a
    to document the lives of tenants, migrants, and uprooted Dust Bowl families?
    a. the Resettlement Administration
    b. the Farm Security Administration
    c. the Agricultural Adjustment Administration
    d. the Southern Tenant Farmers' Union

64. Which New Deal legislation banned child labor and established a minimum wage   a
    and maximum hours for the work week?
    a. the Fair Labor Standards Act
    b. the National Labor Relations Act (Wagner Act)
    c. the National Industrial Recovery Act
    d. the Social Security Act

65. What feature of the Agricultural Adjustment Act of 1938 established the basic   c
    framework of federal agricultural policy for decades to come?
    a. The government encouraged farmers to destroy crops, dump milk, and, if
       necessary, slaughter animals to reduce surpluses.
    b. In order to boost agricultural production the government made loans to
       farmers to invest in more land, machinery, and labor.
    c. In years of big harvests and low prices, the government would make loans to
       farmers and store their surplus crops in government warehouses.
    d. The government encouraged the survival of the family farm by withholding
       aid to agribusiness.

66. A conservative coalition in Congress thwarted Roosevelt during his second term in   d
    all the following ways *except*:
    a. passing the Hatch Act to forbid federal workers from participating in electoral
       campaigns
    b. slashing relief appropriations
    c. rejecting Roosevelt's proposal to reorganize the executive branch into
       superdepartments under the president's direct authority
    d. rejecting the Fair Labor Standards Act

67. Which of the following statements is *not* true about the New Deal?   a

    a. The New Deal brought about full economic recovery, and by 1939 unemployment was no longer a serious problem.
    b. The New Deal vastly increased the power and prestige of the presidency.
    c. The New Deal assumed a fundamental governmental responsibility to promote economic prosperity and the well-being of all citizens.
    d. As the New Deal evolved, it acted as a broker for all organized interest groups—including agriculture and labor, not just business.

68. Which of the following New Dealers is *mismatched* with the department or agency she or he headed?   a   SG

    a. Henry Wallace—Civil Works Administration
    b. Harry Hopkins—Works Progress Administration
    c. Frances Perkins—Department of Labor
    d. Hugh Johnson—National Recovery Administration

ESSAY QUESTIONS

69. What were the causes of the depression? What was the effect of the stock-market crash on business? On workers? On consumers?

70. Compare and contrast President Hoover's and President Franklin Roosevelt's   SG attempts to deal with the depression and its victims. Why did each president follow his particular course?

71. Compare the first "Hundred Days" of the New Deal with the "Second New Deal." What were the major goals of each? What were the major accomplishments?

72. What was the experience of farmers during the depression, and what New Deal programs were established to remedy their problems? Did some farmers benefit more than others from certain New Deal legislation? Which of today's agricultural policies had their roots in the New Deal?

73. How did New Deal policies affect the following groups: blacks, women, organized workers? Did the New Deal address all their problems?

74. How did Roosevelt shape the New Deal—as a personality, a politician, a statesman? How did Eleanor Roosevelt shape the New Deal as First Lady?

75. Who were the New Deal's opponents? Why did they object to New Deal programs, and what alternatives did they offer? How much popular support did these opponents have?

76. How did the New Deal change attitudes about the role of government in the economy, and the government's responsibility for the social welfare of ordinary Americans? What economic and social-welfare programs today trace their origins to New Deal legislation?

77. Did the New Deal seriously threaten capitalism, as some conservatives claimed?
Was the New Deal essentially reformist or revolutionary? Why?

MAP QUESTIONS

Choose the letter on the accompanying map of the United States that correctly identifies
each of the following:

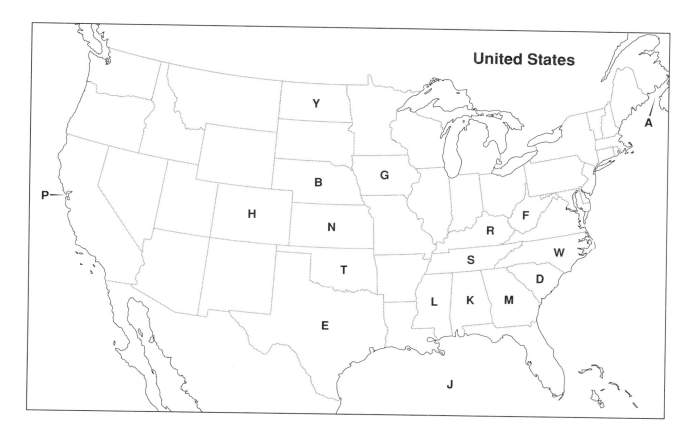

78. Tennessee   S

79. Kentucky   R

80. North Carolina   W

81. Georgia   M

82. Alabama   K

83. Oklahoma   T

84. Iowa   G

85. Texas   E

86. North Dakota   Y

87. Bay of Fundy   A

CHAPTER 25

American Life in a Decade of Crisis at Home and Abroad

IDENTIFICATIONS

Identify the following. Be as specific as possible, and include names, dates, and relevant facts as appropriate. Be sure to explain the *significance* of the person or term.

1. Walter Reuther

2. John L. Lewis

3. Sidney Hillman

4. the Congress of Industrial Organizations

5. Little Steel

6. Battle of the Overpass

7. Memorial Day Massacre

8. the Scottsboro Boys

9. *repatriados*

10. John Collier

11. Father Divine

12. John Reed Clubs

13. the Popular Front

14. General Francisco Franco, Spanish Loyalists

15. the Good Neighbor policy

16. Benito Mussolini

17. *Mein Kampf*, National Socialist Party

18. *Anschluss*

19. Jesse Owens, Joe Lewis

20. Neville Chamberlain

21. Manchukuo

22. *All Quiet on the Western Front*

23. Neutrality Acts

24. the Ludlow Amendment

25. German-American Bund, Silver Shirts

26. Nuremberg Laws

27. *Kristallnacht*

28. the vessel *St. Louis*

MULTIPLE-CHOICE QUESTIONS

Choose the answer that *best* completes the statement or answers the question.

29. In 1937 strikers at General Motors plants in Flint, Michigan,   d
    a. were aided by their wives, sisters, and daughters who organized the Women's Auxiliary and the Women's Emergency Brigade.
    b. were attacked with tear gas by police.
    c. suffered from bitter cold when GM executives cut off the heat in the occupied plants.
    d. all of the above

30. The unemployment rate in the 1930s never fell *below*   b
    a. 5 percent.
    b. 14 percent.
    c. 34 percent.
    d. none of the above

31. Which statement best represents the economic status of farm families during the   b
    1930s?
    a. Because farm families were property owners, they did not suffer as much as other segments of society during the depression.
    b. A quarter of all farm families had to accept public or private assistance.
    c. In rural America, bankruptcies, foreclosures, and the abandonment of farms were rare because communities stuck together.
    d. Three-fourths of the farms folded during the depression.

32. The Committee for Industrial Organization was established   **d**
    a. to organize skilled workers.
    b. by industrialists to undermine the power of labor unions.
    c. by President Roosevelt as one of his "alphabet agencies" to address economic problems.
    d. to organize all workers in a particular industry, regardless of race, gender, or degree of skill.

33. In 1937 U.S. Steel responded to the newly formed Steel Workers' Organizing   **c**
    Committee by
    a. living up to its reputation as "the crouching lion in the pathway of labor" and crushing the new union.
    b. countering with the establishment of a company-sponsored employee association.
    c. recognizing the union, granting a wage increase, and agreeing to a forty-hour week.
    d. engaging in a protracted dispute with the union which included a major strike over union recognition.

34. In 1937 the workers at the two GM Fisher Body plants conducted   **a**
    a. a sit-down strike.
    b. a boycott.
    c. a wildcat strike.
    d. a work slowdown.

35. Which statement best describes union membership in the 1930s?   **b**
    a. Unions lost members because unemployed workers would accept low wages and poor working conditions to get a job.
    b. Unions gained membership, growing from only 3 million in 1933 to over 8 million in 1941.
    c. Union membership held steady at approximately 5 million members throughout the 1930s.
    d. Unions gained members because a big effort was made to organize low-wage workers including agricultural laborers, department-store clerks, and restaurant, supermarket, and laundry workers.

36. At the Ford Motor Company, the "Service Department" was   **d**
    a. organized to provide social services to laid-off workers.
    b. the first customer service department in a major company to manage customer problems.
    c. a philanthropic social club of Ford executives.
    d. a squad of union-busting thugs.

37. All the following industries bitterly resisted unionization in the 1930s *except*:   **b**
    a. Little Steel
    b. U.S. Steel
    c. Ford Motor Company
    d. the textile industry

38. Why did powerful corporations finally cave in to unionization after years of resistance? **d**
    a. worker militance and the tactical skills of new labor leaders
    b. management's fear of violence and sabotage
    c. the new climate of government sympathy for union activities
    d. all of the above

39. During the depression the attitude of most Americans toward whether married women should work was **a**
    a. the overwhelming belief that a wife should not work if her husband had a job.
    b. the belief that this was a personal choice.
    c. the recognition that most married women worked out of economic necessity.
    d. a commitment to the feminist idea that women had just as much right to careers as men.

40. The CIO campaign to organize female clerical workers met with little progress primarily because **c**
    a. women saw their jobs as temporary and had no interest in unions.
    b. women clerical workers were already well paid.
    c. male bosses and male union leaders opposed female unionization.
    d. all of the above

41. Which statement best expresses the mobility of black Americans during the 1930s? **c**
    a. Black Americans poured into northern cities in a "great migration" in search of employment.
    b. Black Americans in record numbers poured into southern cities in search of employment.
    c. The depression markedly slowed down the urbanization of black Americans.
    d. The depression made little difference because the majority of blacks had migrated to northern cities earlier in the century.

42. The Scottsboro boys were **a**
    SG
    a. black teenagers sentenced to death by an all-white jury for allegedly raping two white women.
    b. one of the most popular swing bands of the 1930s.
    c. the main characters in Clifford Odets's play *Waiting for Lefty*, about labor unrest and a strike.
    d. young, unemployed Mexican-American farm workers who were forced by relief officials to return to Mexico.

43. A protest under the banner "Don't Shop Where You Can't Work" was **b**
    a. organized by housewives against stores which fired married women.
    b. organized by blacks against businesses which only hired whites.
    c. organized by Mexican-American migrant workers in towns which prohibited employment of immigrants.
    d. organized by union organizers in company stores where the company refused to recognize the union.

44. During the depression, the American Communist party made a major effort to recruit   d

    a. women.
    b. students.
    c. union members.
    d. blacks.

45. Labor relations in California's agricultural regions in the 1930s were marked by   c

    a. cooperation between farm laborers and producers because farms were small and workers were treated like family.
    b. cooperation because producers recognized they were dependent on labor to harvest perishable crops.
    c. numerous strikes over poor working conditions and near-starvation wages.
    d. the successful alliance of Mexican-Americans and "Okies" in taking over some of the region's largest agribusinesses.

46. Mexicans in cities such as Los Angeles experienced all the following during the depression *except*:   b
    PT

    a. prejudice on the part of the Anglo population
    b. free round-trip transportation to Mexico and back to ensure an ample supply of cheap labor during harvest time
    c. arrest and deportation
    d. rejection by New Deal work programs

47. "Zoot suits"   a
    PT

    a. were a style of dress favored by male Mexican-American youth.
    b. was a slang term for the overalls worn by women factory workers.
    c. was a Chicago gangster.
    d. was a popular radio comedian.

48. The Indian Reorganization Act of 1934   c

    a. turned Indian reservations into living museums in order to promote tourism in western states.
    b. granted Indian tribes the right of self-government and encouraged the renewal of traditional tribal culture.
    c. halted the sale of tribal lands to individuals and enabled tribes to regain title to their unallocated lands.
    d. allowed whites to buy up remaining tribal land.

49. Which of the following did *not* occur during the depression?   c
    SG

    a. Birth and marriage rates declined.
    b. Urbanization and population growth slowed.
    c. Immigration into the United States from Europe and Mexico increased greatly.
    d. High-school enrollment increased sharply.

50. All the following led to the increased use of contraceptives in the 1930s *except*:   d
    a. A federal court lifted the ban against importing or mailing birth-control information.
    b. The Sears, Roebuck catalog began to advertise contraceptives.
    c. The Federal Council of Churches declared contraception morally acceptable.
    d. The federal government distributed free contraceptives to low-income married couples at health clinics.

51. Which section of the country experienced the greatest population growth in the 1930s?   b
    a. Florida
    b. the Pacific region
    c. the North
    d. the southwestern "Sunbelt," especially Texas

52. All the following were popular pastimes during the depression *except*:   b
    a. going to the movies   SG
    b. watching television
    c. listening to the radio
    d. listening to swing played by the big bands of Benny Goodman, Count Basie, and Glenn Miller

53. When Lee De Forest asked, "What have you done to my child?" he was protesting   b
    a. the child star system in Hollywood.
    b. the mediocre quality of radio programming.
    c. the cuts made to his best-selling "sex" novel.
    d. the foster care programs which allowed the government to take the children of the poor.

54. All the following boosted attendance at movies in the 1930s *except*:   c
    a. the introduction of double features
    b. the introduction of drive-in theaters
    c. the development of "3-D" technology
    d. the affordability of the twenty-five-cent admission

55. The Frank Capra films *Mr. Deeds Goes to Town* and *Mr. Smith Goes to Washington* were   b
    a. comedies which lampooned New Deal policies.
    b. patriotic and idealistic portrayals of the triumph of "the people" over entrenched interests.
    c. realistic docu-dramas about social problems.
    d. gangster movies showing gritty images of urban America.

56. Which performers transcended the usual stereotyped roles Hollywood offered   c
    blacks and women in the 1930s?
    a. Bill Robinson and Shirley Temple
    b. Butterfly McQueen and Vivien Leigh
    c. Paul Robeson and Mae West
    d. all of the above

57. The class struggle and the decadence of capitalism were the themes of all the   d
    following *except*:
    a. Clifford Odets's play *Waiting for Lefty*
    b. Jack Conroy's novel *The Disinherited*
    c. Josephine Herbst's novel *Pity Is Not Enough*
    d. William Saroyan's play *The Time of Your Life*

58. Stalin's call for a worldwide "Popular Front" against fascism   a
    a. prompted American Communists to switch from attacking Roosevelt to prais-
       ing him.
    b. was manifested in 1939 when the Soviet Union and Germany signed a pact
       agreeing not to make war on each other.
    c. had little influence on American politics and culture because American intel-
       lectuals were deeply isolationist in the late 1930s.
    d. inspired American radicals and intellectuals to fight the Loyalists in the Span-
       ish Civil War.

59. Which writer captured the political idealism of the Spanish Civil War in a novel?   d
    a. John Steinbeck
    b. William Faulkner
    c. James T. Farrell
    d. Ernest Hemingway

60. All the following were examples of the affirmative cultural nationalism characteris-   b
    tic of the late 1930s *except*:
    a. Aaron Copland's *Billy the Kid* and George Gershwin's *Porgy and Bess*
    b. John Dos Passos's *U.S.A.* and Nathanael West's *Miss Lonelyhearts*
    c. the paintings of Thomas Hart Benton, Grant Wood, and Anna "Grandma"
       Moses
    d. the photojournalism of James Agee and Walker Evans

61. The most important trend in industrial design in the 1930s was   c
    a. art nouveau.
    b. the influence of the arts and crafts movement.
    c. streamlining.
    d. cubism.

62. The Futurama exhibit at the New York World's Fair of 1939 featured a vision of   d
    a. space travel in the future.
    b. an automated home of the future.
    c. "Better Things for Better Living Through Chemistry."
    d. a complex interstate highway network of the future.

63. The radio adaptation of *War of the Worlds* was about   d
    a. World War I.
    b. the Spanish Civil War.
    c. class warfare.
    d. Martians landing.

64. Franklin Roosevelt's Good Neighbor policy   b
    a. proclaimed "Speak softly, and carry a big stick."
    b. declared "No state has the right to intervene in the internal or external affairs of another" in Latin America.
    c. led to a non-aggression pact with the Soviet Union.
    d. led to a scrupulous "hands-off" policy in Latin America, even in instances where American interests were threatened.

65. Adolf Hitler advocated all the following *except*:   c
    a. anti-Semitism.
    b. nationalism.
    c. pacifism.
    d. expansionism.

66. British Prime Minister Neville Chamberlain proclaimed "peace in our time" after   a
    a. appeasing Hitler by agreeing to cede the Sudetenland to Germany.
    b. signing the Versailles treaty.
    c. signing a non-aggression pact with the Soviet Union.
    d. announcing his Good Neighbor policy.

67. Japan demonstrated its expansionist policies in 1931–32 by invading   d
    a. the Philippines.
    b. Pearl Harbor.
    c. Mongolia.
    d. Manchuria.

68. Which of the following helped convince Americans that United States participation   c
    in World War I was a mistake that should not be repeated by getting involved a   SG
    second time?
    a. the Ludlow Amendment
    b. Roosevelt's "Quarantine the Aggressors" speech
    c. the Nye Committee hearings
    d. the *St. Louis* incident

69. The "peace strike" of 1936 consisted of   **b**
    a. workers striking in defense industries.
    b. students boycotting classes to attend antiwar events.
    c. a general strike which paralyzed the country.
    d. women protesting the militarism of male-dominated governments.

70. Which of the following was antiwar?   **c**
    a. *War of the Worlds*
    b. *It Can't Happen Here*
    c. *All Quiet on the Western Front*
    d. *Their Eyes Were Watching God*

71. All the following took strongly anti-Nazi positions in the 1930s *except*:   **a**
    a. Ambassador Joseph P. Kennedy   **SG**
    b. the journalist Dorothy Thompson
    c. the poet Archibald MacLeish
    d. the cultural critic Lewis Mumford

72. Which of the following did the Roosevelt administration object to the most   **d**
    because it threatened the economic interests of the United States?
    a. the *Anschluss* between Austria and Germany
    b. the Italian invasion of Ethiopia
    c. the Munich Pact, which handed the Sudetenland over to Germany
    d. Japanese aggression against China

73. Which statement best represents the United States' response to reports of the   **b**
    German persecution of Jews?
    a. The United States expressed sympathy for the plight of the Jews and liberal-
       ized its restrictive immigration laws.
    b. The United States expressed sympathy for the plight of the Jews, but refused
       to liberalize its restrictive immigration laws.
    c. Americans overwhelmingly supported legislation to admit twenty thousand
       German refugee children.
    d. The United States sponsored the ship *St. Louis* to rescue 900 Jews for reset-
       tlement in America.

ESSAY QUESTIONS

74. Describe the psychological impact of poverty and unemployment during the
    depression. How did individuals and families respond to hardships?

75. In 1933 less than 3 million workers belonged to unions. By 1941 over 8 million
    did. How and why did this "unionization of vast sectors of America's industrial
    work force" come about? Which workers were still almost totally unorganized in
    1941?

76. How did the depression bring "mixed blessings" for women? And why did Senator Robert Wagner refer to women as "the first orphan in the storm"? Discuss employment and unionization, the family, the women's movement, and New Deal policies.

77. What was the experience of blacks, Hispanics, and native Americans during the depression? What kind of discrimination did these groups face? What government policies affected Hispanics and native Americans?

78. Compare the mood of intellectuals in the early 1930s with that of the late 1930s. How did the Popular Front affect American culture? How did the cultural nationalism of the late 1930s manifest itself? Give examples from literature, art, and music.

79. Describe the role of mass culture (radio, movies, music) as a form of escapism during the depression. How did films reflect values or social problems of the era?

80. What was Americans' mood regarding the prospect of war in the late 1930s? Why did they have this attitude? What were the Neutrality Acts and the Ludlow Amendment?

81. What economic interests did the United States have in Latin America and China? What was Roosevelt's Good Neighbor policy? What was the Open Door policy, and how did the United States react to Japanese aggression in China?

82. How did the hysterical reaction to Orson Welles's radio adaptation of *War of the Worlds* reflect apprehension over international events? Describe the rise of fascism in Germany, Italy, and Japan. How did the United States respond to fascist activities in the late 1930s?

83. What was the experience of Jews in Germany in the late 1930s, and what was the response of the United States? What effect did Jewish refugees have on American life and culture?

MAP QUESTIONS

Choose the letter on the accompanying map of Europe that correctly identifies each of the following:

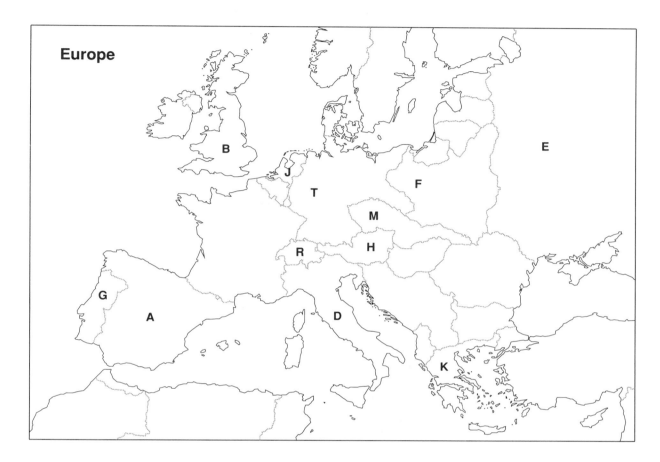

84. Spain	A
85. Soviet Union	E
86. Italy	D
87. Germany	T
88. Austria	H
89. Czechoslovakia	M
90. Poland	F

CHAPTER 26

Waging Global War, 1939–1945

IDENTIFICATIONS

Identify the following. Be as specific as possible, and include names, dates, and relevant facts as appropriate. Be sure to explain the *significance* of the person or term.

1. cash-and-carry

2. Henry L. Stimson

3. Committee to Defend America First

4. Wendell L. Willkie

5. lend-lease

6. Atlantic Charter

7. Tripartite Pact

8. Pearl Harbor

9. James F. Byrnes and the Office of War Mobilization

10. Dr. New Deal and Dr. Win the War

11. Smith-Connally Act

12. Manhattan Engineering District

13. Office of War Information

14. *One World*

15. Rosie the Riveter

16. eight-hour orphans and latch-key children

17. Civil War II and Double V

18. Congress of Racial Equality

19. A. Philip Randolph, Brotherhood of Sleeping Car Porters

20. Detroit Race Riot of 1943

21. zoot suit riots

22. Operation Torch and Operation Overlord

23. Battle of the Atlantic

24. Battle of the Bulge

25. "the new Missouri Compromise"

26. Yalta agreements

27. Hiroshima and Nagasaki

MULTIPLE-CHOICE QUESTIONS

Choose the answer that *best* completes the statement or answers the question.

28. In response to the outbreak of World War II, the United States revised its neutral-   a
    ity statutes so that
    a. belligerents could purchase weapons as long as they paid for them in cash
       and took them away in their own ships.
    b. American merchant vessels might be able to carry cargoes to belligerents'
       ports.
    c. no weapons could be sold to any nation participating in the European war.
    d. only Britain, and not Germany, would be able to buy weapons from the
       United States.

29. In the fall of 1939, an overwhelming majority of the American people believed that   b
    a. the United States should have nothing whatsoever to do with European
       affairs.
    b. it was important to save England and France from defeat, but even more
       important for the United States to stay out of war.
    c. England was just as much to blame for starting World War II as was Germany.
    d. the United States should declare war on Germany because the defeat of En-
       gland would pose a threat to American security.

30. In September 1940, in an effort to bolster American security and at the same time help England, President Roosevelt concluded an executive agreement with Prime Minister Churchill that   c
    a. sold American tanks and cruisers to Great Britain on a deferred payment schedule.
    b. allowed Britain to use American air bases in exchange for a guarantee of safe Atlantic passage for American merchant vessels.
    c. transferred fifty overage American destroyers to Britain in exchange for leases on British air and naval bases in the Western Hemisphere.
    d. drew up a timetable for eventual American participation in the war against Hitler.

31. The Committee to Defend America First argued that   d
    a. the United States was endangered by internal subversion, not possible German invasion.
    b. the United States had to defend itself by going to war against Germany before Germany invaded the United States.
    c. United States security could best be protected by strengthening the American economy and not wasting money on a costly military buildup.
    d. the United States had the strength to stand alone regardless of Hitler's victories in Europe.

32. Lend-lease   c
                    SG
    a. was favored by isolationists as a way to prevent the United States from having to fight in World War II.
    b. favored the Germans because they were considered better credit risks than the British and Russians.
    c. was extended to both Britain and the Soviet Union to help them defeat the Nazis.
    d. was one of the most unpopular policies of the Roosevelt administration because it was pulling the country into a war the majority wished to avoid.

33. Which of the following sequences of events is correct?   a
                                                                SG
    a. United States sends aid to Britain and Russia; Japan attacks Pearl Harbor; United States declares war on Japan; Germany and Italy declare war on the United States
    b. United States declares war on Germany; Japan attacks Pearl Harbor; United States declares war on Japan; United States sends aid to Britain and Russia
    c. United States declares war on Japan; Japan attacks Pearl Harbor; Germany and Italy declare war on the United States; United States sends aid to Britain and Russia
    d. Germany, Italy, and Japan declare war on the United States; Japan attacks Pearl Harbor; United States declares war on the Axis; United States sends aid to Britain and Russia

34. In 1940 and 1941 President Roosevelt wished to prolong negotiations with the   **b**
Japanese rather than go to war, despite continued conflicts and Washington's
overt bellicosity toward Japan. Why?

    a. The negotiations had been making substantial progress and most of the
    points of disagreement were being resolved.
    b. Roosevelt knew that he did not have a large enough navy to fight both Japan
    and Germany.
    c. The American people were virulently anti-Japanese and therefore the anti-
    interventionist sentiment regarding Asian affairs was very strong.
    d. The Japanese had ended their expansion and were looking forward to a cen-
    tury of coprosperity.

35. War between Japan and the United States came about because of the Japanese   **d**
attack on

    a. Midway.
    b. the Philippines.
    c. Alaska.
    d. Hawaii.

36. Which of the following did *not* occur during the first few months of American par-   **a**
ticipation in World War II?

    a. The United States unleashed its massive army and navy and brought German
    and Japanese aggression to a halt.
    b. Germany sank hundreds of Allied merchant ships in the North Atlantic.
    c. Nazi U-boats bottled up Chesapeake Bay for six weeks.
    d. Nazi armies continued rapid, forceful, and seemingly unstoppable advances
    in Europe and North Africa.

37. The various federal agencies created during World War II to coordinate the war   **b**
effort did all the following *except*:

    a. limit or stop the production of civilian goods
    b. impose strict ceilings on corporate profits
    c. mediate disputes between management and labor
    d. impose strict price controls

38. Which of the following did *not* occur during World War II?   **b**

    a. The government imposed wage-and-price controls and rationing to combat   **SG**
    inflation.
    b. The government took over many industries and strictly limited the profits of
    others.
    c. The government raised the income tax and introduced the payroll-deduction
    system to collect it more efficiently.
    d. Farm income soared, unemployment disappeared, and real wages increased.

39. What impact did the wartime economy have on the distribution of American incomes?   c

    a. Because of war profiteering, the proportion of wealth controlled by the richest 5 percent of the population soared to nearly one-third.
    b. Because of government wage controls, the proportion of wealth controlled by the poorest 40 percent of the population dropped to about 10 percent.
    c. The size of the middle class doubled—the only significant shift in income distribution in the twentieth century.
    d. The middle class stagnated as it found itself caught between wage freezes and soaring inflation.

40. How did World War II affect organized labor in the United States?   d

    a. It expanded and grew wealthier.
    b. It was able to gain unprecedented fringe benefits.
    c. It generally obeyed a no-strike pledge.
    d. all of the above

41. The Smith-Connally Act   a

    a. limited the right to strike in a facility deemed essential to the war effort.
    b. guaranteed labor the right of union membership.
    c. prohibited government employees from joining unions or engaging in political activity.
    d. eliminated all federal restrictions on the right to strike.

42. What role did the American scientific community have in World War II?   c

    a. The government insisted that scientific inquiry should not be interrupted by the war.
    b. Most of the nation's scientists opposed the war and refused to have anything to do with it.
    c. Scientists participated actively in developing new weapons, chemicals, medicines, and medical techniques that would advance the fight against the Axis powers.
    d. There was a constant conflict between scientists and the military because the military refused to allow scientists a role in the weapons race.

43. The Manhattan Engineering District was   d

    a. the area in New York City where expatriate German scientists settled during World War II.
    b. the code name for the Soviet espionage network specializing in secret scientific American projects during World War II.
    c. the area in New Mexico where navy scientists worked on new sonar devices during World War II.
    d. the secret $2 billion project to develop an atomic bomb.

44. Which of the following is *not* true regarding the government's management of   a
    public opinion during World War II?

    a. Publishers and broadcasters were allowed to say and report whatever they
       thought would be in the best interest of the public and the war effort.
    b. Government propaganda played up the barbarism of the Axis nations.
    c. Americans were able to see and hear more war news than they had ever been
       able to before.
    d. The government tightly restricted reports of casualty figures and pictures of
       dead soldiers on battlefields.

45. In the 1942 midterm elections, the political tenor of congressional politics took a   b
    decided turn

    a. to the left.
    b. to the right.
    c. away from support of the war.
    d. none of the above

46. Which of the following was *not* one of the changes in the American "social topog-   c
    raphy" that occurred during World War II?

    a. Millions of Americans moved to the West Coast states.
    b. Many Americans moved far from their hometowns and their traditional
       values.
    c. The family unit was strengthened, and divorce rates dropped, as Americans
       united in the effort to defend the nation.
    d. Some 6 million Americans left agrarian areas and moved to cities.

47. Which of the following statements accurately describes conditions in American   d
    education during World War II?

    a. Hundreds of thousands of teachers quit to join the armed forces or to take on
       better-paying war work.
    b. Students abandoned the schools in record numbers to take jobs or join the
       armed services.
    c. Colleges admitted an unprecedented number of women.
    d. all of the above

48. During World War II, the publishing industry experienced the beginnings of a   a
    major change, which was marked by

    a. the acceptance of quality paperback books.
    b. the creation of the Government Printing Office.
    c. the decline of magazines and the rise of radio.
    d. the first million-seller in publishing history.

49. How did World War II affect millions of American women?   b

    a. The federal government adopted a policy of gender equality in all federal hiring and in all companies doing business with the government.
    b. The proportion of women in the labor force rose from one-quarter to more than one-third, as more than 6 million women went to work outside the home.
    c. Because of the importance of their war work, women for the first time achieved equal pay for equal work.
    d. The public attitude toward women's employment underwent a transformation, as the majority of Americans began to admit that they approved of married women working outside the home.

50. A. Philip Randolph's call for a massive march on Washington led to   b
                                                                          SG
    a. an executive order permitting the military to evacuate and intern Japanese living on the West Coast.
    b. an executive order prohibiting employment discrimination and creating a Fair Employment Practices Committee.
    c. passage of the Smith-Connally Act restricting union strikes and protests.
    d. prosecution of the sailors involved in the "zoot suit" riot against the Chicanos.

51. The condition of American blacks improved during World War II through all the   c
    following means *except*:

    a. sit-ins in cities such as Denver, Detroit, and Chicago
    b. a federal executive order prohibiting discriminatory employment practices
    c. a massive march on Washington by 100,000 blacks
    d. the migration north of 700,000 blacks looking for greater educational and economic opportunities

52. Which of the following was *not* one of the causes of the racial friction in wartime   d
    cities like Detroit?   PT

    a. inability to find decent, affordable housing
    b. rising expectations of blacks who had come to cities from rural southern poverty
    c. white workers' open hostility to having to work with blacks
    d. shortage of factory jobs for blacks from the rural South

53. Why was the National Congress of American Indians organized during World War   a
    II?

    a. The federal government had been considering ending all reservation, tribe, treaty, and trust protections enjoyed by native Americans.
    b. The army and the navy had refused to accept native Americans because they described themselves as being from separate nations.
    c. Native Americans were requesting exemption from military service in exchange for manufacturing war supplies on their own reservations.
    d. The federal government needed a forum in which to discuss how the post-war European settlement would affect the future of native Americans.

54. Which of the following groups experienced the least amount of discrimination and prejudice in the United States during World War II?   c

   a. Mexican-Americans
   b. Jewish-Americans
   c. German-Americans
   d. Japanese-Americans

55. The United States government interned over 100,000 Japanese-Americans during World War II for all the following reasons *except*:   d

   a. There was deeply rooted anti-Japanese sentiment on the West Coast.
   b. Some politicians and farmers hoped to be able to take over Japanese-American landholdings.
   c. After Pearl Harbor, white Californians were worked up into a frenzy about possible Japanese sabotage.
   d. FBI and military intelligence had uncovered a Japanese-American espionage network in California.

56. One of the purposes of opening a "second front" was to   a

   a. force Hitler to transfer troops and thereby lessen the pressure on the Red armies.
   b. assist the British army in North Africa and protect British control of the Suez Canal.
   c. liberate Italy as soon as possible so that American troops would be free to turn to the war in the Pacific.
   d. force Japan to transfer troops and thereby lessen pressure on the American armies.

57. Which of the following is out of chronological order?   d

   a. Allied invasion of Italy
   b. Allied invasion of France
   c. Battle of the Bulge
   d. Allied invasion of North Africa

58. By the summer and early fall of 1944, all the following nations had been taken over by the Soviet Union *except*:   b

   a. Poland
   b. Turkey
   c. Romania
   d. Bulgaria

59. The costly battle that essentially exhausted Germany's reserves and opened the way into Germany was the   c

   a. Battle of Leningrad.
   b. Battle of Iwo Jima.
   c. Battle of the Bulge.
   d. Battle of the Atlantic.

60. The battle that ended the Japanese offensive and forced Japan to revert to defend-   a
ing what it had earlier occupied was the   SG
    a. Battle of Midway.
    b. Battle of the Bulge.
    c. Battle of the Philippine Sea.
    d. Battle of Iwo Jima.

61. Although Japan's sea and air power was totally shattered by the end of 1944, why   b
didn't the imperial government surrender to the United States?
    a. President Roosevelt refused to allow a surrender until a full-scale invasion of
       Japan could be accomplished.
    b. Japanese military leaders refused to allow the civilians in the government to
       negotiate a peace.
    c. The tripartite pact required that Japan continue fighting until Germany had
       been victorious in Europe.
    d. all of the above

62. The "Big Three" were   c
    a. Mussolini, Hitler, and Tojo
    b. Churchill, Stalin, and de Gaulle
    c. Roosevelt, Churchill, and Stalin
    d. Hitler, Stalin, and Tojo

63. Which of the following leaders is correctly matched with his main goals for the   d
postwar era?
    a. Roosevelt: retain imperial possessions and a balance of power against Russia
    b. Stalin: peace, open trade, and national self-determination
    c. Churchill: a permanently weakened Germany and a sphere of influence in
       Eastern Europe
    d. none of the above

64. At the Tehran Conference, all the following were agreed upon *except*:   a
    a. elections to be held in Soviet-controlled Eastern Europe
    b. the invasion of France
    c. the division of Germany
    d. Soviet entry in the war against Japan

65. In the election of 1944,   b
    a. Franklin Roosevelt won the largest electoral victory of his career.
    b. the major issues were the personalities of the candidates.
    c. the American people announced that they were hungry for more New Deal
       social programs.
    d. the Roosevelt coalition of urban voters and organized labor fell apart.

66. At the time of the Yalta Conference in February 1945,   c
    a. the American army was just about to enter Berlin.
    b. the war in the Pacific was coming to a rapid close.
    c. Russian troops had overrun Eastern Europe and were fifty miles from Berlin.
    d. Russia was near military collapse.

67. At the Yalta Conference, Stalin agreed on all the following *except*:   d
    a. entry into the war against Japan
    b. recognition of Jiang Jieshi as the ruler of China
    c. establishment of democratic governments in Eastern Europe and free elections in Poland
    d. withdrawal of all troops from Eastern Europe as soon as the war was over

68. In March and April of 1945, why did the United States reject a concentrated Anglo-   a
American thrust to Berlin?
    a. Eisenhower wanted to minimize American casualties and also reassure Stalin that there would be no separate peace with Germany.
    b. Roosevelt believed that postwar stability could best be accomplished if Russia was assured of domination in Eastern Europe.
    c. Churchill feared alienating Stalin and thereby endangering the Suez Canal.
    d. Most leaders and advisers in the American government thought that Soviet Communism was a desirable system.

69. After Harry Truman became president, disagreements between the United States   b
and the Soviet Union increased, mainly over
    a. the Pacific war.
    b. Eastern Europe.
    c. the development of the atomic bomb.
    d. opening the second front.

70. After what event did the Japanese government finally begin to discuss acceptance   c
of surrender terms?
    a. the Battle of Iwo Jima
    b. the dropping of unconditional surrender as a prerequisite
    c. the atomic bombing of Hiroshima and Nagasaki
    d. the threatened invasion of Japan by the Soviet Union

71. In the election of 1940,   d
    a. the Republicans ran an outspoken supporter of greater aid to the British.
    b. Roosevelt endorsed the nation's first peacetime draft.
    c. the Republican candidate attacked the president as an interventionist leading the country to war.
    d. all of the above

72. Which of the following would *not* have been a likely response of an American in   a
    1942 to the suggestion that the Nazis were engaged in the mass extermination of
    European Jews?

    a. The United States should establish an agency to assist in the rescue and relo-
       cation of those condemned to the death camps.
    b. Jewish Communists were responsible for the war, and Hitler was justified in
       his treatment of the Jews.
    c. It was just a Jewish problem, of small concern to anyone else.
    d. It was probably just propagandists' lies.

73. The Axis powers included   b

    a. Germany, Russia, and Japan.
    b. Japan, Germany, and Italy.
    c. Italy, Austria, and France.
    d. the United States, France, and Britain.

ESSAY QUESTIONS

---

74. Explain the domestic impact of World War II. What changes in American society
    were brought about because of the war? Consider the following: the powers of
    the federal government—especially the presidency, the role of the "military-indus-
    trial complex," economic concentration, income distribution, the farmer, labor,
    racial minorities.

75. Chart the gradual movement of the United States to war from the late 1930s to late
    1941. What was the role of public opinion in shaping American policy during
    these years? Did the United States at a certain point abandon non-intervention
    and neutrality? When? Why?

76. What were the points of contention between the United States and Japan in the
    1930s and early 1940s? To what extend did the contention result from different
    views of each other, and to what extent was there a real threat? What were the
    steps that brought the two nations into armed conflict? Could armed conflict have
    been avoided?

77. A Nazi commander said that "the Americans can't build planes, only electric ice-
    boxes and razor blades." Yet during the war the nation achieved, according to
    your text, "a miracle of war production." Describe that miracle, and explain how
    it came about.

78. How and why did the role of American women change during World War II? Why
    was that change temporary? What sort of work did women do, and how were they
    received in their work? Why were the employment opportunities and public
    recognition available to women during the war important? Why, nevertheless,
    were the gains made by women less substantial than those made by blacks during
    the same years?

79. How and to what extent did American blacks achieve economic and social ad-   **PT** vances during World War II? How did wartime ideology affect these reforms? What did Jackie Robinson mean when he declared, "I'm damned if I'm going to let the Alabama version of the Germans kick me around."

80. Compare the situations faced by American blacks, native Americans, Mexican-Americans, Japanese-Americans, and Jews during World War II. Why were they confronted by these problems? Explain and account for the American reaction to the Holocaust.

81. Compare the war in Europe with the war in the Pacific. What were the goals in each theater of war? What were the major obstacles in each theater? What different strategies and techniques were employed?

82. Describe the functioning of the "Grand Alliance" during World War II. Why did it hold together? How did the personalities of the leaders of the Alliance affect its functioning? What points of disagreement began to develop as the war progressed?

83. Why did the United States drop atomic bombs on Hiroshima and Nagasaki? What   **SG** are various explanations that have been offered? Do you feel the United States' actions were justified? Why or why not?

MAP QUESTIONS

Choose the letter on the accompanying map of the European theater of war that correctly identifies each of the following:

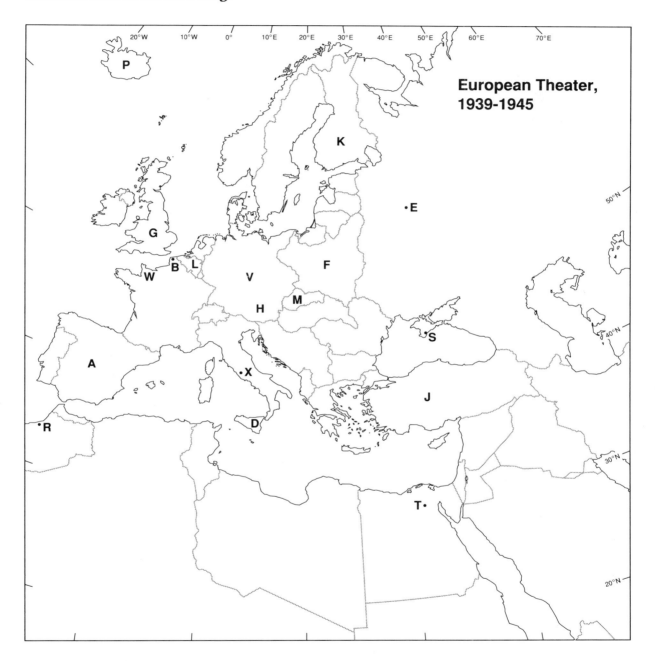

European Theater, 1939-1945

84. Poland   F

85. Belgium   L

86. Dunkirk   B

87. Iceland   P

88. Moscow   E

89. Yalta   S

90. Casablanca   R

91. Sicily   D

92. Cairo   T

93. Rome   X

94. Normandy   W

Choose the letter on the accompanying map of the Far Eastern theater of war that correctly identifies each of the following:

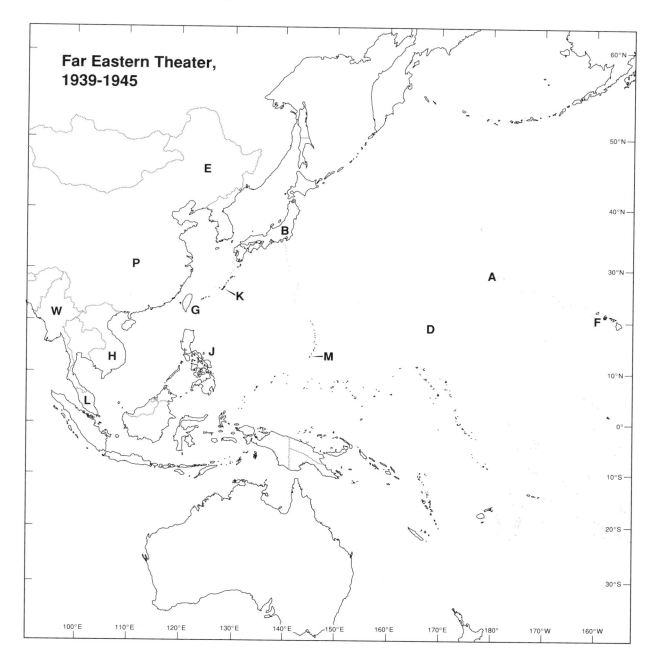

Far Eastern Theater, 1939-1945

95. Japan   B

96. Manchuria   E

97. Pearl Harbor   F

98. Burma   **W**

99. Guam   **M**

100. Midway   **A**

101. Okinawa   **K**

CHAPTER 27

Cold War America, 1945–1952

IDENTIFICATIONS

Identify the following. Be as specific as possible, and include names, dates, and relevant facts as appropriate. Be sure to explain the *significance* of the person or term.

1. Cold War

2. Servicemen's Readjustment Act of 1944

3. Bretton Woods Agreement

4. Employment Act of 1946

5. George Frost Kennan

6. containment policy

7. Iron Curtain speech

8. Truman Doctrine

9. Marshall Plan

10. NATO

11. Jiang Jieshi versus Mao Zedong

12. NSC-68

13. Federal Civil Defense Administration   PT

14. Taft-Hartley Act

15. President's Commission on Civil Rights, *To Secure These Rights*

16. J. Strom Thurmond and the Dixiecrats

17. Henry Wallace and the Progressive party

18. Fair Deal

19. Federal Employee Loyalty Program

20. House Un-American Activities Committee

21. Alger Hiss and Julius and Ethel Rosenberg

22. Joseph R. McCarthy

23. McCarran Internal Security Act, McCarran-Walter Immigration and Nationality Act

MULTIPLE-CHOICE QUESTIONS

Choose the answer that *best* completes the statement or answers the question.

24. Why had Harry Truman been selected as Roosevelt's running mate in 1944?   c
    a. He was a committed New Dealer.
    b. He had wide knowledge of world affairs.
    c. He was a safe, nondescript, middle-of-the-road politician.
    d. He was the candidate of organized labor, which was one of the Democratic party's major interest groups.

25. Early in his presidency, Harry Truman   d
    a. replaced New Deal liberals in the cabinet.
    b. gave key executive posts to old political cronies—the "Missouri Gang."
    c. proposed a twenty-one-point economic-reform program to help the common people against the special interests.
    d. all of the above

26. The United States demobilized rapidly at the end of World War II, and millions of   a
    American soldiers and sailors returned home within a year, because
    a. both the American people and the troops themselves threatened a massive political backlash if they weren't home by Christmas.
    b. President Truman wanted to bring them home to their loved ones as rapidly as possible.
    c. the nation's business leaders pressured Congress to solve a crippling labor shortage.
    d. Congress was worried that if the servicemen stayed in Europe any longer they would develop a lust for killing.

27. All the following were problems potentially facing returning servicemen after   b
    World War II *except*:
    a. a blood lust for killing developed during the war
    b. inability to pay for a college education
    c. sexual problems
    d. a drastic housing shortage

28. All the following contributed to the postwar economic boom in the United States   a
    except: SG

    a. reparations taken from Germany and Japan
    b. wartime savings and pent-up consumer demand
    c. spending made possible by the GI Bill of Rights
    d. new industries and improved production techniques

29. The Bretton Woods Agreement   b

    a. established international oil policy for the major powers of Europe.
    b. established the American dollar as the standard for other foreign currencies, and established a system of trade and international finance.
    c. was an agreement between the United States and Great Britain over the protection of British colonies in Asia.
    d. proposed a system of financial assistance for the beleaguered economies of Western Europe.

30. The Employment Act of 1946   c

    a. established full employment as a federal goal.
    b. gave the president broad powers to achieve maximum employment.
    c. committed the federal government to assuring economic growth.
    d. made Keynesian economics an officially recognized government approach to maximum employment.

31. What was the major postwar economic problem facing the nation?   d

    a. deflation
    b. unemployment
    c. currency reform
    d. inflation

32. The massive labor strikes of 1945–1946 resulted in all the following *except*:   a

    a. a law giving the president authority to draft workers who struck in vital industries
    b. a series of inflationary wage-and-price agreements
    c. growing public hostility to unions
    d. a split between the president and the nation's labor leaders

33. Which of the following provides accurate evidence of the American people's   b
    assessment of the first twenty months of Harry Truman's presidency?

    a. W. C. Fields had become an ardent Truman supporter.
    b. In November 1946 the Republicans gained control of Congress for the first time since 1928.
    c. John L. Lewis took the United Mine Workers out on strike twice, and Truman nationalized the mines twice.
    d. The Democrats gained control of twenty-five governorships in the elections of 1946.

34. In Poland during 1945 and 1946,   c
    a. free elections were held, in accordance with the Yalta agreements, but the Soviet Union nullified the results.
    b. Americans of Polish ancestry who had formed a Thaddeus Kosciusko Brigade fought a guerrilla war against the pro-Soviet Polish government.
    c. the Soviet Union barred free elections and suppressed the democratic parties.
    d. the United States organized an airlift to provide food and supplies to the people of Warsaw.

35. What "lesson" of recent history impressed President Truman and his advisers and   d
    formed a basic diplomatic tenet of his administration?
    a. A war on two fronts was difficult to win.
    b. International peace could be achieved only when the Soviet Union felt secure on its borders.
    c. The Japanese had an innate national tendency toward competition and aggression.
    d. Appeasement toward aggressive dictators leads not to peace but to greater violence and bloodshed.

36. Why did the Truman administration adopt a "get tough" policy toward Poland in   d
    1945–1946?
    a. Truman worried that the American economy would be imperiled by Soviet domination in Eastern Europe.
    b. Democrats feared the domestic political repercussions of appearing to be "soft" on communism.
    c. Truman advisers argued that American generosity or conciliation could lead to a Soviet invasion of Europe.
    d. all of the above

37. George Kennan's sixteen-page cable from Moscow said that   a
    a. conflict with the Soviet Union was inevitable, so the United States had to pursue a firm policy of containing Russian expansion.
    b. the focus of world communism was shifting to China, and the United States should abandon its preoccupation with affairs in Eastern Europe.
    c. the Soviet Union was interested mainly in securing its borders, so the United States should encourage its domination of Eastern Europe.
    d. conflict with the Soviet Union was inevitable, so the United States should, if at all possible, invade Russia and halt its expansive tendencies.

38. When Winston Churchill spoke in Missouri about an "iron curtain," he was refer-   b
    ring to
    a. the division that had developed between President Truman's loyal supporters in his home state and his opponents in the rest of the country.
    b. a division between Soviet-dominated Eastern Europe and the rest of the continent.
    c. the barrier that had to be established in order to contain communism within its existing boundaries.
    d. the atomic espionage ring supposedly organized by Klaus Fuchs.

39. All the following were the ways in which the American-Soviet conflict after World   c
    War II was waged *except*:
    a. economic pressure
    b. propaganda and subversion
    c. direct military confrontation
    d. nuclear intimidation

40. According to the Truman Doctrine,   a
    a. the United States had to support free people everywhere who were resisting
       subjugation by armed minorities or by outside pressures.
    b. the United States had the right to intervene in any Latin American nation that
       was threatened by communism.
    c. members of labor unions that went on strike in vital industries would be sub-
       ject to arrest or military draft.
    d. the federal government had to enlarge the New Deal programs in the areas of
       economic security, conservation, and housing.

41. The purpose of the Marshall Plan was to   d
    a. help the hungry and homeless of Europe.
    b. help stop the spread of communism in Europe.
    c. help expand sales of American goods in Europe.
    d. all of the above

42. Which of the following is out of chronological order?   d
    a. Marshall Plan
    b. Soviet blockade of Berlin
    c. NATO established
    d. Churchill's "Iron Curtain" speech

43. The purpose of the Berlin airlift of 1948–1949 was to   b
    a. demonstrate to Stalin that American B-29s could fly great distances while car-
       rying atomic bombs.
    b. provide thousands of tons of food and fuel that were necessary for Berliners
       to survive the Soviet blockade.
    c. help nearly 100,000 Berlin residents escape to West Germany.
    d. land nearly 50,000 American troops in Germany to prevent Soviet aggression.

44. Which of the following European nations would *not* have been a member of   c
    NATO?
    a. Great Britain
    b. Italy
    c. Yugoslavia
    d. Norway

45. Which of the following people did *not* agree with and encourage Truman's "get   **b**
tough with Russia" policy in the late 1940s?   **SG**
    a. Winston Churchill
    b. Henry A. Wallace
    c. George Frost Kennan
    d. Senator Arthur Vandenberg

46. What was Republican John Foster Dulles referring to when he spoke of "the worst   **a**
defeat the United States has suffered in its history"?
    a. the establishment of the communist People's Republic of China
    b. the Japanese attack on Pearl Harbor
    c. the loss of Eastern Europe to communism
    d. the provisions of the Yalta agreements

47. The conclusions of NSC-68 included all the following *except*:   **c**
    a. The Soviet Union had aggressive intentions and desired world domination.
    b. The United States had to embark on a massive military buildup to meet the
       Soviet challenge.
    c. In order to defeat the Soviet Union, the United States had to cultivate good
       relations with the People's Republic of China.
    d. The American people would have to persuaded to support higher taxes.

48. As part of the campaign to be prepared for a nuclear war, individual Americans or   **d**
government agencies did the following: **PT**
    a. issued metal dog tags to students so that their bodies might be identified in
       the event of a nuclear war
    b. acted as Sky Watchers to guard against Russian planes
    c. wore aluminum pajamas and lead-foil brassieres
    d. all of the above

49. What country, according to Harry Truman, was the "Greece of the Far East"?   **a**
    a. Korea
    b. Japan
    c. Taiwan
    d. Vietnam

50. The Korean War was an example of all the following *except*:   **b**
    a. limited war
    b. the triumph of military over political leadership
    c. the containment policy
    d. war without congressional approval

51. Between 1950 and 1953, the United States   **c**
    a. pared back its defense budget from $60 billion to $13 billion.
    b. closed down many military bases around the world.
    c. increased military aid to Jiang Jieshi and the French army in Indochina.
    d. increased trade with the Soviet Union and mainland China as a way of dimin-
       ishing their aggressive tendencies.

52. The Taft-Hartley Act   **a**

   a. outlawed the closed shop and permitted the president to call an eighty-day cooling-off period to delay a strike.
   b. became known as the Magna Carta of the labor movement because of the rights that it ensured for unions.
   c. constituted a slave-labor bill that crippled the labor movement in the United States.
   d. was the cornerstone of President Truman's Fair Deal.

53. The relationship between President Harry Truman and the Eightieth Congress can   **b** be described as

   a. cordial, because Truman knew that he was unpopular and needed to court Republican votes in order to win reelection in 1948.
   b. antagonistic, because Congress was controlled by the Republicans and Truman was a Democrat.
   c. cool but cooperative, as Congress tried to push Truman toward support of further New Deal–type legislation.
   d. a two-year honeymoon, because the Democrats had regained control of Congress, and Truman was able to capitalize on Roosevelt's aura.

54. In the years immediately after World War II, American civil-rights leaders   **c**

   a. ended most of their activity in the South because of intimidation, repression, and murder.
   b. found themselves shut out of the White House because of Harry Truman's fear of alienating southern white Democrats.
   c. launched aggressive voter-registration drives in the South.
   d. were revealed by congressional investigations to be pro-communist.

55. What was President Truman's motive in adopting an active pro-civil-rights policy   **d** beginning in 1946?

   a. He believed that every American should enjoy the full rights of citizenship.
   b. He wanted to cultivate the black vote for future elections.
   c. He felt that racial inequality in the United States undercut American foreign policy in its contest with the Soviet Union.
   d. all of the above

56. The Dixiecrats   **a**

   a. were white supremacists who were determined to protect the southern way of life against an oppressive central government.
   b. bolted the Democratic party and supported Thomas Dewey in the 1948 presidential election.
   c. formed the core of Harry Truman's support in the solid South during the 1948 election.
   d. none of the above

57. In 1948 Harry Truman's chances of reelection looked grim for all the following   b
    reasons *except*:
    a. Southern segregationists had split with the Democratic party over the civil-rights plank in the party platform.
    b. Republican candidates Dewey and Warren ran a vigorous, aggressive campaign that kept Truman on the defensive.
    c. Left-wing Democrats had formed a splinter party that claimed to be the true heir of New Deal liberalism.
    d. The Republican platform approved much of the New Deal and the Truman administration's bipartisan foreign policy.

58. Truman was able to stage an upset victory in the election of 1948 because   c
       SG
    a. he gave in to southern wishes and ran on a weak civil-rights platform.
    b. he chose the staunch anticommunist Richard M. Nixon as his running mate.
    c. he re-created the old New Deal coalition and won an even greater percentage of the black vote than had Roosevelt.
    d. He wooed the left wing of the Democratic party with promises to reach an accord with the Soviet Union and drop the Employee Loyalty program.

59. Which of the following was accomplished during Truman's presidency?   a
       SG
    a. The armed forces were desegregated.
    b. A national health-insurance system was started.
    c. Labor unions were strengthened by government backing for the closed shop.
    d. A federal anti-lynching law was enacted.

60. Which of the following was *not* one of the signs in 1946–1948 of changing   d
    national attitudes toward civil-rights issues?
    a. The Supreme Court declared segregation in interstate bus transportation unconstitutional.
    b. Many states and cities passed fair-employment-practices and public-accommodations laws.
    c. The Brooklyn Dodgers hired the first black player in major-league baseball.
    d. Southern segregationists bolted the Democratic party over the presidential nomination.

61. Which of the following was *not* one of the reasons that many Americans became   b
    concerned about the nation's security during the late 1940s?
    a. The communists were victorious in China.
    b. The Soviet Union beat the United States in the race to develop a hydrogen bomb.
    c. A major spy network was discovered to have given American military information and atomic secrets to the Russians during World War II.
    d. Congressional investigations into communist influence in American life dominated the news.

62. Between 1947 and 1951, the loyalty boards that were established to root out subversives in government service   c

    a. uncovered evidence of massive subversion and espionage within the Departments of State and Defense.
    b. restricted their investigations to potential subversives in high-risk areas of government service.
    c. forced nearly three thousand government employees to resign and fired some three hundred on charges of disloyalty.
    d. restored to federal government employees a sense of calm and confidence that had been missing since the end of World War II.

63. In the late 1940s and early 1950s, what did Marvel Comics, the House Un-American Activities Committee, Hollywood, and some thirty-nine state legislatures have in common?   d

    a. They were all revealed to be riddled with communist spies and other subversives.
    b. They all took vigorous stands against the witch hunting of Senator Joseph McCarthy.
    c. They all participated in the crusade to clear Alger Hiss and Julius and Ethel Rosenberg of charges that they passed secrets to the Soviets.
    d. They all contributed to the anticommunist hysteria of the period and tried to root out subversives in American society.

64. The House Un-American Activities Committee was   a

    a. responsible for a series of highly publicized hearings designed to expose communist influence in American life.
    b. the name that Senator Joseph McCarthy gave to the House Armed Services Committee.
    c. declared by the Supreme Court to be in violation of basic civil liberties and therefore unconstitutional.
    d. shut down by President Truman as a signal to the nation that the crusade against communist subversion would be directed from the White House.

65. In 1951 the Supreme Court asserted in *Dennis* v. *U.S.* that   b

    a. it was illegal to advocate the overthrow of the government.
    b. Congress had the power to curtail freedom of speech when its members concluded that national security demanded such restriction.
    c. Congress had no right to restrict the purely political activities of any organization, regardless of the popularity of that organization's views.
    d. none of the above

66. Alger Hiss   **c**
    a. charged that Whittaker Chambers had committed espionage in the 1930s by giving Hiss secret State Department documents to be transferred to the Soviet Union.
    b. was indicted for espionage and, after a first trial ended in a hung jury, was convicted of espionage in 1950.
    c. was accused of being a communist and stealing state secrets in the 1930s, and was convicted of lying under oath.
    d. described Richard Nixon's campaign for the Senate against Helen Gahagan Douglas as "the most treasonable conspiracy in American history."

67. Which of the following people was convicted and executed for conspiring to commit espionage?   **d**
    a. Alger Hiss
    b. "Red Dean" Acheson
    c. Whittaker Chambers
    d. Julius Rosenberg

68. Senator Joseph McCarthy won strong backing from all the following groups *except*:   **b**
    SG
    a. midwestern Republicans angered by Truman's support of New Deal reforms and a foreign policy with a Europe-first emphasis
    b. eastern, upper-class, Protestant Democrats and Republicans, such as Dean Acheson and Nelson Rockefeller
    c. traditionally Democratic Catholic ethnics, such as Polish-Americans and Irish-Americans
    d. working- and lower-middle-class Americans who shared his resentment of the privileged Ivy League–educated eastern politicians prominent in government and especially in the State Department

69. When General Dwight Eisenhower received the Republican nomination for president in 1952, which wing of the party was he viewed as representing?   **a**
    a. the moderate eastern wing
    b. the conservative isolationist wing
    c. the hard-line anticommunist wing
    d. the pro–Defense Department wing

70. The Republicans were victorious in the 1952 election because of   **d**
    a. the Korean stalemate and Eisenhower's pledge to go to Korea.
    b. wage-and-price freezes and government corruption.
    c. Stevenson's intellectualism and Eisenhower's military stature and infectious smile.
    d. all of the above

71. Which of the following quotations is correctly matched with the person who made   c
it and the person or persons to whom it refers?

    a. "pink right down to her underwear"—Joseph McCarthy about Ethel Rosenberg
    b. "bright young men who are born with silver spoons in their mouths"—Richard Nixon about Alger Hiss and Whittaker Chambers
    c. "We are the first victims of American fascism."—Ethel Rosenberg about herself and her husband
    d. ". . . you're a dirty s.o.b., but there are times when you've got to have an s.o.b. around, and this is one of them"—Harry Truman referring to Adlai Stevenson

---

ESSAY QUESTIONS

72. In what ways did the Cold War "affect American life as decisively as any military   PT
engagement that the nation had ever fought"? Discuss, for example, the impact of and on the following: the military; Americans' views of their role in the world; domestic politics, political parties, New Deal liberalism, and American conservatism; civil liberties; and learning to live in a nuclear age.

73. Examine Harry Truman as president. What were his beliefs? What was his foreign policy? His domestic policy? Was he an effective president? What were his most significant accomplishments, and his most significant failures?

74. Explain the challenges and fears facing the United States at the end of World War II as it converted to a peacetime economy. To what extent was that conversion successful? Why did the nation experience prosperity rather than economic disaster?

75. Discuss the origins of the Cold War. Explain the differences in policy, goals, and assumptions between the United States and the Soviet Union. Is it possible to assess "blame" for the Cold War, or were both sides equally responsible? Explain the fundamental features of United States Cold War policy in the late 1940s and early 1950s.

76. What was the "containment policy"? How did the Truman administration imple-   SG
ment it in Europe and in Asia?

77. What were the causes of the Korean War? How did it affect American foreign policy? What precedents did it set? What was the *significance* of the conflict between President Truman and General MacArthur?

78. What substantive accomplishments were achieved in civil rights during the Truman administration? To what extent were those accomplishments the work of Truman, and to what extent were they the product of outside groups, other branches of the government, and political pressures? What evidence is there that the mood of the country with regard to civil rights was shifting during these years?

79. What were the issues and who were the personalities in the 1948 and 1952 presidential elections? Explain the reasons for and impact of splinter parties in 1948. Why did the Republicans lose in 1948 but win in 1952?

80. What were the causes of the anticommunist hysteria that swept the nation in the late 1940s and early 1950s? Why did McCarthyism receive so much support?

81. How did the domestic anticommunist crusade affect the following: politics, the labor movement, education, civil liberties, and foreign policy? Give specific examples of the crusade. Discuss especially Joseph McCarthy and the Hiss and Rosenberg cases. Evaluate both the positive and negative effects of the crusade.

MAP QUESTIONS

Choose the letter on the accompanying map of Europe and the Middle East that correctly identifies each of the following:

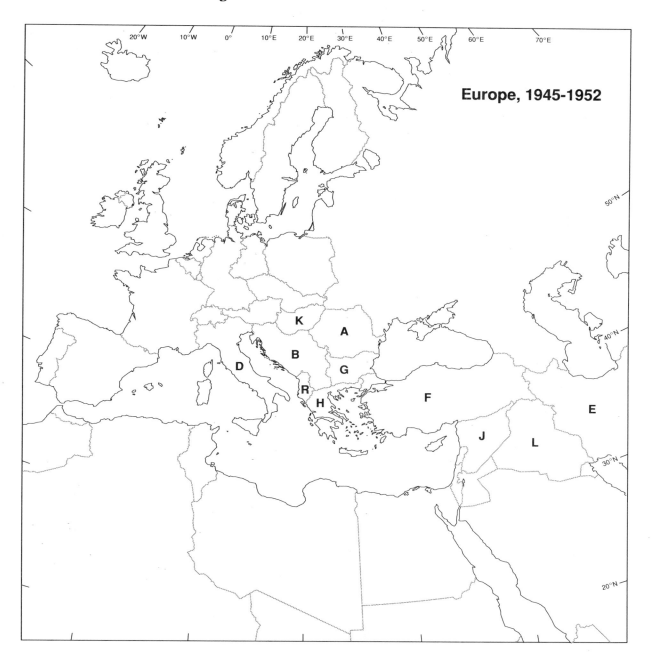

Europe, 1945-1952

82. Iran   E

83. Greece   H

84. Turkey   F

85. Romania   A

86. Albania   R

87. Yugoslavia   B

Choose the letter on the accompanying map of East Asia that correctly identifies each of the following:

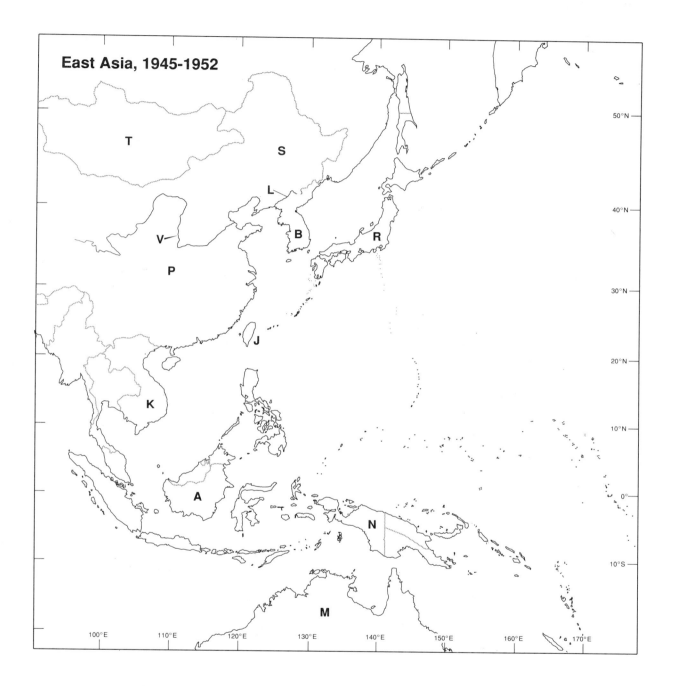

East Asia, 1945-1952

88. Manchuria   S

89. Korea   B

90. French Indochina   **K**

91. Taiwan   **J**

92. Yalu River   **L**

CHAPTER 28

America at Midcentury

IDENTIFICATIONS

Identify the following. Be as specific as possible, and include names, dates, and relevant facts as appropriate. Be sure to explain the *significance* of the person or term.

1. strontium-90

2. Joseph McCarthy

3. House Un-American Activities Committee

4. John Birch Society

5. *Brown* v. *Board of Education of Topeka*

6. *Jencks* v. *United States*, *Yates* v. *United States*

7. the Beats, Allen Ginsberg, Jack Kerouac

8. Earl Warren

9. Southern Manifesto

10. Governor Orval E. Faubus, Little Rock's Central High School

11. Civil Rights Act of 1957, Civil Rights Act of 1960

12. John Foster Dulles

13. 1955 Geneva East-West summit

14. Allen Dulles

15. Ho Chi Minh, Vietminh, Dienbienphu

16. Domino Theory

17. Ngo Dinh Diem

18. Gamal Abdel Nasser, Aswan Dam, Suez Canal

19. Eisenhower Doctrine

20. Mark I, ENIAC

21. George Meany, AFL-CIO

22. Levitt & Sons, Levittown

23. Dr. Benjamin Spock, *Baby and Child Care*

24. Rosa Parks

25. Dr. Martin Luther King, Jr., the Southern Christian Leadership Conference

26. Operation Wetback

27. *Sputnik*

MULTIPLE-CHOICE QUESTIONS

Choose the answer that *best* completes the statement or answers the question.

28. What kind of popular films expressed the mood of the 1950s?   c
    a. screwball comedies
    b. gangster films
    c. horror films
    d. *film noir*

29. Dwight Eisenhower's presidency was characterized by all the following *except*:   a
    a. feuds with Congress
    b. a restrained view of presidential authority
    c. delegating affairs of government to subordinates
    d. bringing factions together

30. What best describes Eisenhower's political ideology?   d
    a. radical right
    b. left-liberal
    c. new conservative
    d. centrist

31. The Interstate Highway Act   d
    a. was the largest and most expansive public-works program in American history.
    b. heightened Americans' dependence on cars and trucks.
    c. accelerated suburban growth and contributed to the decay of central cities.
    d. all of the above

32. President Eisenhower was associated with each of the following *except*:   a

    SG

    a. bringing about the downfall of Joseph McCarthy by publicly denouncing his irresponsible accusations
    b. appointing Earl Warren as chief justice of the United States
    c. bringing an end to the Korean War with the signing of an armistice in 1953
    d. warning the nation about the growing power of the military and big industrial corporations in American life

33. What happened to the works of Ralph Waldo Emerson, Henry David Thoreau, and Mark Twain during the McCarthy Era?   b

    a. Joseph McCarthy insisted that such American authors constitute the sole English curriculum in public schools.
    b. They were banned in the U.S. Information Agency's overseas libraries.
    c. They were quoted extensively in the Army-McCarthy hearings.
    d. none of the above

34. The "new conservatives" advocated all the following *except*:   c

    a. victory over communism instead of containment
    b. a return to older moral standards
    c. gun control
    d. the impeachment of Supreme Court Justice Earl Warren

35. Which of the following was a major Supreme Court civil-rights case?   a

    a. *Brown* v. *Board of Education of Topeka*
    b. *Jencks* v. *United States*
    c. *Yates* v. *United States*
    d. all of the above

36. Southern states responded to the Supreme Court ruling which outlawed segregation in schools by   b

    a. resentfully complying.
    b. refusing to comply.
    c. welcoming the ruling as a step forward for social progress.
    d. establishing separate but equal schools for blacks.

37. What did Eisenhower call "the biggest damn fool mistake I've ever made"?   c

    a. failing to publicly confront Joseph McCarthy
    b. sending troops to Vietnam
    c. appointing Earl Warren to the Supreme Court
    d. appointing John Foster Dulles as secretary of state

38. The Civil Rights Act of 1957   b

    a. was opposed by President Eisenhower because he believed one couldn't change the hearts of men with laws.
    b. established a permanent commission on civil rights with broad investigatory powers.
    c. empowered federal officials to register blacks to vote.
    d. overturned the doctrine of "separate but equal" in education.

39. The Cold War philosophy of John Foster Dulles was   c
   a. pacifism.
   b. conciliation.
   c. anticommunism.
   d. creeping socialism.

40. The "New Look" defense program in the 1950s depended on   c
   a. strengthening the army and navy.
   b. new methods of guerrilla warfare learned in Vietnam.
   c. nuclear bombs and the planes to deliver them.
   d. clandestine CIA operations.

41. The CIA was responsible for all the following in the 1950s *except*:   d
   a. secretly returning the deposed shah of Iran to power
   b. intervening in elections in the Philippines to ensure a pro-American government
   c. supporting a coup in Guatemala and instituting a military dictatorship
   d. intervening in East Germany and Hungary when the Soviet Union crushed popular insurrections

42. The United States' initial involvement in Vietnam consisted of   b
   a. furnishing aid to the nationalist coalition, the Vietminh.
   b. furnishing aid to the French, who were trying to reconquer their former colony.
   c. committing American troops to assist the French.
   d. committing atomic weapons to assist the French.

43. Eisenhower's "Domino Theory" about the successive fall of countries to communism referred to   d
   a. Central America.
   b. the Middle East.
   c. Central Europe.
   d. Indochina.

44. Ngo Dinh Diem, the president of South Vietnam who was backed by the United States, lacked popular support in his country for all the following reasons *except*:   c
   a. There was widespread corruption in his government.
   b. He refused to institute land reform for the peasants.
   c. His Buddhism alienated the predominantly Catholic population.
   d. He refused to hold the promised elections to unify North and South Vietnam.

45. Eisenhower's greatest crisis in the Middle East began when Egyptian leader Gamal Abdel Nasser   b
   a. nationalized the oil wells in Egypt.
   b. seized the Suez Canal.
   c. seized the Aswan Dam.
   d. invaded Israel.

46. In 1956 President Eisenhower responded to the aggression of England, France, and Israel against Egypt by   c

    a. commending their action and offering military assistance.
    b. threatening nuclear war if they did not withdraw from Egypt.
    c. initiating a U.N. resolution condemning the aggression and calling for their withdrawal from Egypt.
    d. offering military assistance to Nasser.

47. The Eisenhower Doctrine declaring that the United States would send military aid and, if necessary, troops to help counter communist thrusts pertained to   a

    a. the Middle East.
    b. Indochina.
    c. Latin America.
    d. Western Europe.

48. Soviet-American relations became strained in 1960 when   b

    a. a Soviet spy plane was shot down within U.S. borders.
    b. an American spy plane was shot down within Soviet borders.
    c. the Soviets resumed atmospheric tests of nuclear weapons.
    d. the United States resumed atmospheric tests of nuclear weapons.

49. Dwight Eisenhower's foreign policy was characterized by all the following *except*:   b

    a. the end of the war in Korea
    b. limitations on the power of the CIA
    c. the avoidance of direct military intervention in Vietnam
    d. the acceleration of the nuclear-arms race

50. Which book described the United States' economy during the postwar era?   c

    a. *Progress and Poverty*
    b. *Looking Backward*
    c. *The Affluent Society*
    d. *The Theory of the Leisure Class*

51. All the following were growth industries during the 1950s *except*:   d

    a. chemicals
    b. electronics
    c. aircraft manufacture
    d. home computers

52. Which did *not* occur in the 1950s?   c
                                           SG
    a. The total number of farms declined as large-scale agribusinesses increasingly dominated farming.
    b. Less than one percent of American business firms earned more than half of all corporate profits.
    c. The portion of the labor force belonging to unions increased from roughly one-quarter to almost one-half.
    d. More than half of the federal budget each year went to finance military preparedness.

53. The professional managerial class in the 1950s was   b
    a. capitalists rather than executives.
    b. conformists.
    c. "inner-directed."
    d. all of the above

54. Which of the following is *not* a factor in the complacency of organized labor in the   d
    1950s?
    a. decent wages and benefit packages
    b. a work week of fewer than forty hours
    c. the self-image of unionized workers as members of the affluent society
    d. success in organizing white-collar workers

55. Which of the following stimuli to consumerism was introduced in the 1950s?   a
    a. credit cards
    b. installment buying
    c. celebrities advertising products
    d. mail-order catalogs

56. Homeownership in Levittown in the 1950s was stimulated by all the following   c
    except: PT
    a. standardized construction methods
    b. extensive car ownership and the expanding highway system
    c. the migration of black Americans from the ghettos to the suburbs
    d. low-cost mortgages from the Federal Housing Administration and the Veter-
       ans Administration

57. The 1950s saw all the following demographic shifts *except*:   c
    a. Some 18 million Americans moved from cities to suburbs.   SG
    b. More than 5 million Americans moved from the North and East to the South
       and West.
    c. Total United States population grew less than in any previous decade of the
       twentieth century.
    d. Millions of rural blacks and Puerto Ricans moved to cities.

58. The population shift to the Sunbelt increased the political power of   b
    a. the Democratic party.
    b. the Republican party.
    c. migrant workers.
    d. organized labor.

59. Which was a cause of the 1950s baby boom?   a
    a. couples marrying at an earlier age
    b. birth control becoming illegal
    c. women leaving the work force
    d. all of the above

60. The child-rearing theories of Dr. Benjamin Spock advocated that   c
    a. babies be fed on a strict schedule to instill orderly habits.
    b. bottle feeding be used instead of breast feeding because fathers could participate more fully in parenting.
    c. full-time mothers comfort crying babies to instill feelings of security and intimacy.
    d. children should be treated like little adults.

61. Which of the following statements about American women in the 1950s is correct?   b
    SG
    a. Women generally married later and had fewer children than they had in the 1930s and 1940s.
    b. Women constituted a smaller percentage of college students and received fewer advanced degrees than they had in the 1920s and 1930s.
    c. The proportion of married women who were employed declined.
    d. A greater proportion of women became involved in the feminist movement than ever before.

62. The most positive image of women in 1950s popular culture was   c
    a. the career woman.
    b. the intellectual.
    c. the housewife.
    d. the political activist.

63. Who was *not* a leading religious popularizer in the 1950s?   d
    a. Billy Graham
    b. Norman Vincent Peale
    c. Fulton J. Sheen
    d. Aimee Semple McPherson

64. Which of the following was evidence of the renewed interest in religion in the   d
    1950s?
    a. Congress added the phrase "under God" to the Pledge of Allegiance.
    b. "In God We Trust" became mandatory on U.S. currency.
    c. Among Hollywood's biggest hits were religious extravaganzas.
    d. all of the above

65. The leading educational theory of the 1950s   c
    a. emphasized "back to basics"—science, math, and history.
    b. encouraged student political activism.
    c. promoted sociability, health education, and self-expression to develop well-rounded students.
    d. rejected sex roles, and encouraged both boys and girls to achieve academically.

66. Which of the following 1950s novels is *not* correctly matched with its topic? **b**
   a. Eudora Welty's *The Ponder Heart*—southern small-town life
   b. Ralph Ellison's *Invisible Man*—dissatisfaction with corporate and suburban life
   c. Philip Roth's *Goodbye Columbus*—upwardly mobile Jews
   d. J. D. Salinger's *The Catcher in the Rye*—alienated youth

67. What was described in 1961 as a "vast wasteland"? **c**
   a. the movie industry because it could not compete with television in popularity
   b. the American education system because it was anti-intellectual
   c. television because of its mediocre programming
   d. the sprawling highway system with its fast-food chains and gas stations

68. About what portion of the American people lived in poverty during the prosperous 1950s? **b**
   a. one-third
   b. one-fifth
   c. one-half
   d. one-tenth

69. The 1955–1956 black boycott of segregated buses in Montgomery, Alabama, led to **a**
   a. affirmation by the U.S. Supreme Court of a lower-court decision outlawing segregation on buses.
   b. the assassination of Martin Luther King.
   c. the voluntary concession by white leaders in Montgomery to integrate buses.
   d. the collapse of the civil-rights movement when black leaders were unable to deliver on their promises of social change.

70. Martin Luther King's philosophy of civil disobedience incorporated **d**
   a. the spirit of evangelical Christianity's sacrifice and redemption.
   b. nonviolent resistance.
   c. direct action.
   d. all of the above

71. Puerto Ricans experienced which of the following when they migrated to the United States from Puerto Rico? **b**
   a. deportation as "undocumented aliens"
   b. reversal in traditional sex roles and parental authority over children
   c. a middle-class lifestyle in the barrio
   d. all of the above

72. The *Asociacion Nacional Mexico-Americana* and the League of United Latin American Citizens   c
    a. established Operation Wetback to help Mexicans swim across the Rio Grande into the United States.
    b. advocated a "Back to Mexico" movement because Hispanics could have freedom and power only in a Hispanic country.
    c. sought to stop abuses against aliens and violations of the rights of Mexican-Americans.
    d. advocated the secession of parts of the southwestern United States that were heavily populated by Mexicans.

73. Federal policies toward Indians during the 1950s   a
    a. enabled nonwhites to take over much of the native American land, while encouraging Indians to move to urban areas.
    b. recognized the importance of Indian culture and helped maintain tribal life.
    c. gave preferential treatment to native Americans over other minority groups and elevated their relative economic status.
    d. thwarted agricultural, lumber, and mining interests in their desire for Indian land by establishing the reservation system.

74. What was the most significant cause of the increase in federal aid to education and the shift to greater emphasis on basic disciplines in the late 1950s?   d
    a. the influx of non-English-speaking Hispanics into the United States
    b. alarm over the popularity of the nonconformist Beats on college campuses
    c. a "war on poverty" that was declared when it became apparent that high-school drop-outs were swelling the welfare rolls
    d. the launch of *Sputnik*, which gave Americans reason to fear that they were intellectually and technologically backward

75. Many middle-class parents objected to rock-and-roll because   a
    a. they linked rock-and-roll with sex and violence.
    b. many rock-and-roll singers such as Elvis Presley were avowed communist sympathizers.
    c. they feared that the black rhythm-and-blues inspiration for rock-and-roll would lead to integration and intermarriage.
    d. rock-and-roll was linked with a widespread drug culture.

ESSAY QUESTIONS

76. How did Eisenhower steer a middle-of-the-road course in his domestic policies? What did he mean when he called his philosophy "dynamic conservatism" and "modern Republicanism"? What style did Eisenhower adopt as an executive?

77. How did McCarthyism reflect the conservative tenor of 1950s politics? Did the Warren court reinforce or counter this conservatism? How?

78. What progress did the civil-rights movement make in the 1950s? Refer specifically to *Brown* v. *Board of Education of Topeka* and the Montgomery, Alabama, bus boycott. How did whites respond to blacks' demand for desegregation? What role did Rosa Parks and Dr. Martin Luther King play in spurring southern blacks to fight for their rights?

79. Discuss Eisenhower's legacy in foreign policy. How successful was he in keeping the peace and easing tensions with the Soviets? In what ways did his policies expand the Cold War and accelerate the nuclear-arms race? **SG**

80. Describe the United States' involvement in Vietnam and the Middle East in the 1950s. Explain the Domino Theory and the Eisenhower Doctrine.

81. What role did women play in the work force and in the family during the 1950s? Did popular culture (television, movies) reflect the reality of women's lives? How did educational institutions reinforce sex roles in the 1950s?

82. In the 1950s, some critics described "an America of mass housing, mass markets, . . . mass media, and mass boredom." Discuss how trends in mass culture developed in the 1950s, focusing especially on the rise of suburbia, television, and consumerism. Why were so many people attracted to mass culture?

83. Does the title of John Kenneth Galbraith's book *The Affluent Society* accurately reflect the economy of the 1950s? How was this affluence measured? What sectors of the economy boomed? How did organized labor, Hispanics (Puerto Ricans and Mexican-Americans), and native Americans fare in this economy?

84. What kinds of dissent existed in the supposedly placid, homogeneous 1950s? Refer specifically to novelists, Beat writers, rock-and-roll, and youth rebellion.

85. How did child-rearing and education theories meet the needs of society in the 1950s? What changes occurred in the late 1950s in education? Why?

MAP QUESTIONS

Choose the letter on the accompanying map of the eastern United States that correctly identifies each of the following:

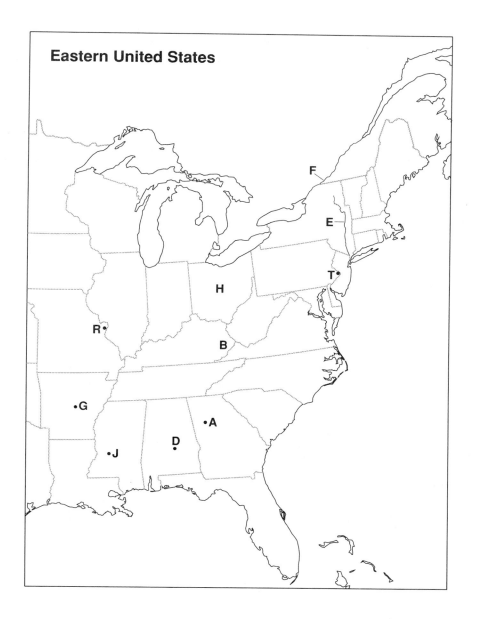

Eastern United States

86. Appalachia   B

87. Montgomery, Alabama   D

88. St. Lawrence Seaway   **F**

89. Little Rock, Arkansas   **G**

90. Levittown   **T**

Choose the letter on the accompanying map of East Asia that correctly identifies each of the following:

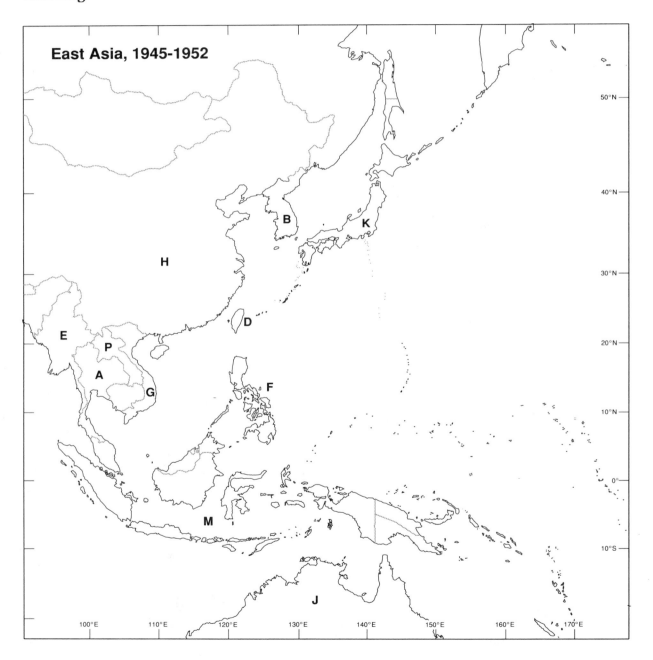

East Asia, 1945-1952

91. Korea

B

92. Taiwan

D

93. Philippines

F

94. Vietnam

G

95. Thailand

A

96. Burma

E

97. Indonesia

M

Choose the letter on the accompanying map of the Middle East that correctly identifies each of the following:

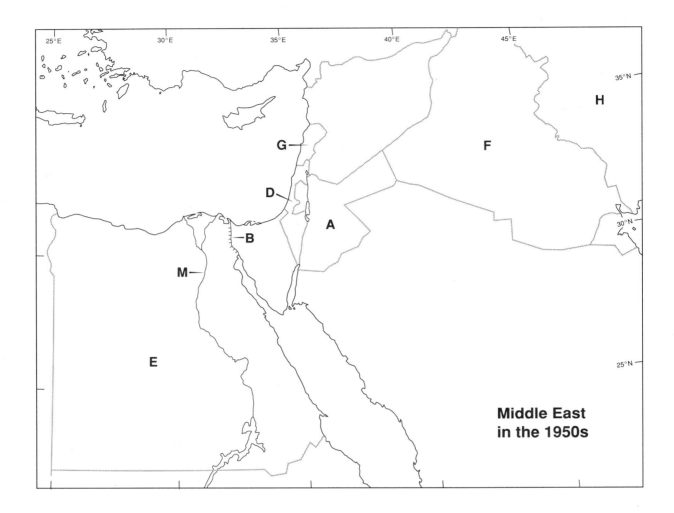

98. Iran   H

99. Egypt   E

100. Suez Canal   B

101. Israel   D

102. Jordan   A

CHAPTER 29

The Turbulent Sixties

IDENTIFICATIONS

Identify the following. Be as specific as possible, and include names, dates, and relevant facts as appropriate. Be sure to explain the *significance* of the person or term.

1. New Frontier

2. Rachel Carson, *Silent Spring*

3. Clean Air Act of 1963

4. freedom rides

5. Congress of Racial Equality

6. Alliance for Progress, Peace Corps

7. Bay of Pigs

8. Cuban missile crisis

9. Ngo Dinh Diem

10. National Liberation Front

11. Civil Rights Act of 1964

12. Michael Harrington, *The Other America*

13. War on Poverty

14. Job Corps, VISTA, Project Head Start

15. Great Society

16. white backlash

17. Barry Goldwater

18. Earl Warren

19. *Miranda* v. *Arizona*

20. Mississippi Summer Project

21. race riots of 1964–1968

22. Kerner Commission

23. Malcolm X

24. Stokely Carmichael and H. Rap Brown

25. Black Panthers

26. National Organization for Women

27. Betty Friedan, *The Feminine Mystique*

28. Gulf of Tonkin resolution

29. Operation Rolling Thunder

MULTIPLE-CHOICE QUESTIONS

Choose the answer that *best* completes the statement or answers the question.

30. Which of the following is *not* true about John F. Kennedy?   a
    a. He had compiled an impressive record of achievement during his years in Congress and had sponsored much notable reform legislation.
    b. He had won a Pulitzer Prize for a book that had been written primarily by one of his staff members.
    c. He was esteemed as a war hero and projected an image of vigor and rugged good looks.
    d. He was the first Roman Catholic to become president of the United States.

31. In the 1960 presidential election, Richard M. Nixon's advantages over his rival,   b
    John F. Kennedy, included
    a. his independence from the crises and scandals of the Eisenhower administration.
    b. his religion and his experience.
    c. his poise, dynamism, and experience in front of the television cameras.
    d. all of the above

32. Which of the following helped to determine the outcome of the 1960 presidential   d
    election?
    a. the television debate
    b. the economy
    c. the U-2 incident
    d. all of the above

33. The results of the 1960 presidential election reflected   a
    a. a widespread desire all around the country for change.
    b. the growing influence of "yellow journalism."
    c. widespread hostility to the idea of a Catholic president.
    d. the enduring popularity of Dwight Eisenhower.

34. President Kennedy's top domestic priority was   b
    a. social legislation to benefit blacks and women.
    b. economic growth through defense spending and incentives to private enterprise.
    c. controlling runaway inflation.
    d. meeting and beating the threat from environmental pollution.

35. Why did the Kennedy administration have such a poor record of legislative   c
    accomplishments?
    a. Members of the administration had no program for reform.
    b. The threat of communism abroad forced the president to turn from domestic affairs and concentrate on foreign affairs.
    c. The administration had received a weak electoral mandate and lacked the votes in Congress.
    d. An economic recession required that the federal government reduce its expenditures, so the administration refrained from proposing new programs.

36. Who said, "There is no sense in raising hell and then not being successful," and   d
    why?
    a. Richard Nixon, to explain why he did not run a more vigorous campaign for president in 1960
    b. Lyndon Johnson, to explain why he was not running for reelection in 1968
    c. Stokely Carmichael, to encourage his Black Power supporters to burn down Chicago
    d. John Kennedy, to justify his failure to press Congress to enact reform legislation

37. Which of the following was *not* one of the accomplishments of the Kennedy   a
    administration?
    a. social legislation to fight poverty and finance medical care for the elderly
    b. a massive arms buildup
    c. wage-and-price restraints to curb inflation
    d. a crash program to put an American on the moon

38. Rachel Carson's *Silent Spring* dealt with   b
    a. the failures of American youth during the placid 1950s.
    b. the hazards of DDT and other pesticides.
    c. the year in which Americans failed to speak out against racial prejudice.
    d. a secret buildup of American military forces in Vietnam during the spring of 1962.

39. Which of the following captures the approach of the Kennedy administration to the issue of civil rights? **c**

    a. a decline in the amount of civil-rights litigation by the Justice Department
    b. acceptance of racial discrimination in federally financed housing
    c. reluctance to take a firm stand followed eventually by the introduction of civil-rights legislation
    d. all of the above

40. Which of the following statements about Martin Luther King, Jr.'s, speech to the 1963 Washington civil-rights rally is correct? **d**
    PT

    a. It spurred the United States Congress to swiftly approve President Kennedy's civil-rights bill.
    b. It was a failure because the turnout at the rally was poor and it came at the end of a long and hot day of lengthy speeches.
    c. It was dramatically interrupted when a white racist shot King as he spoke on the steps of the Lincoln Memorial.
    d. It turned a political rally into a historic event and recalled the nation to the ideals of justice and equality.

41. Which of the following statements about the Bay of Pigs invasion is accurate? **a**

    a. The Cuban exiles were captured without ever having established a defensible beachhead.
    b. The CIA-conceived invasion of Cuba triggered a general uprising that nearly toppled Fidel Castro's regime.
    c. After the invasion failed, President Kennedy went on television to apologize for his administration's effort to overthrow the Castro regime.
    d. It was the first and last effort of the Kennedy administration to overthrow Fidel Castro.

42. The most serious conflict between the United States and the Soviet Union during the Kennedy administration occurred over **b**

    a. Berlin.
    b. Cuba.
    c. Vietnam.
    d. Turkey.

43. Which of the following correctly suggests the Kennedy policy toward the Soviet Union in 1963? **c**

    a. an embargo of Cuba and development of new nuclear weapons
    b. compromise on Berlin and conflict over Vietnam
    c. a major wheat sale and a nuclear test-ban treaty
    d. a summit conference marred by the downing of an American spy plane

44. On the basis of which of the following assumptions did the Kennedy administration formulate its policy toward Vietnam?   d
    a. Allowing aggression to go unchecked could lead to a wider war.
    b. Communism was a monolithic movement under the direct control of Moscow and Beijing.
    c. Conflicts fomented by the communist leadership were tests of the United States', and the president's, will.
    d. all of the above

45. The policy of the Kennedy administration toward Vietnam included   a
    a. sending some 16,000 military advisers to South Vietnam and attempting to move South Vietnamese peasants into fortified villages to isolate the Vietcong.
    b. sending American troops to protect Premier Ngo Dinh Diem from an expected military coup.
    c. withdrawal of American troops and negotiations with the Soviet Union to install a neutral premier.
    d. an embargo of the South to force Premier Ngo Dinh Diem to deliver on his promise of land reform.

46. The man accused of assassinating John F. Kennedy was   c
    a. William Miller.
    b. Medgar Evers.
    c. Lee Harvey Oswald.
    d. Jack Ruby.

47. Who was thought of by his liberal critics as "a Machiavelli in a Stetson"?   b
    a. John F. Kennedy
    b. Lyndon B. Johnson
    c. Richard M. Nixon
    d. Hubert H. Humphrey

48. Which of the following suggests Lyndon Johnson's policy on civil rights?   c
    a. a cautious "wait and see" attitude that betrayed fear of upsetting his southern constituents
    b. emphasis on increased educational opportunities for blacks, but failure to address immediate economic concerns
    c. enactment of a sweeping civil-rights law that granted the federal government new powers to fight segregation
    d. high-flown speeches that failed to produce significant legislation because of a continuing southern filibuster

49. Which of the following was *not* one of the training programs enacted during the Johnson administration?   d
    a. VISTA
    b. Project Head Start
    c. Job Corps
    d. Peace Corps

50. Who ran against Lyndon Johnson for president in the 1964 election?   **b**
    a. Richard Nixon
    b. Barry Goldwater
    c. Hubert Humphrey
    d. Eugene McCarthy

51. In the 1964 presidential election,   **a**
    a. Lyndon Johnson won over 60 percent of the popular vote while the GOP carried only Arizona and five Deep South states.
    b. the GOP nearly defeated Lyndon Johnson, who had alienated northerners because he was southerner, and southerners because he was too liberal.
    c. the GOP successfully branded Johnson as an irresponsible liberal whose reelection would lead to depression and war in Vietnam.
    d. Lyndon Johnson won a sweeping electoral victory but was unable to help the Democratic party make gains in either the Senate or the House of Representatives.

52. All the following are considered major Great Society programs *except*:   **d**
    a. the Voting Rights Act
    b. the Medical Care Act
    c. the Appalachian Regional Development Act
    d. the Interstate Highway Act

53. President Johnson's vision of a Great Society was one in which   **a**
    a. American society could be transformed by consensus, poverty would be eliminated, and economic opportunity would be available for all.
    b. inequalities between social classes could be eliminated by government wealth-redistribution schemes.
    c. individuals and corporations could work as partners to eliminate poverty without the need for elaborate government-sponsored social-welfare programs.
    d. independent farmers and small shop owners would once again form the backbone of a free and democratic citizenry in the Jeffersonian mold.

54. To what extent did Lyndon Johnson succeed in bringing about his Great Society, and why?   **b**
    a. All the legislation proved to be no more than gigantic boondoggles because the programs were ill-conceived and underfinanced.
    b. Some of Johnson's programs significantly improved the quality of American life, but the major thrust to provide economic opportunity for all was derailed by the war in Vietnam.
    c. Because of the sweeping Johnson programs, poverty was reduced to less than 5 percent of the population for the first time in American history.
    d. Because Congress was generally hostile to most features of Johnson's program, it refused to approve anything more than minimum appropriations, thereby crippling and dooming the programs from the start.

55. In the 1960s some Americans called for the impeachment of Chief Justice Earl   c
Warren because
    a. the Court issued a string of decisions declaring unconstitutional most of the
    liberal Great Society programs of the Johnson administration.
    b. the Court was dominated by five old men who believed in judicial restraint
    and stubbornly refused to decide on any of the major social or political issues
    of the day.
    c. the Court was responsible for a series of extremely liberal decisions that its
    critics thought overstepped the bounds of its constitutional authority.
    d. members of the Court had begun to lobby openly for a more vigorous American military policy in Vietnam.

56. Which of the following was *not* one of the decisions of the Warren court?   d
    a. Bible reading and prayer were not permissible in public schools.
    b. States could not ban the use of contraceptives.
    c. The Constitution protected all sexually explicit material that has any literary
    or scientific or artistic value.
    d. The Constitution protected a woman's right to an abortion.

57. In *Miranda* v. *Arizona*, the Supreme Court declared that   a
    a. police had to advise a suspect of his or her constitutional right to remain
    silent and to have a counsel present during interrogation.
    b. state laws prohibiting marriage between persons of different races were
    unconstitutional.
    c. the federal courts possessed jurisdiction over state apportionment systems to
    ensure that the votes of all citizens carry equal weight.
    d. states could not establish racially segregated schools even if the schools were
    supposed to have equal facilities.

58. By 1964 what had become the major thrust of young black activists?   b
    a. mass lobbying for the legal prohibition of discrimination in public accommodations and facilities
    b. voter-registration drives in southern states
    c. encouragement of economic opportunity for blacks by making Small Business
    Administration loans available for minority-owned companies
    d. encouragement of the development of a separate and distinct sense of African
    culture and heritage among American blacks

59. Which of the following helped to transform southern politics during the 1960s?   d
    a. *Wesberry* v. *Sanders*
    b. Twenty-third Amendment
    c. Voting Rights Act of 1965
    d. all of the above

60. What major change occurred for black Americans in the mid-1960s as a result of southern black activism, court decisions, and federal legislation?   c

    a. Unemployment for blacks had been cut in half and was approaching the rates for white Americans.
    b. Racial discrimination had been eliminated from all spheres of American life.
    c. Black voter registration jumped, and for the first time since Reconstruction blacks became a force to be reckoned with in southern politics.
    d. Blacks were elected to top government positions in all southern states.

61. Between 1964 and 1968, some urban blacks around the country expressed their reaction to the civil-rights movement by   a

    a. looting, rioting, and destroying white property.
    b. launching the most vigorous voter-registration drive in American history.
    c. organizing a series of mass demonstrations and marches that paralyzed city affairs for days at a time.
    d. staging sit-ins at banks in order to get more loans for black-run businesses.

62. Which of the following was an explanation offered for the destructive race riots that swept American cities between 1964 and 1968?   d

    a. They were revolutionary violence to overthrow a racist, reactionary society.
    b. They were evidence of a communist plot to subvert the United States.
    c. The riots amounted to senseless outbursts by a small number, but they brought great distress to all.
    d. all of the above

63. The recommendations of the Kerner Commission report included   b

    a. strengthened local police forces to ensure that law and order could be maintained in the nation's cities.
    b. 2 million new jobs, 6 million units of public housing, the end of de facto school segregation, and a national system of income supplementation.
    c. financing a system of medical care for the elderly through the social-security system.
    d. a 20 percent increase in the defense budget, a fivefold increase in the purchase of intercontinental ballistic missiles, and the building of nuclear submarines armed with Polaris missiles.

64. Malcolm X advocated all the following *except*:   c

    a. Blacks should separate themselves from whites.
    b. Blacks should be proud of their blackness and their African roots.
    c. Blacks should rely on nonviolence and should earn their freedom by passive resistance.
    d. Blacks should control their own destinies.

65. In the 1960s many native Americans began to demand that the federal government   **a**
   a. take action to redress long-standing discrimination and poverty.
   b. provide public-works projects to improve the reservations.
   c. end the practice of keeping them on reservations.
   d. allow them to leave the United States and establish a new homeland on a South Pacific island.

66. The person largely responsible for kindling the ethnic pride and solidarity of   **b**
   Mexican-Americans in the 1960s was
   a. Carmen Miranda.
   b. César Chávez.
   c. Martin Luther King, Jr.
   d. Mario Savio.

67. In the 1960s Betty Friedan and other women began to call for   **c**
   a. a chance to prove themselves as wives, mothers, and homemakers.
   b. more concern for the political and social problems of blacks, native Americans, and Chicanos, and less emphasis on the personal, selfish concerns of middle-class American women.
   c. equality with men and an opportunity to control their own lives and define their own goals.
   d. a revolution in attitudes toward sex roles so that American men would be more like John F. Kennedy.

68. The most widespread technique used by feminists in the 1960s to recruit supporters and help transform women's perceptions of themselves and society was   **d**
   a. public bra burning.
   b. mass rallies.
   c. sit-ins at all-male bars and social clubs.
   d. consciousness-raising discussion groups.

69. What policy did Lyndon Johnson follow with regard to American involvement in   **a**
   Vietnam?
   a. gradually escalate the direct American role in the war
   b. rapidly send American ground troops in for a massive invasion of North Vietnam
   c. gradually withdraw while asking for United Nations mediation
   d. pull out immediately and declare that the United States had achieved its goals

70. The Gulf of Tonkin resolution   b

    a. advocated the use of nuclear weapons against North Vietnam if that govern-
       ment did not accede to American demands.
    b. authorized the president to take all necessary measures to repel any armed
       attack against American forces and to prevent further aggression in Vietnam.
    c. condemned United States involvement in Vietnam and demanded that Ameri-
       can troops be withdrawn immediately.
    d. constituted a congressional explanation to the American people of the John-
       son administration's immediate and long-term foreign policy goals in South-
       east Asia.

71. Opponents of American involvement in the Vietnam War said that   d

    a. the war was a civil conflict in which the United States had no business
       meddling.
    b. the war would force drastic cutbacks in Great Society social programs.
    c. the United States could never win the war without impossible expense.
    d. all of the above

72. How did ordinary Americans feel about continued United States involvement in   c
    the war in Vietnam?

    a. Most believed that the war was immoral and that the United States should
       withdraw immediately.
    b. They generally believed that the government should be conducting the war
       more vigorously and should commit more American ground troops.
    c. They were ambivalent, wanting to get out but not wanting to give up.
    d. They wanted the United States to win but not to endanger American soldiers,
       so they supported use of tactical nuclear weapons.

73. Which of the following was *not* said by Lyndon B. Johnson?   a

    a. "Khrushchev wants to rub dirt in my nose."
    b. "Eighteen months from now ol' Landslide Lyndon will be Lame-duck
       Lyndon."
    c. "a raggedy-ass fourth-rate country"
    d. "I feel like a hitchhiker caught in a hailstorm on a Texas highway. I can't run,
       I can't hide, and I can't make it stop."

74. Which of the following statements was *not* made by a leading black American in   b
    the 1960s?

    a. "If tokenism were our goal, this administration has moved us adroitly toward
       its accomplishment."
    b. "We're eyeball to eyeball, and I think the other fellow just blinked."
    c. "I mean, don't be trying to love that honky to death. Shoot him to death."
    d. ". . . political power comes through the barrel of a gun."

75. The purpose of the 1964 Freedom Summer in Mississippi was

    a. to protest the escalation of the Vietnam War.
    b. to help and encourage blacks to become registered voters.
    c. to force the Interstate Commerce Commission to declare segregated transportation facilities unconstitutional.
    d. to persuade the state legislature to ratify the Equal Rights Amendment.

    b
    SG

76. Which of the following leaders most closely followed the example of Martin Luther King, Jr., using religion and nonviolent resistance to battle for social justice?

    a. H. Rap Brown
    b. César Chávez
    c. Malcolm X
    d. George Wallace

    b
    SG

77. Resort to war was avoided in the Cuban missile crisis when

    a. the United States agreed to remove its missiles from Turkey in exchange for the Soviets taking their missiles out of Cuba.
    b. Kennedy agreed to remove Western troops from East Berlin in exchange for Khrushchev's order to dismantle Soviet missiles in Cuba.
    c. the United States agreed to stop its bombing of North Vietnam in exchange for the Soviets' removal of missiles with nuclear warheads from Cuba.
    d. Khrushchev agreed to remove Soviet missiles from Cuba in exchange for Kennedy's pledge not to invade that country.

    d
    SG

78. Belief in the Domino Theory would most likely lead a person to support

    a. federal intervention in the South to protect freedom riders and other civil-rights activists.
    b. a test-ban treaty with the Soviets against further atmospheric and ocean firing of nuclear weapons.
    c. American intervention in the war in Vietnam to prevent a Vietcong victory.
    d. appointment of more conservative justices to the Supreme Court to prevent it from falling completely under the influence of Warren liberals.

    c
    SG

79. The feminist revival in the 1960s was brought about by

    a. continuing employment discrimination.
    b. the publication of Betty Friedan's *The Feminine Mystique*.
    c. the sexism women activists encountered in the peace and civil-rights movements.
    d. all of the above

    d
    SG

ESSAY QUESTIONS

80. Why did the civil-rights movement gain momentum in the early 1960s, crest, and then rapidly recede? How and why did the movement change during those years? What political, social, and economic gains were achieved? What was not achieved? Discuss blacks, Chicanos, and native Americans.

81. What does the author of your text mean when he talks about "the sense of new beginnings that prevailed in the early sixties"? What were the major accomplishments of the period?

82. Explain and describe the "image" projected by John F. Kennedy. Why was this image important? In what sense did it represent a new mood in the country? To what extent did the image match the reality of John Kennedy?

83. Discuss the accomplishments and failures of John F. Kennedy's thousand-day presidency.

84. To what extent did the foreign policy of the Kennedy administration represent new departures for the United States, and to what extent was it a continuation of previous administrations' foreign policies? Discuss especially Cuba, the Soviet Union, and Southeast Asia.

85. Discuss Lyndon Johnson's vision for a Great Society. To what extent was Johnson able to deliver on his promises? To what extent did he fail? Why? Discuss, especially, taxes, civil rights, and poverty.

86. How did the Supreme Court in the 1960s change the tenor of American life and, at the same time, inflame the heated political climate? What were the major Court decisions?

87. Why did some black Americans reject liberal solutions and turn to violence in the mid-1960s? Compare the Black Power, Red Power, and Brown Power movements of the later 1960s. To what extent did they differ? What were the major successes and failures of these groups?

88. In the 1960s American women "were vigorously taking control of their own lives and defining their own goals." Examine why many American women began to challenge the role that had been defined for them in the 1950s, and explain how the other political and social-reform movements of the 1960s shaped this second feminist wave.

89. Why did Lyndon Johnson choose to escalate American participation in the Vietnam War gradually? To what extent did that policy succeed? What did the American people think of the war? What role did public protests and television play in shaping American public opinion?

MAP QUESTIONS

Choose the letter on the accompanying map of Indochina that correctly identifies each of the following:

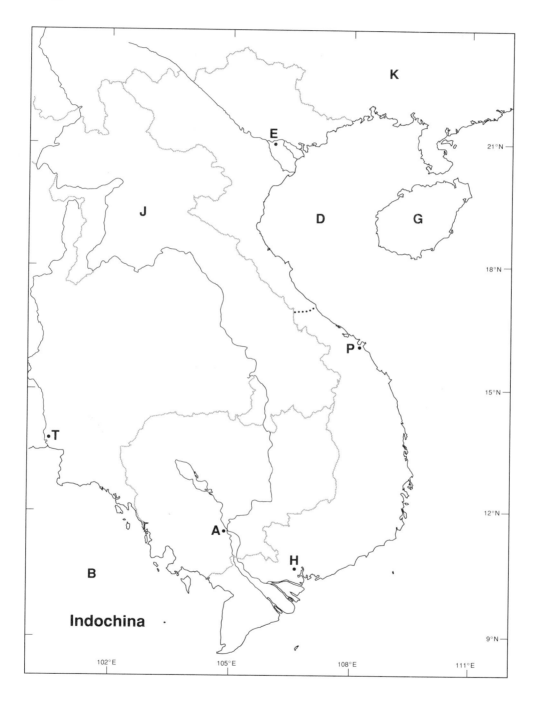

90. Gulf of Tonkin   **D**

91. Hanoi   **E**

92. Saigon   **H**

93. Pnompenh   **A**

94. Danang   **P**

95. Laos   **J**

CHAPTER 30

A Troubled Journey: From Port Huron to Watergate

IDENTIFICATIONS

Identify the following. Be as specific as possible, and include names, dates, and relevant facts as appropriate. Be sure to explain the *significance* of the person or term.

1. Berkeley Free Speech Movement, Mario Savio

2. Students for a Democratic Society, Port Huron Statement

3. Woodstock

4. New Left

5. red-diaper babies

6. napalm and Agent Orange

7. hippies, Yippies

8. Timothy Leary

9. Charles Manson

10. Haight-Ashbury

11. *Roe* v. *Wade*

12. U.S.S. *Pueblo*

13. Eugene McCarthy

14. Tet offensive

15. détente

16. Nixon Doctrine

17. William Calley and My Lai

18. Khmer Rouge, Pol Pot, Kampuchea

19. Paris Accords

20. OPEC oil embargo

21. Henry Kissinger, shuttle diplomacy

22. Family Assistance Plan

23. New Federalism

24. the plumbers

25. Pentagon Papers

26. *Swann* v. *Charlotte-Mecklenburg Board of Education*

27. Spiro Agnew

28. Committee to Re-Elect the President, "dirty tricks"

29. Carl Bernstein, Bob Woodward, and "Deep Throat"

30. Saturday Night Massacre

MULTIPLE-CHOICE QUESTIONS

Choose the answer that *best* completes the statement or answers the question.

31. Which of the following best describes American youths of the 1960s?   a
    a. They were apolitical and conservative, seeking mainly a good job, a new car, a pleasant suburban home, and a secure place in the system.
    b. They were radicals who were deeply involved in political action and espoused cultural and political revolution.
    c. They generally preferred drugs to beer.
    d. As their numbers dwindled, they developed increasing uncertainty about their own collective identity.

32. Most of the early Students for a Democratic Society and New Left members were   b
    a. from working-class families.   SG
    b. children of parents who had been radicals and activists in the 1930s and 1940s.
    c. from upper-class families who were unhappy with the declining status of the "eastern liberal establishment."
    d. students who were already active in sororities and fraternities.

33. Student activists of the early 1960s were likely to admire all the following Americans *except*:   c
    a. Elvis Presley
    b. Allen Ginsberg
    c. Doris Day
    d. John F. Kennedy

34. What were the goals of the Students for a Democratic Society?   d
    a. a society in which democratic institutions were fully protected from subversion by the international communist conspiracy
    b. control of both the Senate and the House of Representatives by the Democratic party, and the recruitment of one million new members of the party at colleges around the nation
    c. 100 percent participation from American colleges in the 1968 national Model Congress to be held in Chicago
    d. the transformation of the United States into a "participatory democracy" in which citizens would have direct political and economic control

35. Which of the following was *not* one of the developments of the early and mid-1960s that tended to radicalize thousands of American students?   a
    a. the American government's refusal to pursue total victory in Vietnam
    b. the perceived impersonality and rigidity of campus administrators
    c. the evident insensitivity of the nation's bureaucratic processes
    d. the apparent inability of mainstream liberalism to achieve swift, far-reaching change

36. Many college students in the 1960s protested   d
    a. college dress codes, strict grading, and required courses.
    b. escalation of the war in Vietnam.
    c. university research that benefited the military-industrial complex.
    d. all of the above

37. What was writer Garry Wills describing when he wrote, "They were ragged kids, comically self-important, a Halloween crew of trick-or-treaters; but the men they walked for could not be treated now, and they had no tricks to play—unless this were their last one, this haunting by proxy."   b
    a. campus hijinks during the 1969 Winter Houseparties at Hamilton College
    b. the 1969 March Against Death that took place in Washington
    c. the attempt to disrupt the nomination of Richard Nixon at the 1968 Republican national convention
    d. the killing of four Kent State University students by National Guardsmen in May 1970

38. At Kent State University in May 1970,   c

    a. campus radicals ambushed National Guard Troop G, wounding eleven and
       killing four.
    b. Ohio governor James Rhodes ordered the National Guard to shoot down all
       campus radicals.
    c. National Guard troops panicked and fired at a crowd of students, wounding
       eleven and killing four.
    d. campus police fired into a women's dormitory, accidentally killing two male
       students who were in the midst of a panty raid.

39. How did most Americans react to the campus convulsions of 1970?   a

    a. They criticized campus protesters for undercutting the nation's foreign
       policy.
    b. They blamed the Nixon administration for widening the war, and they
       applauded the goals of the campus demonstrators.
    c. They retreated from traditional American policies and sought new answers in
       mystic cults, communes, or the ecology movement.
    d. They became increasingly radicalized and in the November election voted for
       radical or left-wing Democratic candidates.

40. Which of the following was an activity that represented the mood on the nation's   b
    college campuses in the fall of 1970?

    a. eating goldfish
    b. racing across campus in the nude
    c. mass student demonstrations against the war in Vietnam
    d. reinstitution of course requirements and strict standards of grading

41. The actions of the New Left during the 1960s had all the following consequences   c
    except:

    a. increased opposition to the war in Vietnam
    b. a conservative reaction against radicals
    c. permanent radicalization of a large portion of American workers and students
    d. major reforms on American college campuses

42. The changes brought about on American college campuses because of student   d
    activism in the 1960s included

    a. elimination of dress codes and curfews.
    b. increased recruitment of minorities.
    c. courses that were more "relevant."
    d. all of the above

43. Which of the following is *not* representative of the trends in popular music during   a
    the 1960s?   PT

    a. Woody Guthrie
    b. Joan Baez
    c. Joe Cocker
    d. Country Joe and the Fish

44. Which of the following would have been the least likely to advocate peace and nonviolence in the 1960s?   b

    a. John Lennon
    b. Charles Manson
    c. Allen Ginsberg
    d. Timothy Leary

45. If you were in San Francisco in 1966, you would go to Haight Street to find   c

    a. the army recruiting office.   PT
    b. the headquarters of the Democratic National Committee.
    c. macrobiotic food, LSD, and psychedelic music.
    d. the headquarters of Young Americans for Freedom.

46. What did the experiences of late 1960s hippies demonstrate?   d

    a. Attempting to go against the Establishment leads mainly to drugs, venereal disease, and crime.   PT
    b. Most Americans would have accepted the communal ethic if the news media had portrayed it favorably.
    c. Countercultures in the United States never can succeed or gain much following because of the power of the American ideology of family and sharing.
    d. It is easier to agree on peace and freedom and love than on who will cook, wash the dishes, and pay the bills.

47. All the following contributed to a "sexual revolution" during the 1960s *except*:   a

    a. the elimination of all state laws infringing on a woman's right to an abortion during the first trimester of pregnancy
    b. waning fear of unwanted pregnancy because of the availability of contraceptives, particularly the Pill
    c. greater permissiveness and openness about sexual activity
    d. the counterculture's "do your own thing" attitude

48. Eugene McCarthy's main issue during his challenge to Lyndon Johnson for the 1968 presidential nomination was   b

    a. the presence of communists in the State Department.
    b. the war in Vietnam.
    c. the war on poverty.
    d. an appeal to the "silent majority" of Americans.

49. As a result of the Tet offensive,   c

    a. American military leaders came to realize that United States forces could never repulse a massive Vietcong offensive, much less regain captured territory.
    b. the nation experienced a resurgence of support for the war effort.
    c. many Americans came to realize that no area of South Vietnam was secure from enemy attack.
    d. Lyndon Johnson trounced Eugene McCarthy in the New Hampshire primary.

50. The Democratic candidate for president in the 1968 election was   **d**
    a. Lyndon Johnson.
    b. Eugene McCarthy.
    c. Robert F. Kennedy.
    d. Hubert Humphrey.

51. All the following occurred in 1968 *except*:   **a**
    a. the nomination of an antiwar Democratic candidate for president
    b. the assassination of a prominent civil-rights leader
    c. the political comeback of a Republican politician
    d. the assassination of a candidate for the Democratic presidential nomination

52. Which candidate for president in 1968 is correctly matched with one of his   **b**
    statements?
    a. Richard Nixon: "There comes a time when an honorable man simply has to
       raise the flag."
    b. George Wallace: "those briefcase-totin' bureaucrats, ivory-tower guideline
       writers, bearded anarchists, smart-aleck editorial writers, and pointy-headed
       professors looking down their noses at us"
    c. Robert Kennedy: "the great majority of Americans, the forgotten Americans,
       the nonshouters, the nondemonstrators . . . who love this country"
    d. Hubert Humphrey: "If any demonstrator ever lays down in front of my car,
       it'll be the last car he'll ever lie down in front of."

53. Which of the following facts about the 1968 election indicates that a new conser-   **a**
    vative majority had supplanted the long-standing New Deal coalition?   **SG**
    a. Between them Nixon and Wallace received a majority of the votes of unskilled
       and semiskilled workers.
    b. Nixon won 43.4 percent of the popular vote.
    c. The great majority of blacks voted for Hubert Humphrey.
    d. Almost all union leaders supported Hubert Humphrey.

54. At the outset of his presidency, Richard Nixon's foreign-policy goals included all   **a**
    the following *except*:
    a. stepping up the war in Vietnam
    b. checking Soviet expansionism
    c. limiting the nuclear-arms race
    d. bringing greater stability to the world

55. Which of the following is true about Henry Kissinger?   **b**
    a. He believed that human nature was basically good and that people would do
       the right thing if left to themselves.
    b. He believed that power alone counted in world affairs.
    c. He came to his foreign-policy post in Washington with little knowledge of
       international relations.
    d. He served as the president's national security adviser but failed to become
       secretary of state because he lacked the willingness to act ruthlessly when
       opponents placed obstacles in his path.

56. The Nixon Doctrine stated that the United States   c
    a. would help to defend, by military means if necessary, the territorial integrity of any nation threatened by communism.
    b. would use force, if necessary, to ensure that Latin American nations elected honest, pro-American governments.
    c. would provide financial and moral support to nations facing communist subversion, but such nations would have to defend themselves.
    d. would work to support human rights around the globe.

57. Which of the following statements most accurately describes conditions in the American army in Vietnam by 1969?   d
    a. Morale had plummeted and drug use had soared.
    b. Racial conflict among American soldiers had increased.
    c. Killing of officers by enlisted men had become more common.
    d. all of the above

58. In the course of the Vietnam War, who wanted to be thought of as "the mad bomber"?   a
    a. Richard Nixon
    b. Lyndon Johnson
    c. Iron Pants Curtis LeMay
    d. Ho Chi Minh

59. President Richard Nixon's policy in Southeast Asia included all the following *except*:   b
    a. escalation of American bombing of North Vietnam
    b. massive increases in American ground forces to invade North Vietnam
    c. secret direct negotiations with North Vietnam's foreign minister, Le Duc Tho
    d. widening of the war by invading Cambodia

60. What was the result of President Nixon's policy of increased heavy bombing of North Vietnam?   c
    a. It caused the People's Republic of China to send a large army to North Vietnam to fight the United States.
    b. It destroyed all chance of a negotiated peace because Le Duc Tho walked out of the Paris peace talks in protest.
    c. It broke the deadlock in the peace talks and got the North Vietnamese to agree to terms.
    d. It brought Nixon close to defeat in his bid for reelection in 1972.

61. The Paris Accords signed in 1973 included all the following *except*:   d
    a. withdrawal of all American troops
    b. return of American prisoners of war
    c. permission for North Vietnamese troops to remain in South Vietnam
    d. resolution of the differences between North Vietnam and the Thieu regime

62. Which of the following events of the Vietnam War is out of chronological order?   **b**

    a. Gulf of Tonkin resolution
    b. Christmas bombing of North Vietnam
    c. Tet offensive
    d. United States–South Vietnam invasion of Cambodia

63. Richard Nixon engineered a dramatic turnaround in American relations with   **a**

    a. the People's Republic of China.
    b. Panama.
    c. the Philippines.
    d. Kampuchea.

64. Which of the following statements correctly summarizes Richard Nixon's foreign   **c**
    policy toward the Soviet Union and the People's Republic of China?

    a. He opened up new initiatives with the Soviet Union in an effort to isolate the
       People's Republic, capitalizing on the Sino-Soviet split.
    b. He listened to his hard-line anticommunist advisers and initiated a new and
       more hostile era of the Cold War against both powers.
    c. He capitalized on their widening split by playing one power off against the
       other.
    d. none of the above

65. The SALT I agreement   **d**

    a. arranged for the Soviet Union's purchase of at least $750 million in American
       grain over a three-year period.
    b. brought about the end of the OPEC oil embargo.
    c. called for a phased withdrawal of American missiles and troops in Europe, in
       exchange for a comparable Soviet withdrawal from Afghanistan.
    d. limited the antiballistic missiles of the United States and the Soviet Union.

66. What was the cause of the 1973–1974 oil embargo?   **a**

    a. United States support of Israel in repelling the attack by Syria and Egypt
    b. refusal of Western Europe to agree to new OPEC price increases
    c. the attempt of the Palestine Liberation Organization to establish an indepen-
       dent Arab Palestinian nation
    d. the Egyptian desire to abandon its alliance with Moscow and forge an alliance
       with Washington

67. In which country did the Nixon administration *not* aid repressive, antidemocratic   **c**
    forces?   SG

    a. Chile
    b. South Korea
    c. West Germany
    d. Angola

68. Why did John Mitchell, E. Howard Hunt, and G. Gordon Liddy arrange the break-in at the Watergate complex?

   c
   SG

    a. to find information about Daniel Ellsberg that would discredit him in the eyes of the peace movement

    b. to destroy the Democratic National Committee's files of potential campaign contributors

    c. to wiretap the telephone of the Democratic National Committee

    d. all of the above

69. "That's one small step for man, one giant step for mankind" describes

   d
   SG

    a. Nixon's decision to resign from the presidency.

    b. the signing of the Paris Accords ending the United States' presence in Vietnam.

    c. the peaceful inauguration of Gerald Ford after the long nightmare of Watergate.

    d. astronaut Neil Armstrong's walk on the moon.

70. During his first two years in office President Nixon did all the following *except*:

   a

    a. reduce the regulatory powers of the federal government

    b. increase social-security benefits

    c. reform the tax system

    d. expand the Job Corps

71. President Nixon's policy of "New Federalism" was designed to

   b

    a. revamp the federal government so that there would be no duplication of effort.

    b. shift power from Washington to the states and communities.

    c. bolster the taxing and regulatory powers of the federal government.

    d. move the capital of the United States to a newly constructed metropolis in the heart of the Sunbelt.

72. The economic problems challenging President Nixon included all the following *except*:

   c

    a. budget deficits

    b. recession

    c. declining prices and wages

    d. balance of trade deficit

73. President Nixon's approaches to solving the nation's economic problems included

   d

    a. deficit spending and reduction of government expenditures.

    b. increasing interest rates.

    c. imposition of wage-and-price controls.

    d. all of the above

74. The voting coalition that Richard Nixon hoped to assemble for the 1972 presidential election consisted of **a**

a. Democratic blue-collar laborers, white southerners, and members of white ethnic minorities.

b. Democratic blue-collar laborers, black southerners, and members of non-white ethnic minorities.

c. eastern liberals, western moderates, and midwestern farmers.

d. white southerners, Vietnam veterans, and the middle class.

75. The Nixon administration's "enemies list" included **b**

a. leaders of North Vietnam, the People's Republic of China, and Kampuchea.

b. prominent Americans who were to be harassed by the government for opposing Nixon's policies.

c. known communists who were working in either the State Department or the Defense Department.

d. Spiro Agnew, William F. Buckley, John Mitchell, G. Gordon Liddy, and Robert Welch.

76. Why did the Nixon administration attempt to halt the publication of the Pentagon Papers? **c**

a. They contained damaging revelations about the Nixon administration's policy in Vietnam.

b. They chronicled two decades of waste, mismanagement, and ineffective weapons systems, and the administration feared that public trust in the defense establishment would be undermined.

c. They revealed a long history of government lies that could further undermine public trust in government statements about the war.

d. They contained embarrassing details of Daniel Ellsberg's psychiatric therapy, and the administration feared that a national hero would be publicly discredited.

77. What was Richard Nixon's reaction to *Swann* v. *Charlotte-Mecklenburg Board of Education*? **d**

a. He denounced the decision to ban school busing, and he asked Congress to enact new laws that would desegregate all schools.

b. He denounced the decision to permit the publication of the secret Pentagon documents, and he ordered the plumbers to discredit Chief Justice Warren Burger.

c. He denounced the refusal of southern states to accept racial equality, and he sent the National Guard to Montgomery and Little Rock to integrate the public schools.

d. He denounced the ruling to uphold school busing, and he asked Congress to enact a moratorium.

78. Which of the following did *not* resign in protest over the Nixon administration's roadblocks to racial equality?   a

    a. the attorney general
    b. the head of the U.S. Commission on Civil Rights
    c. top Justice Department lawyers
    d. the head of the Equal Employment Opportunity Commission

79. All the following were successful Nixon appointments to the Supreme Court *except*:   b

    a. William Rehnquist
    b. Clement Haynesworth
    c. Lewis Powell
    d. Harry Blackmun

80. The Burger court shifted to the right on all the following subjects *except*:   c

    a. civil liberties
    b. community censorship
    c. abortion
    d. police power

81. Who, according to Vice President Spiro Agnew, were "curled-lip boys in eastern ivory towers" and "nattering nabobs of negativism"?   d

    a. white supporters of George McGovern
    b. entrenched bureaucrats in the Federal Reserve System
    c. antiwar protesters
    d. television network newscasters

82. How did Democrats react to Vice President Agnew's attacks in 1970?   a

    a. They reversed their previous positions on abortion, gun control, and the legalization of marijuana.
    b. They barnstormed the country in support of their positions, declaring that it was "time to rip away the rhetoric and to divide on authentic lines."
    c. They authorized a special committee that would harass Agnew and attempt to discredit him through dirty tricks.
    d. all of the above

83. George McGovern overwhelmingly lost the 1972 presidential election because   d

    a. his vice-presidential running mate had received electric-shock therapy for nervous depression.
    b. he endorsed income redistribution and the decriminalization of marijuana.
    c. the Nixon campaign kept information about the Watergate burglary contained.
    d. all of the above

84. What did the "White House tapes" reveal?   **b**
    a. that the burglary at Democratic headquarters was simply a third-rate caper, and no one on the White House staff had been involved
    b. that President Nixon had ordered a cover-up in the Watergate affair
    c. that President Nixon had been having an affair with his secretary for three years
    d. that President Nixon had attempted to halt the "dirty tricks" of his supporters but had failed

85. President Richard Nixon   **c**
    a. was impeached by the House of Representatives for obstruction of justice, abuse of power, and contempt of Congress.
    b. resigned to allow Vice President Spiro Agnew to take over the reigns of power and end the nation's long nightmare.
    c. resigned from office before the House of Representatives could impeach him, which it was likely to do.
    d. none of the above

ESSAY QUESTIONS

86. Discuss the rise and decline of college student radicalism in the period 1960 to   SG
    1970. What caused the radicalism? Who became radicalized? What forms did radical protest take? Why did radical protest wane?

87. Compose a profile of the student of the 1960s. Describe the "youth culture" of   PT
    the decade. How did political events affect the youth culture, and how did the youth culture affect the politics of the period?

88. What were the issues, and who were the personalities, of the 1968 presidential campaign? What conclusions can you draw from the results of that year's political events? What, in particular, was the connection between domestic politics and foreign policy?

89. In the late 1960s a new electoral majority began to evolve. What were the components of this new majority, and how was it different from the old New Deal coalition? What was the importance of this new electoral majority? What changes in American politics did the elections of 1968 and 1972 reveal?

90. What was Richard Nixon's "Grand Design" in foreign policy? What were his foreign-policy goals? Discuss, specifically, his policies toward Southeast Asia, the Soviet Union, China, and the Middle East. What role did Henry Kissinger play?

91. Evaluate the following policies of Richard Nixon with regard to the Vietnam War: "peace with honor," Vietnamization, "the mad bomber," and ending the war by widening it.

92. What were the domestic accomplishments—both positive and negative—of the Nixon administration? How did Nixon deal with the economic and social problems facing the nation?

93. What were the issues and events of the "Watergate" scandal? Who was involved? What were the lessons? What was the impact on the American political system?

94. How and why did opposition to the Vietnam War grow? Who supported the war, and who opposed it? What role did student protests play in ending the war?

95. How and why did a more conservative mood evolve in the nation during the late 1960s and early 1970s? How did this mood evolve out of radicalism? What happened to the New Left, and why?

MAP QUESTIONS

Choose the letter on the accompanying map of China and Indochina that correctly identifies each of the following:

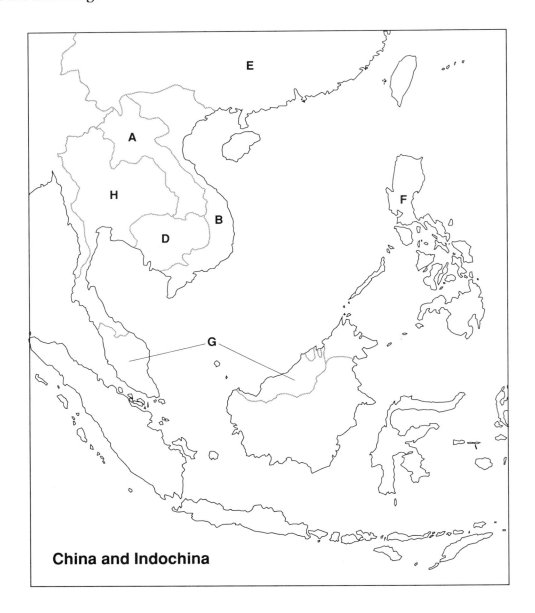

China and Indochina

96. Vietnam   **B**

97. Cambodia   **D**

98. Laos   **A**

99. Philippines   **F**

Choose the letter on the accompanying map of the Middle East that correctly identifies each of the following:

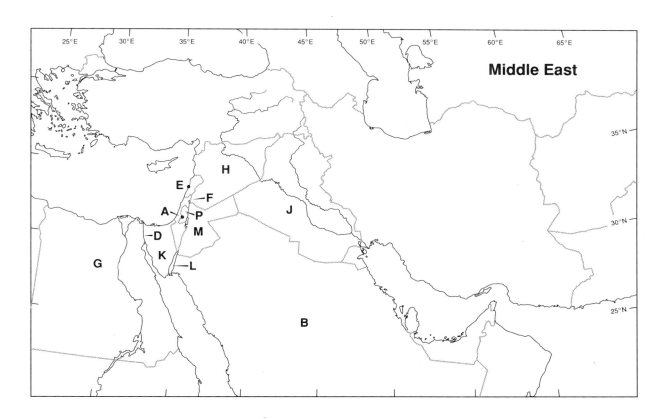

100. Sinai Peninsula   **K**

101. Syria   **H**

102. Egypt   **G**

103. Golan Heights   **F**

104. West Bank   **P**

105. Suez Canal   **D**

106. Jerusalem   **A**

107. Saudi Arabia   **B**

Choose the letter on the accompanying map of Africa that correctly identifies each of the following:

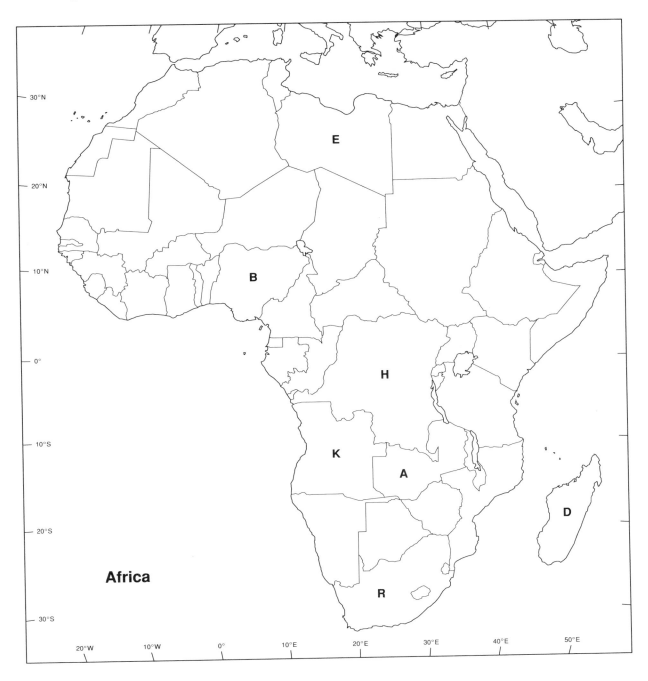

108. South Africa

109. Nigeria

110. Angola

R

B

K

Choose the letter on the accompanying map of South America that correctly identifies each of the following:

111. Chile

112. Brazil

D

F

CHAPTER 31

New Problems, Old Verities: From Watergate to the Present

IDENTIFICATIONS

Identify the following. Be as specific as possible, and include names, dates, and relevant facts as appropriate. Be sure to explain the *significance* of the person or term.

1. Mayagüez incident

2. Panama Canal treaties

3. Salt II

4. Zbigniew Brzezinski

5. MX missile

6. Camp David Accords

7. stagflation

8. Shah Reza Pahlavi

9. Ayatollah Ruhollah Khomeini

10. New Right

11. PACs

12. Reaganomics

13. Caspar Weinberger

14. George Schultz

15. Sandinistas and contras

16. Palestine Liberation Organization

17. Strategic Defense Initiative ("Star Wars")

18. Yuppies

19. the Me Generation

20. Steven Jobs and Stephen Wozniak

21. the Great Bull Market

22. Equal Rights Amendment

23. pro-life and pro-choice

24. American Indian Movement

25. Jerry Falwell and the Moral Majority

26. Old Time Revival Hour, PTL, and the 700 Club

27. Jesse Jackson, rainbow coalition

28. Gramm-Rudman Act

29. Iran-contra scandal

30. INF treaty

MULTIPLE-CHOICE QUESTIONS

Choose the answer that *best* completes the statement or answers the question.

31. All the following were conditions facing the United States in the late 1970s *except*:   a
    a. plummeting energy prices
    b. Americans being held hostage
    c. unemployment and recession
    d. inflation

32. Who became president upon the resignation of Richard Nixon?   b
    a. Ronald Reagan
    b. Gerald R. Ford
    c. Jimmy Carter
    d. Nelson Rockefeller

33. After resigning from the presidency, Richard Nixon   c
    a. was convicted of obstruction of justice but received a suspended sentence.
    b. ran for the Republican nomination for governor of California but was defeated by Ronald Reagan.
    c. was pardoned by President Ford for any and all crimes committed while in office.
    d. became American ambassador to China during the Ford administration.

34. How did President Ford try to curb inflation?   **d**
    a. voluntary wage-and-price restraint
    b. reductions in federal spending
    c. support for increases in the discount rate
    d. all of the above

35. All the following contributed to Jimmy Carter's election victory in 1976 *except*:   **a**
    a. his clearly defined economic and social program
    b. his reputation as an outsider to Washington politics
    c. his pledge never to lie to the American people
    d. his avowed faith as a "born-again" Christian

36. Which of the following was one of President Carter's high priorities in interna-   **b**
    tional affairs?
    a. reasserting American rights in the Panama Canal Zone
    b. attending to human-rights violations around the world
    c. isolating China from other nations
    d. none of the above

37. Which of the following correctly summarizes the Carter administration's policy   **c**
    toward the area of the world with which it is paired?
    a. Panama: fortification of the canal and the Canal Zone against the threats of
       the Panamanian dictator
    b. Soviet Union: growing détente and continued expansion of economic and
       cultural relations
    c. China: restoration of full diplomatic relations
    d. Middle East: use of American troops to stop the Egyptian invasion of Israel

38. During the Carter presidency, the American economy was marked by   **d**
    a. the worst depression since the 1930s.
    b. rapid business expansion and record low unemployment.
    c. creeping inflation brought about by steady business growth.
    d. business stagnation and skyrocketing inflation.

39. What, according to President Carter, was the cause of the nation's woes in the late   **a**
    1970s?
    a. a failure of the American people to have confidence in their nation and gov-
       ernment
    b. the government's inability to reduce the burgeoning budget deficit
    c. collusion by foreign nations to make the United States a second-rate power
    d. his own inability to understand the big picture or articulate a clear set of
       policies

40. What events precipitated the 1979 seizure of over fifty American hostages in Iran?   **b**
    a. the return to power of Shah Reza Pahlavi with the assistance of the CIA
    b. the return to power of Ayatollah Khomeini, and the arrival of the shah in the United States for cancer treatment
    c. the collision of an American helicopter and a transport plane in the Iranian desert
    d. the invasion of Iran by the Soviet Union

41. All the following are true about Ronald Reagan *except*:   **c**
    a. He had been a paid spokesman for a major American corporation.
    b. As a Hollywood actor he had played opposite a chimpanzee in a movie.
    c. He had been an enthusiastic conservative Republican since the 1930s.
    d. As governor of California, he popularized conservative ideas while showing himself to be flexible and capable of compromise.

42. In the 1980 presidential election,   **d**
    a. Reagan won by a razor-thin margin, but the Republicans lost seats in both the House and the Senate.
    b. Carter lost, but he held such traditional New Deal Democratic voters as blue-collar workers and white southerners.
    c. Reagan won in a landslide by capturing all western and northeastern states, although the solid South remained firmly Democratic.
    d. Reagan won about 51 percent of the popular vote, and Republicans gained control of the Senate for the first time since 1955.

43. Of the following economic policies of the Reagan administration, which is *not* considered a component of "Reaganomics"?   **a**
    a. increased discount rates
    b. tax cuts
    c. spending cuts
    d. deregulation

44. President Ronald Reagan's economic policies during his first term brought about   **d**
    a. a severe recession.
    b. foreign trade deficits.
    c. an economic surge.
    d. all of the above

45. The experience of Houston, Texas, in the 1970s and 1980s demonstrates that   **b**
    a. Texans are concerned about environmental issues.   **PT**
    b. the international oil market can affect all regions of the United States.
    c. if America develops its domestic sources of oil, the nation will be shielded from international economic pressures.
    d. the boom-town mentality is a nineteenth-century phenomenon that cannot occur in twentieth-century America.

46. What effect did OPEC's pricing policies have on American oil companies?

    a. Gulf, Texaco, and Exxon withdrew from Mideast oil exploration in order to concentrate on the development of American reserves.
    b. Domestic firms suffered as Americans reduced their oil consumption.
    c. The skyrocketing price of foreign oil brought skyrocketing profits for the five biggest domestic American companies.
    d. Gulf and Texaco pulled out of Houston, Texas, and moved their headquarters to Saudi Arabia.

    c
    PT

47. To what was Ronald Reagan referring when he spoke of the "evil empire"?

    a. the Soviet Union
    b. the growing federal bureaucracy
    c. the New Deal electoral coalition
    d. the People's Republic of China

    a

48. The "contras" were

    a. formed by members of the Palestine Liberation Organization to overthrow the Israeli government.
    b. established and financed by the CIA to undermine the Sandinista government in Nicaragua.
    c. the name that President Reagan gave to all American hostages around the world.
    d. bands of evangelical Christians who traveled the country inveighing against sexual permissiveness and secular humanism.

    b

49. Which of the following events symbolized President Ronald Reagan's Middle Eastern policy during his first term?

    a. an Egyptian-Israeli peace treaty signed by Menachem Begin and Anwar el-Sadat
    b. a CIA-financed coup in Iran
    c. a terrorist explosion that killed 239 American marines stationed at poorly guarded barracks in Beirut, Lebanon
    d. all of the above

    c

50. The Strategic Defense Initiative

    a. was a method of neutralizing the growing peace and antinuclear movement.
    b. proposed a vast system of space-based lasers and other high-tech defenses against nuclear missiles.
    c. was foreshadowed in a 1940 Reagan film called *Murder in the Air*, which featured an "Inertial Projector" that destroyed enemy aircraft by invisible rays.
    d. all of the above

    d

51. President Reagan's accomplishments during his first term included all the follow-   a
    ing *except*:

    a. reducing the federal budget and the federal deficit, improving the nation's balance of trade, and implementing the social agenda of the New Right
    b. ending inflation and revitalizing American capitalism
    c. rebuilding the military and making the nation once again "stand tall" in the world
    d. maintaining a personal popularity that was impervious to the ups and downs of his policies

52. Yuppies were known for   b

    a. their refusal to follow social norms, their use of psychedelic drugs, and their wild clothing.
    b. their preoccupation with physical fitness, psychic harmony, a tasteful lifestyle, and money.
    c. their participation in the environmental movement, particularly the campaign against nuclear power.
    d. their leadership of the antiwar movement during the early 1970s.

53. All the following are examples of consumer electronics products that began to   c
    shape American society in the 1980s *except*:

    a. videocassette recorder
    b. personal computer
    c. television
    d. compact disc

54. If you took a survey of mid-1980s college students, you would find that most of   d
    them

    a. believed that it was very important to develop a meaningful philosophy of life.
    b. believed that women were inferior to men and should be protected by special federal legislation.
    c. had turned their backs on the materialism of American culture.
    d. were interested in academic programs that would prepare them for specific well-paying careers.

55. The administration that ran up the biggest federal budget deficits in American his-   d
    tory was that of   SG

    a. Franklin Roosevelt.
    b. Lyndon Johnson.
    c. Ulysses Grant.
    d. Ronald Reagan.

56. All the following administrations are particularly associated with corruption and   b
wrongdoing in government *except* that of   SG

   a. Ulysses Grant.
   b. Herbert Hoover.
   c. Warren Harding.
   d. Richard Nixon.

57. Beginning in the 1970s, what was the policy of the federal government toward   c
native Americans?

   a. termination of all Indian-aid programs and relocation in cities so that they
      would disappear as a distinct ethnic group
   b. continuation of the government's traditional paternalism
   c. greater autonomy for native Americans in managing their affairs—such as
      schools and federal-aid programs
   d. relocation of Indian tribes from valuable land in the Sunbelt to undeveloped
      tracts in Alaska

58. All the following represent the changing situation of the American Indian from the   d
1970s onward *except*:

   a. a new direction of federal Indian policy
   b. the renewal of tribal life and a flowering of ethnic pride
   c. willingness of whites to recognize the validity of ancient Indian treaties
   d. record low rates of unemployment, alcoholism, and disease

59. When some people in the 1980s chanted "AIDS is a cure, not a disease," they   a
meant that

   a. AIDS would "cure" a person of homosexuality because the person would die.
   b. AIDS was actually a cure for the common cold.
   c. the number of AIDS cases was being exaggerated by gay-rights groups.
   d. those afflicted with AIDS should look on the bright side of things and not
      dwell on the negative aspects of the disease.

60. Which of the following correctly suggests 1980s attitudes about sexuality?   b

   a. declining number of unmarried couples living together
   b. increased use of condoms
   c. growing patronage of gay bathhouses
   d. popularity of the slogan "Make Love, Not War"

61. What was the role of religion in post-1970 America?   c

   a. It became increasingly irrelevant as the "Me Generation" turned inward and
      concentrated on personal goals and materialistic pursuits.
   b. It gained new visibility as a champion of liberal reform.
   c. It gained increased visibility and played a more decisive cultural and political
      role than it had for years.
   d. It became discredited because of a series of scandals involving television
      preachers.

62. Which of the following issues did evangelical Christians target after 1970?   **d**

    a. abortion

    b. homosexuality

    c. public-school prayer

    d. all of the above

63. Geraldine Ferraro was   **a**

    a. Walter Mondale's running mate in 1984.

    b. evangelist Jim Bakker's illicit sexual partner.

    c. Gary Hart's running mate in 1980.

    d. the keynote speaker at the 1988 Democratic National Convention.

64. The Reagan administration came to support the widow of an assassinated politi-   **b**
cian who had led the opposition to the corrupt and tyrannical government of

    a. South Africa.

    b. Philippines.

    c. Panama.

    d. Iran.

65. In 1988 an American warship, under fire from gunboats of this nation, shot down   **c**
a passenger plane of this nation, killing all 290 aboard.

    a. North Korea

    b. Libya

    c. Iran

    d. Cuba

66. The Gramm-Rudman Act of 1985   **d**

    a. granted Indian tribes the right to manage federal-aid programs on the reser-
vations and to oversee their own schools.

    b. approved covert aid to the Nicaraguan contras.

    c. enacted a 25 percent income-tax cut over three years.

    d. mandated automatic across-the-board spending cuts if the normal budget
process did not achieve a balanced federal budget.

67. All the following became new Supreme Court justices during the Reagan presi-   **a**
dency *except*:

    a. Robert Bork

    b. Antonin Scalia

    c. Sandra Day O'Connor

    d. Anthony Kennedy

68. The Iran-contra scandal highlighted to many Americans   b

    a. a pattern of corruption in Pentagon procurement.
    b. President Reagan's passive, casual managerial style, and the fact that he often didn't fully know what was going on.
    c. that many of the president's closet associates and advisers, such as Lyn Nofziger and Michael Deaver, had caused the president's problems.
    d. that Vice President Bush had been a strong supporter of selling arms to Egypt and using the profits to support opponents of Ferdinand Marcos.

69. What did Michael Deaver, Lyn Nofziger, and Edwin Meese have in common?   c

    a. They were key figures in shaping the policies that culminated in the Iran-contra scandal.
    b. They were unsuccessful Reagan nominees to the Supreme Court.
    c. They were accused or convicted of using their high positions in the Reagan administration to promote ventures that would benefit themselves.
    d. They were television evangelists whose ministries were rocked by a series of scandals in the late 1980s.

70. What seems to account for the vast popularity that Ronald Reagan maintained during his eight years as president?   c

    a. his skill as an administrator and manager
    b. his exhaustive familiarity with the issues
    c. his ability to articulate the beliefs, aspirations, and fears of millions of Americans
    d. all of the above

71. The 1987 INF Treaty was a major milestone in nuclear-arms control for all the following reasons *except*:   a

    a. It resulted in a 45 percent reduction in the world's nuclear arsenal.
    b. It eliminated an entire class of existing nuclear weapons.
    c. It provided for on-site inspection to verify compliance.
    d. It revived the long-dormant arms-control process.

72. Although Ronald Reagan had been a vigorous "Cold Warrior" throughout his political career, he was able to bring about a remarkable easing of Cold War tensions because of   d

    a. his personal rapport with Mikhail Gorbachev.
    b. his massive military buildup.
    c. the influence of Nancy Reagan.
    d. all of the above

73. All the following were candidates for the Republican presidential nomination in 1988 *except*:   b

    a. former secretary of state Alexander Haig
    b. senator Lloyd Bentsen
    c. evangelist Pat Robertson
    d. congressman Jack Kemp

74. Which of the following statements from the 1988 presidential campaign is correctly matched with the person who made it?   **d**

    a. "He was born with a silver foot in his mouth." (Michael Dukakis about Alexander Haig)
    b. "What is it about the Pledge of Allegiance that so upsets him?" (George Bush about Jesse Jackson)
    c. "Wouldn't it be nice to be the iceman so you never make a mistake?" (Gary Hart about J. Danforth Quayle)
    d. "This election is not about ideology, it's about competence." (Michael Dukakis about George Bush)

75. The outcome of the 1988 presidential election suggested all the following conclusions *except*:   **a**

    a. The growing excitement of presidential politics is leading to increased voter participation.
    b. Television has great power to shape political reality.
    c. The old "New Deal coalition" has disintegrated.
    d. Voters seem to want to curb executive power by keeping the legislative branch in the control of the opposite party.

76. In which two periods did the federal government make its greatest efforts to protect black Americans by passing civil-rights laws and constitutional amendments?   **c**
SG

    a. in the 1920s and 1930s
    b. during the administrations of Ronald Reagan and George Bush
    c. during Reconstruction and the 1960s
    d. during World Wars I and II

77. Each of these was a muckraking writer whose book helped to secure passage of federal legislation *except*:   **a**
SG

    a. John Hay
    b. Upton Sinclair
    c. Michael Harrington
    d. Rachel Carson

78. Which of the following happened to the majority of southern blacks in the years between Reconstruction and 1900?   **b**
SG

    a. They were driven out of the South by poverty and discrimination.
    b. They became tenant farmers and sharecroppers on lands owned by whites.
    c. They got jobs in the factories opening in the Midwest and Far West.
    d. They became independent, landowning small farmers.

79. What accounts for the "two worlds of contemporary black America"?   **d**

    a. white racism
    b. structural changes in the economy
    c. new opportunities for blacks to acquire a college education
    d. all of the above

ESSAY QUESTIONS

80. In what sense was the United States in the 1980s a nation in transition? Discuss the "profound economic, social, and political changes" that the nation experienced during the fifteen years between the resignation of Richard Nixon and the inauguration of George Bush.

81. How did the American experience in the Vietnam War shape American foreign policy in the later 1970s?

82. What economic problems confronted the United States from the late 1970s to the late 1980s? Discuss, especially, the effect of oil on the economy. How did presidents Ford, Carter, and Reagan deal with those problems, and with what success?   PT

83. What were the major domestic and foreign challenges facing the Ford administration? How did the president meet those challenges? Why did Ford lose the election of 1976?

84. Did President Carter have greater success in foreign or domestic affairs? Explain. When he left office in 1981, his presidency was thought to have been a failure. Why? Do you agree with that assessment?

85. Explain the elements of the "Reagan Revolution's" social, ideological, and political foundations; Reagan's managerial style; and the sources of his personal popularity.

86. What were Ronald Reagan's domestic goals? Which of those goals was he able to accomplish during his two terms? What were the major components of "Reaganomics"? Did Reaganomics work?

87. What policies did the Reagan administration follow regarding the Soviet Union, the Caribbean and Central America, the Middle East? Explain how the administration pursued a massive military buildup yet also brought about a revival of détente.

88. Compare and contrast the "old immigrants" (pre-1880s), the "new immigrants" (1880s to 1920), and the post-1960 immigrants. What ethnicities composed each group? Why did each group come? What characteristics did each display? How did each fare in America and why?   SG

89. Compose an ethnic profile of the United States in the 1980s. Who are the major groups, and the fastest-growing groups? How did conditions of native Americans and women change during the 1980s?

MAP QUESTIONS

Choose the letter on the accompanying world map that correctly identifies each of the
following:

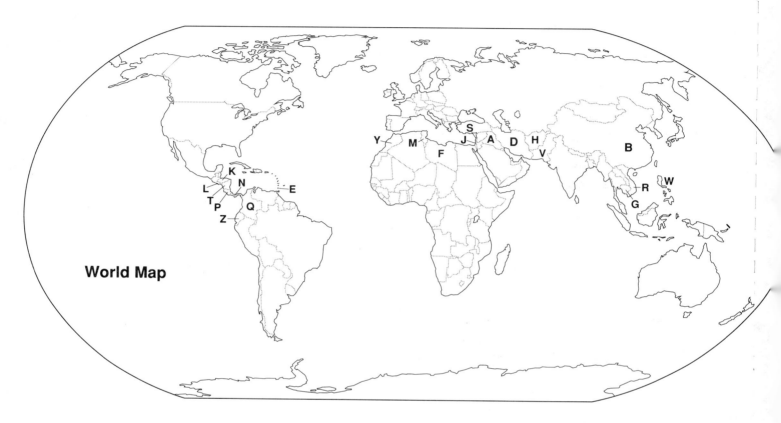

World Map

90. Iran   D

91. Israel   J

92. Lebanon   S

93. Tunisia   M

94. Libya   F

95. Iraq   A

96. Afghanistan   H

97. China   B

98. Vietnam   R

99. Cambodia   G

100. Philippines   W

101. Grenada   E

102. Costa Rica   P

103. Panama   N

104. Nicaragua   T

105. El Salvador   L

Final Examination Questions for Chapters 15-31

Identify the following. Be as specific as possible, and include names, dates, and relevant facts as appropriate. Be sure to explain the *significance* of the person or term.

1. black codes

2. scalawags and carpetbaggers

3. Red River War and Wounded Knee

4. *Munn* v. *Illinois*

5. Eugene Debs

6. horizontal and vertical integration

7. Jane Addams, Hull House

8. new immigrants and old immigrants

9. the "new woman"

10. Chautauqua

11. Populist party

12. Teller and Platt amendments

13. Federal Reserve Act

14. Frederick W. Taylor's *Principles of Scientific Management*

15. Fourteen Points

16. dollar diplomacy

17. Harlem Renaissance

18. Sacco and Vanzetti

19. National Labor Relations Act

20. the Hundred Days

21. the Good Neighbor policy

22. John L. Lewis

23. lend-lease

24. Yalta agreements

25. containment policy

26. Joseph R. McCarthy

27. *Brown* v. *Board of Education of Topeka*

28. Levittown

29. Gulf of Tonkin resolution

30. New Frontier

31. *Roe* v. *Wade*

32. Pentagon Papers

33. SALT II

34. American Indian Movement

MULTIPLE-CHOICE QUESTIONS

Choose the answer that *best* completes the statement or answers the question.

35. Which of the following presidents had to confront the fewest grave national prob-   a
    lems during his term of office?
    a. Calvin Coolidge
    b. Franklin Roosevelt
    c. Woodrow Wilson
    d. Lyndon Johnson

36. Which of the following wars resulted in the fewest American deaths?   b
    a. Vietnam War
    b. Spanish-American War
    c. Korean War
    d. World War I

37. Which of the following is in the correct chronological order?   c

    a. Harlem Renaissance, ratification of Nineteenth Amendment, Treaty of Versailles, Dust Bowl
    b. Dust Bowl, Treaty of Versailles, Harlem Renaissance, ratification of Nineteenth Amendment
    c. Treaty of Versailles, ratification of Nineteenth Amendment, Harlem Renaissance, Dust Bowl
    d. ratification of Nineteenth Amendment, Treaty of Versailles, Dust Bowl, Harlem Renaissance

38. In which of the following years would you have been *most* likely to encounter government suppression of dissent and civil liberties in the United States?   d

    a. 1896
    b. 1960
    c. 1932
    d. 1918

39. Which of the following periods was considered a "reform" era?   a

    a. 1910–1915
    b. 1945–1960
    c. 1890–1895
    d. 1920–1930

40. The mass media played an important role in   d

    a. the 1960 presidential election.
    b. the Spanish-American War.
    c. the 1928 presidential election.
    d. all of the above

41. Which of the following can be considered an era of feminist activity?   b

    a. the 1920s
    b. the 1910s
    c. the 1930s
    d. the 1950s

42. The United States entered its first peacetime military alliance in   c

    a. 1889.
    b. 1933.
    c. 1949.
    d. 1919.

43. At what point could the United States be described for the first time as "second to none in economic and military power"?   a

    a. after World War II
    b. after World War I
    c. after the Spanish-American War
    d. after the Vietnam War

44. Which of the following presidents is responsible for the biggest public-works pro-   **b**
    ject in American history?

    a. Woodrow Wilson
    b. Dwight Eisenhower
    c. Franklin Roosevelt
    d. Jimmy Carter

45. Which of the following was a period of rapid inflation?   **c**

    a. 1920–1930
    b. 1875–1885
    c. 1975–1980
    d. all of the above

46. Of the following wars, there was the *least* amount of domestic resistance to Amer-   **d**
    ican participation in

    a. the Vietnam War.
    b. World War I.
    c. the Korean War.
    d. World War II.

47. The presidential candidate who received the highest percentage of the popular   **a**
    vote in American history was

    a. Lyndon Johnson in 1964.
    b. Franklin Roosevelt in 1936.
    c. William McKinley in 1900.
    d. Richard Nixon in 1972.

48. In which of the following decades was the American birthrate highest?   **b**

    a. the 1960s
    b. the 1950s
    c. the 1930s
    d. the 1970s

49. In which of the following years did New York, Chicago, Detroit, and Washington,   **c**
    D.C., have the highest percentage of black residents?

    a. 1879
    b. 1940
    c. 1960
    d. 1919

50. Since the 1890s, the United States has had a consistently close diplomatic relation-   **d**
    ship with

    a. France.
    b. Germany.
    c. the Netherlands.
    d. Great Britain.

51. All the following provisions of the Constitution have been added since the Civil   a
    War *except*:
    a. equality for all citizens regardless of race, sex, or national origin
    b. the direct election of senators
    c. the limitation of a president to two terms in office
    d. the right of the federal government to levy an income tax

52. Which of the following presidents was elected by a minority of the popular vote?   d
    a. John F. Kennedy
    b. Harry S Truman
    c. Woodrow Wilson
    d. all of the above

53. Which of the following is in the correct chronological order?   b
    a. American diplomatic recognition of the Soviet Union, World War I, the Cold
       War, presidency of Franklin Roosevelt
    b. World War I, presidency of Franklin Roosevelt, American diplomatic recogni-
       tion of the Soviet Union, the Cold War
    c. World War I, diplomatic recognition of the Soviet Union, the Cold War, pres-
       idency of Franklin Roosevelt
    d. presidency of Franklin Roosevelt, diplomatic recognition of the Soviet Union,
       World War I, the Cold War

54. Which of the following is in the correct chronological order?   c
    a. Clayton Antitrust Act, Interstate Commerce Act, Taft-Hartley Act, Wagner Act
    b. Taft-Hartley Act, Wagner Act, Interstate Commerce Act, Clayton Antitrust Act
    c. Interstate Commerce Act, Clayton Antitrust Act, Wagner Act, Taft-Hartley Act
    d. Interstate Commerce Act, Clayton Antitrust Act, Taft-Hartley Act, Wagner Act

55. In which of the following are the labor unions listed in their correct order of   a
    founding?
    a. Knights of Labor, American Federation of Labor, Industrial Workers of the
       World, Congress of Industrial Organizations
    b. American Federation of Labor, Congress of Industrial Organizations, Knights
       of Labor, Industrial Workers of the World
    c. Industrial Workers of the World, Knights of Labor, Congress of Industrial
       Organizations, American Federation of Labor
    d. Congress of Industrial Organizations, Knights of Labor, American Federation
       of Labor, Industrial Workers of the World

56. In which of the following are the movements listed in the correct chronological   c
    order?
    a. woman suffrage, black civil rights, gay liberation, student peace movement
    b. black civil rights, student peace movement, woman suffrage, gay liberation
    c. woman suffrage, student peace movement, black civil rights, gay liberation
    d. student peace movement, woman suffrage, gay liberation, black civil rights

57. Which of the following is in the correct chronological order?　　　　　　　**d**

    a. Glenn Miller, Elvis Presley, Scott Joplin, the Beatles
    b. Scott Joplin, Glenn Miller, the Beatles, Elvis Presley
    c. Elvis Presley, Glenn Miller, the Beatles, Scott Joplin
    d. Scott Joplin, Glenn Miller, Elvis Presley, the Beatles

58. All the following women were known primarily for their reform efforts *except*:　　**b**

    a. Carrie Chapman Catt
    b. Sara Orne Jewett
    c. Jane Addams
    d. Frances Willard

59. Which of the following was *not* an American businessman?　　　　　　　**a**

    a. Alger Hiss
    b. J. Pierpont Morgan
    c. Ivan Boesky
    d. Abraham Levitt

60. Which of the following American politicians did *not* run for president?　　　**b**

    a. Henry A. Wallace
    b. Henry Cabot Lodge
    c. J. Strom Thermond
    d. Robert La Follette

61. Which of the following was *not* a vice president of the United States?　　　**c**

    a. Spiro Agnew
    b. Chester A. Arthur
    c. George Wallace
    d. Harry S Truman

62. Which of these black leaders has the *least* in common with the other three?　　**d**

    a. Marcus Garvey
    b. Malcolm X
    c. Stokely Carmichael
    d. Booker T. Washington

63. All the following were prominent labor leaders *except*:　　　　　　　**a**

    a. Big Jim Pendergast
    b. John L. Lewis
    c. Terence V. Powderley
    d. A. Philip Randolph

64. A prominent American naval officer was　　　　　　　　　　　　**b**

    a. George Armstrong Custer.
    b. Chester Nimitz.
    c. John J. Pershing.
    d. Douglas MacArthur.

65. What do presidents Franklin Roosevelt, Richard Nixon, and Woodrow Wilson have   c
in common?
    a. They all were presidents who drew the United States into a major war.
    b. They all were presidents who came to office while the nation was in the grip
       of a grave economic crisis.
    c. They all were presidents who significantly expanded the powers of the execu-
       tive branch of the federal government.
    d. none of the above

66. What do Theodore Dreiser, Jack Kerouac, John Steinbeck, and Richard Wright   d
have in common?
    a. They all wrote novels about the experiences of blacks in America.
    b. They all were short-story writers who wrote most of their stories while in
       exile in Paris.
    c. They all were novelists whose books appealed primarily to a growing middle-
       class genteel readership.
    d. They all wrote novels that were critical of American culture, customs, or
       society.

67. Which of the following was a black American poet?   a
    a. Langston Hughes
    b. Josiah Strong
    c. Kate Chopin
    d. James T. Farrell

68. Which of the following court cases expanded the rights of individuals?   b
    a. *Plessy* v. *Ferguson*
    b. *Miranda* v. *Arizona*
    c. *Dennis* v. *U.S.*
    d. all of the above

69. Which of the following applied to the most limited geographical area?   c
    a. Truman Doctrine
    b. Eisenhower Doctrine
    c. Carter Doctrine
    d. Reagan Doctrine

70. At a certain point during the last 125 years, there was a major transformation of   d
the American people's expectations of what their federal government could and
should be. When did that transformation occur?
    a. the Gilded Age
    b. the Vietnam War
    c. the Roaring Twenties
    d. World War II

71. Which statement accurately reflects conditions in American agriculture over the last century?   **a**
    a. periods of great prosperity, periods of economic collapse, declining numbers and increasing size of farms
    b. fairly consistent prosperity until the 1970s and 1980s
    c. lack of profitability throughout the century, and an inability to attract capital investment
    d. declining productivity, government refusal to assist farmers, and renewed interest in farming as a way of life in the post–World War II era

72. Which of the following statements most accurately represents national voting patterns over the past century?   **b**
    a. a decline in the number of national political parties
    b. a general long-term decline in voter participation
    c. growing ideological split between the two major political parties
    d. greater emphasis on voter qualifications

73. Over the past century, the Supreme Court has   **c**
    a. steadfastly remained the most conservative branch of the federal government
    b. been insulated from controversial political debates or partisan political pressures.
    c. become increasingly activist on behalf of political ideologies of either the right or the left.
    d. maintained a firm rule that only constitutional or other legal precedents should be taken into consideration in deciding a case.

74. Which of the following women has the least in common with the other three?   **d**
    a. Betty Friedan
    b. Susan B. Anthony
    c. Alice Paul
    d. Sarah Orne Jewett

75. Which of the following is the most recent major wave of immigration to the United States?   **a**
    a. Asian
    b. Irish
    c. German
    d. Italian

76. Since the late nineteenth century, a major thrust of American reformers has been   **d**
    a. education.
    b. civil rights.
    c. economic democracy.
    d. all of the above.

77. Since the late nineteenth century, American troops have invaded all the following areas *except*:   **b**
    a. Siberia
    b. Pakistan
    c. Honduras
    d. Southeast Asia

78. Which of the following statements about American cities in the past century is *not* correct?   **c**
    a. They grew rapidly in size and geographical extent.
    b. They became concerned with parks, monuments, and other social amenities.
    c. They dealt effectively with municipal corruption and crime.
    d. Their social structure and ethnic mix became increasingly complex.

ESSAY QUESTIONS

79. How have the patterns of American family life changed over the last century? How have class and race affected family life?

80. Compare and contrast the World's Columbian Exposition of 1893 with the New York World's Fair of 1939–1940. How does each, in its own way, reflect the idea of progress that prevailed in the nation at the time?

81. Much of the story of the United States in this century can be understood by examining the consequences of what the text calls a "remarkable period of industrial growth" in the late nineteenth century. Trace the political, social, and economic consequences of that industrial growth during the last one hundred years.

82. Trace the waves of reform sentiment that have swept over the United States at various times during the last 125 years. When have reform movements flourished, and when have they floundered? What have reformers focused on at various periods? What factors—domestic and international—affect the urge for reform?

83. Trace the development of the United States as a global power, from the late nineteenth century to the present. What basic principles have guided American foreign policy during that period?

84. What impact have twentieth-century wars had on American culture and politics, labor and business, the economy, and civil liberties? Compare and contrast the domestic impact of World War I, World War II, and the Vietnam War.

85. What changes have occurred in national politics over the last century? How have national political campaigns changed? How has the electorate changed? How has the political process itself changed? To what extent is it more democratic? Compare two presidential campaigns, or the political functioning of two presidential administrations.

86. To what extent has the role of women in American society changed over the last century, and to what extent has it remained the same? During what decades did the most significant changes occur, and during what decades were there the fewest changes? Consider the role of women in the workplace, in politics, and in the home. Consider both institutional changes and changes in attitudes and outlook.

87. How have the rights of minorities in American society been protected or impinged upon over the past century? Consider minorities classified by the following: race, religion, nationality, sexual preference, and point of view. What has helped to shape the treatment that such minorities have received at different times?

88. In Chapter 4 the text says, "The Declaration [of Independence] never claimed that perfect justice and equal opportunity existed in the United States; rather, it challenged the Revolutionary generation and all who later inherited the nation to bring this ideal closer to reality." To what extent have Americans living during the last century remained true to their Revolutionary heritage?

89. How has organized protest or rebellion been part of American life and politics over the last century? Consider the efforts of labor, individual-rights, and peace activists, as well as of groups that have adopted illegal or extralegal methods of achieving their goals.

90. The United States has always been a culturally pluralistic society. Explain this pluralism by examining some of the "competing" cultures that have shaped American society over the past century.

91. The urban landscape of America has changed dramatically over the last century. Pick two American cities and examine how they have changed from the late nineteenth century to today. Discuss, for example, the economy, physical layout, population base, and culture of the two cities.